SAHARA | Desert of Destiny

SAHARA

Desert of Destiny

by
GEORG GERSTER
translated by
STEWART THOMSON

NEW YORK
Coward-McCann, Inc.

English Translation © 1960 by Barrie & Rockliff
(Barrie Books Ltd.)

FIRST AMERICAN EDITION 1961

Library of Congress Catalog
Card Number: 61-5422

Contents

In Place of a Foreword

I feel I owe the geographers an apology for the title of this book. They like to speak of the Nile as a Saharan river, of the railway-line between Wadi Halfa and Khartoum as a Trans-Saharan railway. They use the word 'Sahara' of the whole vast area of desert between the Atlantic and the Red Sea. This book, however, is only concerned with the French Sahara, with four and a half million square kilometres, on which eight hundred and seventy thousand people live. That is almost three quarters of the total area covered by the Sahara but with only one third of its inhabitants. The frontiers of the French Sahara are sometimes natural, sometimes political. In the West it meets the Spanish Sahara and the Atlantic Ocean, in the East the (former Anglo-Egyptian) Sudan, Libya and Tunisia; in the North it is bounded by Tunisia, Morocco and 'the frontier where the edible dates begin'—next to Algeria—and its southern limits are marked by the Cram-Cram plant (Cenchrus biflorus), which is peculiar to the Sudanese steppes.

I make my apology, however, with a fairly easy conscience, for not only has the Sahara in the West always been generally accepted as distinct from the Libyan Desert in the East but in more recent times, thanks to a gigantic human effort, the Western part of the desert has become *the* Sahara: the scene of a great adventure and experiment, which has echoed round the world. This is the theme of my report.

G.G.

SAHARA | Desert of Destiny

Here too are the backward-grazing oxen,
which graze backwards for the following
reason. Their horns are bent forward, so
that they move backwards as they graze, for
they cannot go forward as their horns keep
thrusting into the ground. Otherwise they
are no different from other oxen except
that their hide is very thick and tough. These
Garamanti hunt the Ethiopians, who live
in caves, with four-horse chariots. For these
Ethiopians who live in caves are the fastest
runners of all the people we have
ever heard of.
HERODOTUS

1. Camels and Horses

SAH'RA is an Arabic word which means dun or mouse-coloured.
For the Arabs it signified originally a flat, barren expanse of grey-
brown earth. This is the meaning it has in pre-islamic Arab literature. Sah'ra is the colour of death. El Yakubi, a geographer of the
ninth century, even uses the word Sah'ra as synonymous with
cemetery. But in the same century it also appears in a work entitled
'The Conquest of North Africa' by an Egyptian Ibn el Hakam,
probably for the first time, to designate a part of the North African
desert.

To the European the oases are part of the Sahara, like emeralds
set in dull bronze. To the casual visitor, in fact, the oases are undoubtedly the highlights of his experience of the desert. But those
who inhabit the desert, and particularly the nomads, still associate
the Sahara with the grey pallor of death. When they speak of it,
they are not thinking of the palm-groves, the wells and the oases as
living islands in an ocean of barren sand and rubble. A Chaambi,
who leaves the El Golea oasis, talks of going into the Sahara.

In terms of space the Sahara has been conquered. If an exhaus-
tive record were to be made of this conquest, much of it would have
to be devoted to the camel, the final page to the helicopter.

The one-humped camel was the first serviceable vehicle in the Sahara. Its main features: four-wheel drive, three gears, large fuel container with reserve-tank, special tyres, fuel gauge, and a particularly strong front-chassis. Contrary to general belief, however, its fuel-consumption is high.

Anything that can stand up to the blazing heat of the desert is invested with mythical powers. This is especially true of the camel. It is reputed to be a fast animal. The Immortals of the Académie Française define the dromedary in their dictionary as follows: 'One-humped species of camel, which moves very fast.' 'A horrible mixture of zoology and etymology,' remarked Emile-Félix Gautier, leading French authority on the Sahara. The Immortals had obviously never sat on a camel's back and tested its speed. The Greek word from which 'dromedary' is derived means 'to run' or 'to hurry,' and presumably the half dozen camel-treks or 'meharées' which have become legendary were also taken as further proof. The Tuareg on their racing dromedaries are alleged to have covered a hundred and fifty, even a hundred and eighty miles in twenty-four hours in pursuit of camel-thieves. A certain Hadji Mohamed from Ouargla had to deliver a letter to Touggourt, a hundred miles away. On the evening of the following day, so the story goes, he was back in Ouargla with the reply. Captain Lecocq, on a punitive expedition with his meharists in an area without water, is said to have covered six hundred miles in ten days and to have found time for two successful engagements. The Saharan who told me of these tremendous achievements—a man of great experience who had been crippled by the bite of a horned viper—was careful to add that the camels had paid the price. The animals are doped and subsequently die of exhaustion.

The touching docility of the camel is admirably brought out in an Arab anecdote. After his mid-day siesta a traveller could find no trace of his 'mehari'. He finally discovered it several hundred yards away. But when he stooped down to pick up the reins from the ground he found they were caught in the hole of a jerboa, a rodent about the size of a rat. Even the almost imperceptible tugging of a mouse had been sufficient to lead the camel!. . . .

So the camel has passed into legend as a fast and docile animal.

The first I ever rode was an obstinate beast with a routine of its own. No amount of persuasion or force would induce it to travel at more than two miles an hour. It bore me with the utmost indifference, even condescension. It showed interest in only two things. The first was green dates. While we trotted through the palm-groves of the oases, its long sinewy neck snaked out from side to side with, as I soon noticed, the greatest deliberation, for on both sides of the narrow path it found a rich harvest of fruit among the luxuriant foliage of the palms. Words of command and even more pressing warnings and admonitions with my feet were of no avail. Like an old sailor who directs a stream of tobacco-juice at the landlubber's feet, the beast spat twice contemptuously, leering back at me. Out in the sand-dunes, however, it developed an un-bridled passion for shoe-soles, whether of rubber or of leather and regardless of the nails. I do not know which astonished me more, the apparent abundance of discarded shoe-soles in the desert or the camel's acquired taste for the dilapidated handiwork of some oasis shoemaker.

This ride from Ouargla to Sedrata was followed by others. In the Hoggar; in the Tassili; in Mauretania. They gave me no reason to change my opinion of the camel, an opinion, incidentally, which is not mine alone. One has only to be present when a camel patrol is going off duty. No horseman ever subjected his mount to such a stream of abuse. The curses generated throughout the centuries by the camel's obstinacy, its look of sophistication and its sulky, yellow-toothed mouth, from which about a hundredweight of saliva slavers every day, must be as countless as the grains of sand on the great dunes of the Erg. One does not have to be a connois-seur to distinguish between a farm-horse and a thoroughbred, but it takes a practised eye to see at a glance the difference between a Mehari—a riding and racing camel—and a pack animal. For the riding camel is not a product of selective breeding. No camel is born a Mehari. If it is lucky it is picked out when young and specially trained. A camel never has breeding, even a 'mehari.' The Mehara one reads of which dance nervously are purely fictitious. Even if one takes into account the high build and long legs of the Mehari, it is still a slow animal. A pack camel in first gear travels at just over two miles an hour. If it is constantly egged on with a stick, it will increase its speed to between three and four miles an hour. The great majority of dromedaries never exceed this snail's pace as long as they live. An exceptionally good riding camel, on days when it is not off its head, will do four miles an hour in first gear— possibly a little more. At a medium trot—if one can accuse such a confirmed saunterer of trotting—it reaches a speed of nearly six miles an hour, but only for short stretches. At a rapid trot—in attack or in flight—the speedometer rises to around twelve miles an hour but in a few minutes the beast is lame. It will only maintain this speed for any length of time if it is doped or goaded so that its flanks become lacerated and bloody. The word 'gallop' is better not mentioned. The dromedary is, to say the least, a reluctant beast. It certainly cannot be accused of lack of self-respect, for when it does gallop, with its legs striking out in all directions, the effect is comic and absurd. Gautier was reminded of a bout of coughing. Another parallel that springs to mind is dancing on a turntable.

And yet we are told that dancing-girls are flattered if they are compared to camels. There is a popular saying that 'Life is a desert and woman is the camel that helps us to cross it.' When Allah created Adam, two lumps of clay were left over, and Allah made one into a camel, the other into a palm tree. The camel and the palm are, therefore, part of the human family, created to make man's life on earth easier. And the nomads of the western Sahara have an explanation for the arrogance, the self-satisfied air of the camel that is both revealing and rewarding: 'The Prophet has a hundred names. Man knows only ninety-nine, but the camel knows the hundredth.'

It is not intelligence or complaisance or agility that has made it man's indispensable companion in the desert. Nor is it frugality, for although this is one of the virtues popularly ascribed to the camel it was certainly not among those bestowed by Allah. It can consume twenty gallons of water at one draught and has a bound-less appetite for solids. At the same time it is both a gourmand and a gourmet. Given the choice it can distinguish between herbs and weeds. It is exceptionally well equipped for desert conditions merely because its meal-times are so elastic not only in terms of hours but even of days.

Its hump is not a water-reservoir, either directly or indirectly. It is quite simply an accumulation of fat and as such is an ideal fuel gauge. The camel driver can tell from the size of the hump how much energy is left. If the camel is driven too hard the hump shrinks. During its annual six-months' vacation when it is grazing from sunrise to sunset, the camel's back is often completely hidden by the hump. Nature, however, can hardly have been thinking of man and his needs when she created the camel's hump. It was a simple expedient to prevent the fat from spreading over the entire body and so storing up heat. The camel's stomach is in three parts and has a capacity of over fifty gallons. The outer wall is specially designed for storing water and food-juices, and camel-drivers have been known, when faced with death by thirst, to kill, and 'tap' a dromedary. Whether the 'water', a greenish, nauseating liquid, was to their taste is another matter. But the really sensational feature of the 'camel-vehicle' is not so much the unusually large fuel tank as the cunningly constructed reserve-tank. Even when the supply of water in the animal's entrails runs out, the camel can still keep going for two or three days. Its body-tissues—and they alone— provide water. That is what is so astonishing. The blood of a human being exposed to hot, dry air becomes sluggish and there comes a moment when it is no longer flowing fast enough to convey the heat to the skin and release it. The result is a heatstroke. But thanks to a remarkable mechanism which is still unexplained, the blood of the camel, even with an unusually heavy loss of water, retains its normal consistency. It can survive a loss of water equivalent to one quarter of its weight, twice as much as humans can survive, and the camel has only to drink for a few minutes to make up the deficiency. Moreover it can tolerate a rise in body temperature from ninety degrees at night to a hundred and five in the daytime without sweating.

The popular misconception about the camel's frugality, docility, speed and endurance is not without its dangers. For the camel has its own method of protesting against unreasonable treatment; it dies.

'Carrying its burden, moving at its habitual pace, uncom-
plaining (at least complaining no more than usual, for Nature has
given it a soft mouth), the exhausted camel plods wearily on. When
it is at the end of its tether, it suddenly stops, like a motor-car that
has run out of petrol, cowers down and dies with considerable
dignity and a far-away expression, as if its thoughts are elsewhere.
It has a slightly roguish look, as though it is about to play one
splendid, final trick on its master.'

In 1901 the French occupied the 'road of palms,' the Touat
oases which are the main gateway to the Western Sahara. Supplies
and reinforcements had to be brought up for thousands of soldiers.
The camels were grossly overloaded and tens of thousands simply
lay down and died in protest. Algeria lost half its camel population
in this one operation. For several thousand miles the desert tracks
were strewn with the corpses of camels, as regular and as numerous
as telephone-poles. Gautier, whom I have already quoted more
than once because he has written more accurately and more
elegantly about the camel than anyone before or since, maintains
that a blind man could have followed those desert tracks merely by
the stench of death. It even carried as far as Paris, where this gruesome massacre created a political scandal.

How did the camel find its way into North Africa? The scholars
are divided. Some believe that it made its first appearance in the
Sahara about the dawn of our history, others that it staged a come-
back. Whichever theory is correct, it seems likely that the camels
came by the same route as the cattle. Tribes in what is today
Ethiopia brought them to Africa through the Gate of Sorrow, the
straits between the Red Sea and the Gulf of Aden. From Ethiopia
the camel migrated down the Nile to Egypt and from there into
Cyrenaica and Fezzan, where the Garamanti made it popular
throughout the Sahara. Some authorities believe that, after the
ethiopian tribes had rounded up wild camels in southern Arabia,
they laid the future ship of the desert on the stocks. And at this
point it is worth noting that, contrary to another popular legend,
no one has ever suffered from sea-sickness on a camel.

This particular ship appears to have been launched before it was
really seaworthy. Gautier points out that the camel has been in use

in North Africa and certainly in Tunisia both as a pack animal and
for riding since the third century. He has found evidence of this in
inscriptions and other archaeological discoveries. In those early
times, to judge by contemporary carvings and paintings, the rider
either sat astride on a sort of basket in front of the hump, or he
clung to a pack saddle on which clay jugs were hung, or he perched
without saddle on the hump itself—the last method hardly seems
conducive to driving in second or third gear. It was not until a light
saddle was invented, which lay over the hump, and the goatskin
water-container came into use that more rapid progress became
possible. From then on the driver used his feet to steer his mount.
I have met Meharists whose whole personality was in their feet,
beautiful, sensitive feet, whereas their hands were utterly devoid of
character and even clumsy. Gautier holds the view that the light
saddle and the leather water-bag were introduced in the fourth
century, which is the period when the camel nomads emerged as
desert pirates. With good reason the famous explorer of the
Western Sahara, Theodore Monod, dedicated his book 'Méharées'
to 'the camel and the goat, the vehicle and the container, sole
conquerors of the Sahara.'

Jean Larteguy gave a more modern version of Monod's dedica-
tion in a reportage on 'The Sahara in the Year One' which he
dedicated to the Jeep and the Dakota, 'which roused the Sahara
from its long sleep and changed its whole way of life.'

The first flight across the Sahara to the Niger was in 1920. The
Lindbergh of the desert, Joseph Vuillemin, later became C.G.S. of
the French Air Force. He turned the Sahara from a dash to a
hyphen linking the Atlas mountains with black Africa. But before
it surrendered, the desert claimed a victim in the most outstanding
and most respected man between Algiers and Timbuctoo, Marie-
Joseph-François-Henri Laperrine.

In the first year of this century Captain Laperrine was made the
officer in charge of the Sahara oases. Even today this post is no
sinecure, but at that time it was a very tough assignment. Anyone
but Laperrine would almost certainly have found it too much for
him. France had taken possession of wide stretches of the desert
but lacked the means to impose her will. Bands of camel nomads,

the desert marauders, continued to raid unprotected oases, to plunder caravans, to make war on one another and to vanish before the superior French defence forces could intervene.

It was Laperrine's idea to set a thief to catch a thief by creating the 'compagnies sahariennes,' a mounted desert gendarmerie to which he recruited the Chaamba, Arab camel-nomads and notorious trouble-makers in the northern desert. Napoleon had set up a dromedary regiment but his Meharists were merely Hussars mounted on camels instead of horses. Neither they nor their mounts felt particularly comfortable. Laperrine's approach was quite different. His point of departure was the camel, the local customs and the native clothes. It was a matter of complete indifference to him what sort of impression his army 'in slippers, shirt and straw hat' made at home. Each Chaambi had two to three animals. They belonged to him, bought out of his pay, and he knew exactly how much he could get out of them without crippling or killing them. There were no stables or barracks. The Meharists, 'sharks in the desert ocean,' remained nomads. So with the minimum outlay—a few French officers and N.C.O.s and two hundred Chaamba—Laperrine produced the maximum results: within a few years he had consolidated France's possessions in the desert and given them peace and security.

During the first world war when the French Sahara became restive, Laperrine, now wearing the stars of a General, was called back to the desert. His second campaign was no less successful than the first. Calm and order were restored. Both from a military and a political viewpoint it was a brilliant achievement. Yet in his lifetime he became a legendary figure for quite other reasons. He had only one passion: the desert. His ability to adapt himself to it was prodigious. He and his mehari seemed to be one; he would fast for days at a time and could live for weeks on a handful of dates or a few millet-cakes, yet when the occasion arose, he had a gargantuan appetite. This is all the more remarkable as he was no giant but a rather small man with short legs and a most unmilitary, high-pitched voice. In the course of innumerable reconnaissance expeditions, on which he crammed his note-books with geographical data, this little man with the squeaky voice filled in the last remaining blank spaces on the map of the Sahara. His powers of endurance, his self-sufficiency and his courage were boundless. Yet he was no fanatic. Wherever he went he inspired confidence by his kindness to the poor, his understanding of the abandoned inhabitants of the desert, his patience and his thoughtfulness.

In 1920 Air Force pilots decided to make the first attempt to fly across the Sahara. Single-engined double-deckers were to set out for the town which still carries in its very name something of the magic that cost so many Sahara travellers their lives: Timbuctoo, the 'Rome of the Niger.' Elaborate preparations were made. The route, the landing-places, the fuel and supply depots were all mapped out with the utmost care. Camel patrols stood by as ambulances, the wireless telegraph was installed at Tamanrasset, and smoke-signals marked the route from Tamanrasset to the Sudan.

General Laperrine, then a man of sixty, was not among those taking part, but shortly after the take-off from Algiers the machine carrying the General in Command had to turn back. It was ordered to fly to Paris immediately. Laperrine leapt into the breach, congratulating himself on a stroke of luck which was, in fact, to be his death-sentence. He joined the expedition at Biskra. One machine crashed while taking off for Ouargla, while a second was compelled to return to Ouargla before it reached Inifel. A third made a forced landing in a sandstorm near Salah. Only a few machines reached Tamanrasset in the Hoggar mountains. The Tuareg led by Laperrine's friend, the Amenokal or elected chieftain Moussa ag Amastane, gave the birdmen an enthusiastic reception. Then Vuillemin and Laperrine set out on the next stage to Tin Zaouaten, but before long both machines were enveloped in a storm of sand and dust and lost their bearings. Laperrine's plane ran out of fuel and had to come down in the desert. In doing so it turned over and out of the crew of three only the pilot was unhurt. Laperrine's left collarbone was broken, his right knee injured and several ribs fractured. Vuillemin meanwhile flew on, unaware of the plight of his companions.

The three men shared out the biscuits and the few tins of food they had brought with them. They rationed the water-supply,

which consisted mainly of cooling water from the plane's engine,
and the meagre patches of shadow cast by the wreckage of the
machine. Over the vast landscape of sand and rubble the air
shimmered in the merciless heat. For two days after the crash they
tried to find a well and a camel-track, which, they calculated, could
not be more than forty miles away. In vain.

'Returned to machine at 9 pm. on 21st. Utterly exhausted'
Lapperine wrote in his diary and his handwriting is that of an
exhausted man. This was Laperrine's last entry. Across the bottom
of the page he drew a final, clear line with his pen, which marked
●the end of his life. A week after their first unsuccessful reconnaissance the pilot and the mechanic made one last attempt to reach
Tin Zaouaten, a distance, they reckoned, of seventy-five miles. The
General was in no condition to walk. They left him two containers
of water and cocoa with a tube in each so that the wounded man
could drink without difficulty, then they set off into the desert. But
the desert still had need of them as witnesses to Laperrine's slow
and painful death. Many hours later, which seemed to them like
days, the two men stumbled back to the wreckage of the plane.
Their compass was out of order; they had walked in a circle.
Twenty days after the crash the pilot and the mechanic were still
alive. They were found near the plane by meharists a hundred and fifty
miles from Tin Zaouaten. Laperrine had died on the 5th of March.

He was buried in the red soil of Tamanrasset close by the heart
of his friend Pater Charles de Foucauld and only a stone's throw
from the spot where the hermit was murdered in 1916. The grave,
surmounted by a small pyramid, lies in the shifting shadow of a
tamarisk tree. The General and the Saint, the soldier and the
mystic—this combination is an essential feature of the history of
the Sahara.

It took General Laperrine seventeen days to die. The desert, one
might say, made his slow death an atonement for the jerricans that
line the desert-tracks where before there had been only the
bleached bones of camels, for the filling-stations in the oases and
the smell of oil and petrol in the palm-groves, for the whole
rattling, rumbling, rasping, roaring mechanised invasion, for the
forced retirement of the camel and the dwindling caravans, for the

abject surrender of the nomads who abandon their tents for a permanent roof, and for the crisis that threatens the desert-dweller's staple food, the date.

Laperrine's death marked the end of one era, the beginning of another, for it heralded the entry of the combustion engine into the desert.

The aeroplane did not have priority in the Sahara, it had simply won a race. The heat that evaporates petrol, the wind that fills the engine with sand, the burning sand that melts the tyres and not least the lack of roads—all these factors obviously handicap the automobile. As early as 1908 a Major Pein tried to cross the Sahara by motor-cycle. All went well as far as Ouargla but before the palms of El Golea came in sight the engine broke down. Not until 1916 did a motor vehicle succeed in reaching In Salah, and a year later a group of five vehicles under General Laperrine's command penetrated as far as this oasis. But Laperrine's attempt to go on to the Hoggar failed. In 1920 a number of trucks got through to Tamanrasset with supplies for the radio station, but of thirty-two that started from Algiers only nine completed the journey. Two made the trip back to Ouargla.

Another two years passed before the first motor-vehicle crossed the Sahara. In the ice-cold night of December 16, 1922 five small Citroëns with caterpillar wheels set off southwards from Toggourt. The prospect of success could hardly have been worse. The leaders of the expedition, G. M. Hardt and L. Audouin-Dubreuil, had deliberately refrained from making any inquiries from mehar-ists about the terrain and possible routes. They wanted to succeed without being in any way indebted to the camel, least of all for scouting services. And succeed they did. On January 7, 1923 they reached Timbuctoo without having lost a single vehicle.

Since then the penetration of the desert has gone forward with giant strides. Citroën's rivals, Renault and Berliet, designed a special six-wheeled vehicle with a petrol-consumption of about fifteen gallons per hundred miles. In 1925 the Latecoere Company started a regular air-service from Toulouse via Casablanca and the rebellious Spanish Sahara to Dakar. One of the pioneers of this service was Antoine de Saint-Exupéry. In 1930 the first Saharan

Rally was held. Forty touring cars crossed the desert without casualty to the banks of the Niger. In 1934 Shell published the first 'Guide to automobile and air travel in the Sahara.' The Dakota and the jeep appeared on the scene and were the progenitors of a whole race of desert vehicles. The scientists of the 'mission Berliet Ténéré', which succeeded in exploring the waterless, almost virgin territory between the Hoggar and Lake Chad, had a small fleet at their disposal: nine Berliet 'Gazelle' trucks, five smaller vehicles adapted to desert conditions, a DC 3, a Cesna and a helicopter. Two thousand years after it was first launched on the desert the camel was about to be thrown on the scrap-heap with a monument to 'The unknown Camel in gratitude.' In the inaccessible mountain wilderness of the Central Sahara where for many centuries only the camel had been able to penetrate, the helicopter like an enormous dragon-fly is now dropping geologists.

In terms of space the Sahara has been conquered. In 1958 in Tamanrasset I met an English student who had hitch-hiked twelve hundred miles from Algiers into the country of the veiled men.

It is surely no mere coincidence that the appeal of adventure in time begins when adventure in space has been satisfied. In the stone chronicles of its rocky walls, in its prehistoric implements, in its pollen and its fossilised soil-deposits the Sahara holds a fascinating and still largely undeciphered record of its own history and that of the human race. Here is a voyage of exploration as enthralling as was the gold of Timbuctoo.

1956 was an 'annus mirabilis'. In January at Edjeleh the first oil-strike was made in the Sahara. In February an expedition led by Henri Lhote struggled up the steep rock face of the Tassili to find what one connoisseur called 'the greatest artistic sensation we have experienced since the discovery of Tutankhamen's tomb.' In April, Professor Quézel came back from the Central Sahara with the material for his sensational pollen analysis. In June Lhote found himself face to face with the White Lady of Aouanrhet, a horned goddess of fertility, while some four hundred miles away to the north at Hassi Messaoud the richest oil-strike so far was being made. . . .

Today the geologists, guarded by machine-guns, are at work

with their hammers. Not that working under military escort is anything new. It has become a tradition, started, it seems, by Georges-
Barthelemy-Mederic Flamand, who, according to Larousse, was:
'French traveller and geologist, born in Paris, died in Algiers
(1861–1919). He carried out interesting research-work into the
geological conditions in North Africa. He took part in the expedition which occupied In Salah in 1899.' Flamand discovered
amongst other things, however, that his military escort took him
for a fool. They used his work as a cloak for their own activities.
The Tidikelt area was still controlled at that time by the Tuareg,
and the veiled men of the Hoggar regarded its capital, the In
Salah oasis, as theirs. Only two Europeans had until then set foot
in the Ksar In Salah: a Scotsman, Gordon Laing, and a German,
Gerhard Rohlfs. In Salah was an important market for slaves,
ostrich feathers, ivory and gold dust, as well as cloth, tea and dates.
The Tuareg had decided that they would make short shrift of any
stranger who crossed a borderline they themselves had laid down.
The successful massacre of an expedition led by Colonel Flatters
in 1881 had gone to their heads. France's vanity was hurt; she took
up this bloody challenge by weaving a myth not only round the
victims but also round their murderers. So the Colonel, who was a
singularly weak and criminally credulous officer, became a martyr
and national hero, while the Tuareg, whose arms were medieval
and who were numerically weak, acquired the reputation of being
invincible. As far as public opinion in France was concerned,
further military adventure in the desert was taboo, but this did not
apply to French military circles. Flamand was naive enough not to
be surprised when an impressive military escort of a hundred and
forty armed men was attached to his geological expedition to
Tidikelt. The Tuareg, on the other hand, had no illusions. Hardly
had Flamand appeared in their territory with his escort when they
attacked. Those who had planned the coup were not surprised.
This masquerade was directed not so much at the Tuareg as at the
Governor-General, a highly circumspect official to whom his career
was everything. He would have refused to sanction an undisguised
military expedition, but he was completely taken in by the façade
of the innocent geologist.

Flamand himself probably saw through the manoeuvre only after the Taureg attack when Major Pein took over the command and military units in battalion strength, summoned by a rocket-signal, appeared as if from nowhere to reinforce the escort. In spite of protests by the geologist there were two bloody engagements and in the closing days of the 19th century In Salah was occupied. France, almost against her will, had moved up to the very threshold of the Hoggar-Tuareg country. The Governor-General, faced with an accomplished fact, had to adapt himself as best he could and make Paris swallow this fresh conquest. As the enterprise had been successful, he did not have much difficulty. Flamand, on the other hand, did not find it so easy to accept the fact that he had been made a fool of. He challenged Captain Pein to a duel with sabres in the sand-dunes near In Salah. What he lacked in experience and practice he made up for in fury. Pein, who was to become a motor-cycling pioneer, almost qualified as the first candidate for In Salah's Christian cemetery.

Flamand was passionately interested in the 'Hadjerat Mektoubat,' the inscribed stones. As a result of years of research and field-work he was able to locate a number of new sites with rock-engravings, and his book 'The inscribed Stones,' which appeared two years after his death, gives a complete account of his investigations. It was the first comprehensive work on the rock-pictures of the Sahara.

The discovery of the Tassili paintings is another story, which, like the research into the Saharan rock-pictures as a whole, started with officers who managed to combine archaeology with the business of war. The real pioneer was Captain Cortier. In 1909 he noticed an animal painted in red ochre on an overhang of rock. He took it to be a bison. In fact it was an ox. Then in 1912, the year in which he defeated the Ajjer-Tuareg, notorious robbers and bandits, at Esseye, Lieutenant Gardel stumbled on a number of paintings near a well on the old caravan-trail to the salt market of Bilma. These paintings belonged to a variety of periods: white antelopes, oxen, horses, Libyan-Berber and Arabic symbols. In 1928/29 Conrad Kilian, the unacknowledged prophet of Saharan oil, reported having found a giraffe, hunting-scenes, and warriors armed with bows and arrows. In 1932 Captain Duprez and Lieutenant Noe came on a number of rock-shelters during a reconnaissance trip into the interior of the Tassili. They stared spellbound at the horse-drawn chariots, the fish, the herds of oxen and the hunting dogs. . . .

2. Appointment with Antinea

'Lhote had an appointment with Antinea. That is the whole secret.'

The administrator of the Tassili district, Captain Rossi, who made this remark to me in Djanet, knows what he is talking about. He makes no secret of the fact that he too is a slave of Antinea. He read 'L'Atlantide' at the age of eighteen and immediately enlisted in the Camel Corps.

Antinea, the heroine of Pierre Benoit's Atlantis novel, claims to be descended from the Atlantids and lives in a mysterious castle in the Hoggar. There she lures two French officers to their death.

Benoit did more than merely add a further three hundred and fifty pages of romantic phantasy to the literature of Atlantis, which Plato's celebrated report alone has swollen to several million printed pages. Antinea is not just the heroine of an adventure-novel. A certain dollar millionaire once went so far as to assure the world at large that Antinea had been found. That was in 1925 when excavations in a tumulus at Abelessa, reputed to contain the ancestress of the Tuareg tribes, yielded the skeleton of a white woman who had been given royal burial.

Antinea is the Lorelei of the desert; her consumption of males is very high. I am thinking of the lieutenants who fall under the spell of sand, rock and solitude, who bury themselves in the Sahara and turn their backs quite happily on careers and the future. I am thinking of the captains who dream not of promotion but of sending a report to the Academy of Science or the Year Book of the Institute of Saharan Studies. Three-quarters of all discoveries in the great desert are made by French officers. And students of the Sahara have General Laperrine to thank, for he himself was hopelessly in love with the desert and therefore raised no objection if a company commander set all his men to digging prehistoric arrow-heads out of the sand. He established a tradition which has continued ever since. But much is also due to Antinea. What Laperrine's spirit alone could not have achieved was accomplished by the lure of Antinea's embrace.

Benoit published his novel in 1919. One of its earliest readers was Henri Lhote. He was sixteen years old, an orphan and poor as a church-mouse, but he had fallen under Antinea's spell. One of his two major ambitions in life was to get to know and explore the desert, from which his brother-in-law occasionally sent him sand roses. His other ambition was to fly. This was soon achieved when he came to do his military service and was sent to an Air Force unit. But his other dream could only be realised by his own efforts.

I have never met Lhote, but I have been present on many occasions—in the tropical tent of a platinum prospector, at the bar in an oil-drillers' camp, in a military fort—when his name cropped up. To judge by these conversations, for every friend Lhote had he had a hundred enemies. His courage, his obstinacy, his endurance and his monastic austerity are beyond question. But, his critics constantly assert, these qualities can hardly be divorced from his overpowering ambition and the urge to assert himself.

Lhote found it none too easy to keep his appointment with Antinea. The opportunity did not come until 1928. He was studying zoology when the Natural History Museum in Paris decided to offer his services to Prince Sixtus of Bourbon-Parma's expedition. He was to join the expedition, which was already in the desert, as a specialist in reptiles. But when Lhote landed at Algiers, he learned that another zoologist had already taken over the work he had been sent to do. He knew no one in North Africa, had no contacts and just enough money to pay his fare back to France. Anyone else but Lhote would probably have taken the next boat. Lhote, however, decided that, as there was nothing to be done with reptiles, he would concentrate on insects. The only official body that could help a young man anxious to explore the desert was the Office for the Preservation of Cultivated Plants. It commissioned Lhote to do locust research. The funds at his disposal were extremely limited but he had at least an official position and was free to roam about the desert. Lhote soon became a locust specialist and was in great demand as a locust-killer. He discovered the breeding grounds of the migratory locust and during one invasion near Timbuctoo was responsible for destroying one and three-quarter million gallons of the insects. For three months, while a Governor in the Niger valley was ill, Lhote acted for him but he declined the offer of a return ticket home. For the second time he crossed the Sahara alone by camel. At the end of 1931, two days before Christmas, he arrived back in Algiers, bronzed and irretrievably dedicated to the desert.

Lhote's scientific colleagues have never quite forgiven him that somewhat adventurous period in his career. He later took his Doctorate. During the German occupation of France he prepared for the examination, but even this was not made easy for him. In a British air-raid he was badly injured and when the examination day came he had to be carried to the Sorbonne on a stretcher. He gained a diploma at the School of Anthropology and was given a senior post at the National Institute for Scientific Research. He was intimately concerned with the Musée de l'Homme, was awarded the Gold Medal of the French Geographical Society 'for twenty-five years of research in the Sahara' and was made an officer of the 'Ordre du Mérite Saharien.' But for all that his critics still seemed to detect traces of the adventurer here and there in his scientific publications—an occasional boldness in interpretation, a pretentious theory, a superficial observation. . . .

Not even his bitterest opponent could deny, however, that Lhote was at home in the Sahara. Since the anti-locust campaign he had kept returning to the desert. In terms of mileage his camel-trips had taken him twice round the world. Only someone who has sat on a camel can appreciate what this means: a 'meharée' of 50,000 miles. 'Lhote knows the Sahara better than anyone.' This tribute by General Meynier, himself a connoisseur of the Sahara, is worth more than any decoration. Lhote only earned it by undergoing immense privation.

Quite a few of the inferences Lhote drew from his finds may have been hasty and in some cases untenable, but the discovery and preservation of the artistic treasures in the Tassili mountains will always be associated with him.

In 1933 a certain Lieutenant Brenans rode into the Oued (Wadi) Djerat at the head of his Camel Corps. It was a routine exercise, the sort of reconnaissance the Meharists were accustomed to. But in the desert no routine is ever entirely without a certain flavour of adventure. Brenans was the first European to enter this canyon, which cuts across the Tassili plateau. Suddenly on the steep walls on either side of the dry river-course he noticed strange figures such as he had never seen before.

'He immediately gave orders to dismount,' writes Lhote. 'He thought he must be dreaming. For he was confronted by pictures of big game cut deep into the rock-face. There were elephants marching with raised trunks, hippopotamus which had come from a nearby pool to graze, rhinoceros with menacing nose-horns, giraffes with outstretched necks as if they were reaching for the tips of the thorn-trees . . . In short, this sun-baked valley presented an astonishing spectacle.'

Brenans continued on his trek till an insurmountable barrier of loose rubble forced him to turn back. He immediately informed the authorities of his discovery. Paris and Algiers despatched pre-historians and geographers. Lhote also made his way there unofficially.

Together with the geographer Perret, Lhote travelled up from Fort Polignac on the northern fringe of the Tassili towards the Oued Djerat till a deserted and overgrown oasis brought them to a stop. The way was blocked by an apparently impenetrable barrier of palm-shoots and creepers. Perret despaired of breaking through but Lhote refused even to consider retreat. He hacked a narrow path through the green wilderness which was more like a tropical jungle than a mountainous desert. His hands and arms streaming with blood, his clothes torn to ribbons by the thorns, Lhote fought his way forward yard by yard with a machete and cleared a path through which the caravan could follow. Beyond the undergrowth the travellers set up camp on the fine sand. A small lake nearby was swarming with fish. A bent pin baited with a piece of date was enough to provide them with a hearty meal. These fish were a relic of the fertile desert, the records of which Lhote was to decipher on the rocky walls of the Tassili.

The various Professors who had come from Paris and Algiers spent several weeks in the desert. Lhote was there for eighteen months. Together with Brenans and, as often as not, by himself he explored the whole expanse of the Tassili and other foothills of the Hoggar mountains. The four camels in which he had invested his entire funds died one after the other. The exhausting treks over barren, sun-baked rubble and boulders were too much for them. Lhote returned to France with little more than a rucksack. But he could not get the rock-frescoes out of his mind, for, in addition to the hitherto unknown carvings he had discovered, he had also stumbled upon paintings on ledges and in hollows under overhangs of rock and sometimes even on the open rock-face itself. To begin with, Brenans had directed him to paintings north of Djanet at the southern end of the Tassili. As Lhote carried on the search and found more and more paintings to copy, his stock of drawing-paper and colours soon ran out.

It was not until 1954 that the Tassili expedition, of which Lhote had been dreaming for twenty years, finally took shape. Other work, the war and his air-raid injuries had all combined to postpone the plan. Even in 1954 it might have come to nothing if the ethnologist, Yolande Tschudi, had not visited the Tassili in the winter of 1950. The main object of her visit was to make an ethnological study of the Tuareg nomads of Ajjer, but a sudden drought had driven them far to the south. This enterprising Swiss scientist therefore spent her time with the rock-paintings. She discovered a number of new ones, copied them carefully and published them in Italy under the patronage of Professor Paolo Graziosi, the leading Italian authority on rock-carvings. The treasure-chamber of Tassili was accessible to all and, when Yolande Tschudi took a few jewels from it, she did so with no ulterior motive. Her sole aim was to serve the cause of human knowledge. But without realising it, she had invaded a province which Lhote regarded as his special preserve. The French authorities who kept jealous guard over their desert were also made painfully aware of the danger that other foreigners might invade the Tassili.

Dawn broke on 20th February, 1954, to reveal a scene of incredible confusion before the fort in the Djanet oasis. Five camel-drivers cursed volubly, while some thirty camels, as was to be expected, wore expressions of supercilious irritation; the four artists and the photographer, whom Lhote had managed to recruit for his expedition, tried in vain to create some sort of order out of chaos.

Djanet is a dream-oasis with its snow-white fort, its gardens of peaches and climbing-roses. In the Oued Edjariou under thousands of palm-trees are small plots of corn, barley and millet. Over them towers a sheer wall of Tassili rock, apricot-coloured in the early-morning sun, leaden in the merciless light of noon, and changing after sunset from burgundy red to inky black. The panorama from Fort Charlet would be world-famous and four-starred in every guide-book if it were not almost as remote and unattainable as the stars. It is fifteen hundred miles from Algiers to Djanet, some six hundred of them over rough and difficult desert-tracks, to say nothing of two hundred and fifty miles through rebel territory in nerve-racking convoys. Djanet is not on any civil air-route. Small wonder, therefore, that the centre of the Tassili area is not even mentioned in the Michelin Guide to Algeria and the Sahara.

Djanet is an Arabic word which virtually means Paradise. "See Djanet and die" is a common saying in the Sahara. Lhote's team, however, had no thought of dying that day in February as they loaded three tons of equipment and supplies on the pack-saddles. The Paradise they were seeking lay in the corroded and weather-beaten frescoes of Tassili.

That expedition is still remembered in Djanet with a mixture of affection and respect. Men who are not easy to impress, because the desert has taught them to be uncompromising with their fellow-men, were unstinting in their praise.

'Tassili,' I heard one say, 'swallowed them and spat them out again, one by one. They came back to organise fresh supplies or for medical attention. They had flowing beards and their clothes were in tatters; they were in the last stages of exhaustion, men of the twentieth century who were living in the stone-age—yet I never saw one of them discouraged, not even Frassati, who had to be sent home eventually because he had lost three stone in weight.'

It was a gruelling, nerve-racking business getting camels up to the plateau through the only pass that pack-animals could negotiate. Some of them collapsed and the men had to take over the loads themselves. Yet this was only a slight foretaste of the trials and privations to come.

The expedition copied the paintings. First of all the outlines of the pictures were traced and transferred to paper which was the same basic colour as the rock itself, then the various tones and shades of the original were filled in. Photographic reproduction was, in most cases, impossible due to lack of space, lack of light or the condition of the rock-face. While the artists were busy copying one picture after another, Lhote combed the surrounding area for new paintings. Hidden under the patina of many centuries, under a crust of sand, mud and dust, they were often hard to find. To take only one example, the expedition camped for a fortnight near the Great Martian God before the wall even showed signs of yielding anything and the phantom of the desert began to emerge under the wet sponge.

As the months passed, the sponge wrought a hundred and one miracles. It turned drab, dark patches on the rocky walls into colours of dazzling brilliance. And the paintings themselves were never in danger. Fortunately the prehistoric artist had made fast his colours by mixing them with milk-protein and agglutinous plant-juices, particularly from the acacia or gum arabic tree. The absorptive quality of the sandstone had also helped to protect them. The sole disadvantage of this improvised method of moistening the walls was that it made frequent inroads into the precious supply of drinking and cooking water.

The expedition copied . . . How simple that sounds! Yet it gave rise to tremendous problems and privations. The men were working at a height of 6,000 to 6,500 feet above sea-level. In winter their hands grew numb with cold, but hardly had they grown accustomed to holding a brush in nerveless fingers than they had to acclimatise themselves to the long Tassili summer. Then came the desert wind, holding up the work for days at a time, soiling the colours, tearing the drawing-paper. One single, random gust was enough to undo the work of weeks. Even in normal circumstances there was the sheer physical strain of working in enclosed spaces under overhanging rocks. They had good reason to understand why Michelangelo contracted a stiff neck when he painted the ceiling of the Sistine Chapel. And copying pictures high up on the walls meant balancing on the drawing-tables like trapeze artists.

These impromptu circus acrobats lived little better than the stone-age artists themselves had lived. The coarse rubble tore their shoes, their clothes hung in rags, they suffered from both hunger and thirst. At night they sought shelter from the bitter cold among the rocks; in the day time they used loose stones to grind the corn.

Lhote had originally planned to complete his self-imposed task in eight months, but at the end of that period only half the work had been done. Both in quantity and in quality the discoveries exceeded all expectations. In the Jabbaren alone, a massif only 800 yards long and 700 yards wide, more than five thousand figures came to light, relics of about a dozen different civilisations, crowded together without any apparent connection and painted one over the other like a palimpsest, some naturalistic, some highly mannered, some boldly abstract, and they covered every conceivable dimension from miniatures to monumental frescoes.

For the second stage of the work Lhote had to recruit further help. Exhaustion and commitments at home had reduced his original team to almost nothing. The winter of 1956/57 was particularly severe. In the Tassili it even snowed, an extremely rare occurrence in the heart of the Sahara. Due to the unusual weather conditions the expedition's return to France was held up and the last member did not reach Paris until 10th July, 1957.

Lhote had every reason to be satisfied with the results. Eight hundred frescoes had been faithfully and accurately reproduced on more than 15,000 square feet of drawing paper. These were by no means all the paintings he and his colleagues had unearthed. The inventory of the Tassili pictures over an area 500 miles long by 40 miles wide contains several thousand items. But Lhote's expedition had confirmed the claim that in the early Stone Age the Central Sahara was densely-populated and had proved that the Tassili plateau was the focal point of unknown prehistoric civilisations and peoples.

Outstanding among these discoveries was the herd of Jabbaren. Lhote found other paintings with even more animals in them but none so rich in line and gradations of colour, none so animated and at the same time so detailed. This is not just a picture of a large number of animals, It shows a complete herd with its leaders, its outrunners, its stragglers and its strays. And yet the artist had managed to treat each individual animal with all the loving care of a master. No two are the same. The reddish-yellow canvas of rock is filled with a wealth of pigmentation which is unique in prehistoric paintings: in addition to red and black, the colours most of the Tassili artists employ, there are violet, yellow, green, and even blue. And the composition is equally varied. Several species of cattle are represented. There are lyre-shaped and broad-spanned horns, short and long, thick and thin horns; some have a strange forward twist, while others are sickle-shaped with the cutting-edge again directed forward. Most of the cattle are in one colour—pale yellow, red, violet, green or blue—but a few are spotted and dappled. The herd is not grazing. It is in full flight, possibly from one grazing-place to another. A herdsman with coffee-coloured skin, red loin-cloth and red headdress is standing behind the main body of the herd with outstretched arms, driving on the stragglers. But the leading animals appear to have run into some obstacle or other. One cow, which the artist has merely sketched in, is lying on the ground. Near the dead animal is a woman, again with coffee-coloured skin and red headdress but with a lighter shade of loin-cloth. She and a group of red-skinned men seem to be hurrying anxiously towards the herd. This particular group, which like several other parts of the picture has not been completed, is nevertheless remarkably effective. From a purely formal point of view it rounds off the whole composition. Not that the artist himself is likely to have concerned himself with the composition. He was clearly more interested in content, in the story. Yet it is precisely the story that remains hidden from us. We cannot even be certain that the slaughtered cow is not a sacrificial offering.

Another picture that stands out in my memory is of three

giraffes. Two of them, males, are fighting, probably for a mate, and the artist has immobilised them in a fantastic 'pas de deux.' The third animal, the female, is looking on curiously. An ostrich is seen fleeing from the dancing giants. In the background two gazelles are making for safety. In the foreground a hunter is creeping up, a bow in his right hand, while with his left he holds an antelope on a short lead as cover. The giraffes, the hunter and the ostrich are clearly intended to form three separate groups.

The coursing-scene: this is a highly dramatic snapshot. The hunting-chariot carries three men. The one in the centre is about to hurl his spear at a buffalo. The driver is standing in front holding the reins. The horse seems to be flying, his fore and hind legs stretched out symmetrically in a gallop. His tail is flowing and ribbons are fluttering from the axle between the seven-spoked wheels.

The idyll: a giraffe with her young. The mother's neck is bent low over the young one, which is shrinking back nervously from a barking dog. On the left of the picture the hunter is approaching with bow and arrow at the ready.

The battle scene: groups of little men in red ochre, some naked, some in loincloths, are fighting. Many are shown in full motion; the main weapon is the bow and arrow. The picture is really an object-lesson to aspiring archers: the arrow is shown being discharged from the bowstring; one sees how the archers stop as they draw back the string and bend the bow. One of the warriors, also shown in action, is swinging a wooden club.

The desert phantom: the largest prehistoric figure so far discovered. The lower part of the picture is missing but the giant must have been about twenty feet high. Lhote was reminded of some figure from space-fiction and he dubbed him the Great Martian God. But this monster could equally well suggest a deep-sea diver or one of those clay figures that feature in the folklore of various countries. The round head without neck is set directly on the shoulders, which are hunched. A series of lines between head and torso were possibly designed to suggest ornaments. The hair is a kind of fringe of banana skins. In the middle of the head are two concentric ovals, possibly an eye. Beneath, to the left near the ornaments, sits a similar but smaller figure.

Much more human is the graceful female figure which Claude Guichard discovered on an overhang of rock in the Aouanrhet Massif. It is hard to say whether she is running or dancing. One foot is just touching the ground, while the other leg is raised ready for the next step. She is wearing a great deal of jewellery, and from the arms, waist and knees hang finely-embroidered tassels. Her shoulders, body, breasts and legs are tattooed or painted. Round her wrists and ankles are plaited bracelets, the hands are hidden in gloves which are knotted with some kind of whipcord. From her head project a cow's horns, between which a field of corn is depicted, its ears showering down over her. The swaying movement of the body, the tasselled fringes lightly blown by the wind and the corn falling like Jupiter's golden rain all give the figure a springlike grace and charm. The cornfield between the horns suggests a goddess of fertility or at least the priestess of some agrarian cult. Lhote, in honour of his teacher the Abbé Breuil, who is particularly devoted to the 'White Lady of Brandberg' in South West Africa, called her the 'White Lady of Aouanrhet.'

That, however, was not all. In a quiet, remote corner of a cave-dwelling in Jabbaren a painting of a woman had been found, which is almost unreal in its beauty. She is more than life-size and painted in white and red. She is kneeling on one knee and leaning her head in the crook of her arm. Her hair is held by a diadem or headband and a veil is draped over her back. She radiates nobility and dignity; her face is turned northwards, towards Greece. She might be a princess, or a priestess or a goddess.

When the sponge passed across the wall for the third time and revealed the figure, Henri Lhote cried: "So we meet at last!" He called her Antinea.

3. Hunters and Herdsmen

'IF only I were down there now,' I burst out.

'You would be disappointed,' replied René Mossu drily. 'The reproductions you saw in the Louvre in Paris are much more striking than the originals. Since Lhote was there, they have become coated with a fresh patina. You would be sadly disillusioned.'

We were on our way by plane from Djanet to Fort Flatters. Directly below us lay the new Mecca of prehistoric art, the largest open-air museum in the world. The Noratlas, commonly known as 'the flying truck,' droned low over Tassili-n-Ajjer. Isolated mountains drifted past like islands washed by a sea of sand; the deep gashes of canyons, their sheer walls vanishing from sight in great heaps of rubble; massif after massif, each one corroded by time, stood out boldly on the high plateau; gloomy clearings amidst tree-trunks of stone, domes, needles and pyramids of rock; abandoned towns in whose ruins one can still pick out the market-place, the streets and lanes, the houses and the palaces . . . the crazy, unpredictable patterns of erosion.

I had met Mossu in Djanet and taken him at first for an American who spoke excellent French. He moved about the desert as if it were a golf-course. Faced with a problem he seemed to weigh an invisible driver in his hand and, eyes narrowed, gauge the distance to an invisible green! Though born in Paris, he had in fact come from the States and was spying out the Sahara on behalf of an American mining company. Had I been his employer, I would have sacked him at once. He showed only mild interest in the things that were everyday talk in the Tassili and Hoggar: diamonds, platinum, asbestos, thorium and uranium. But he would go to endless trouble to see one rock-carving. The frescoes of the Sahara were his hobby.

Remembering Lhote's magnificent exhibition in Paris, I remarked that the paintings from Tassili had enormously enriched the world's store of artistic beauty. A new province had been discovered, in which the art-lover is dazzled and amazed, yet which is somehow not altogether unfamiliar.

'As long as he's interested only in form and colour' Mossu agreed. 'The specialist is also naturally excited by this discovery. But he does not feel quite so happy in his mind. For he is faced by a great many new and unsolved problems, unanswered questions. He is rather like an accountant who wants to draw up a balance-sheet but is confronted every now and then by a new item in the inventory which he had not noticed before. Lhote's discovery at Tassili, to which further material was added in 1959 and 1960, was the biggest and most spectacular of those items. But it is by no means the only one. Lhote himself provided additional material when he made the first systematic inventory of the rock-carvings in the Oued Djerat in 1959. His team copied 4,000 of these, partly by means of a new process using fluid rubber. Amongst them are the largest prehistoric carvings ever known: giraffes more than 20 feet high, rhinoceros 25 feet long and elephants 15 feet high. But quite apart from Lhote's discoveries, ever since the desert woke from its Rip van Winkle sleep not a month has passed without another set of rock-carvings being unearthed. In the last few years alone about twenty thousand figures have been discovered on the rock-walls of the Sahara. And that,' added Mossu, 'is an under- rather than an over-estimate.'

The sinking sun had set the Tassili mountains on fire. The propellors were dipped in glowing lava. In the dry gullies the shadows were lengthening like rivulets of blue ink. While darkness crept over that magnificent, melancholy landscape, Mossu and I compared notes on our common hobby, rather like two students outside the examination-room quickly refreshing their memories.

The Sahara picture-gallery tells a story of constant coming and going in the desert, of successive civilisations, races, peoples, tribes and clans, which may have brought their own art with them or may equally well have taken over an artistic tradition already in existence and carried it on. But what do the many different styles represent? Is each one the expression of an individual artist? Or of a school? Or of a clan? Did these styles develop simultaneously and independently or in some chronological sequence? Can any chronological order, relative and absolute, be traced? Which civilizations, races, peoples, tribes and clans are involved? Was the Sahara inhabited by black, brown, red or white people?

These are only a few of the questions we asked one another. The original list was much, much longer.

A scientific study of the rock-carvings of the Sahara can be made from two different angles. It can compare these artistic creations of prehistoric man with those of more recent periods. It is also possible, on the other hand, to leave aside all idea of foreign influences and contacts and attempt to arrange the carvings in some kind of order based on the works themselves.

The first approach has been tried but it leads nowhere. The Sahara rock-carvings are certainly not isolated phenomena. Some specimens remind one of the rock sculpture in Eastern Spain and the bushman art of South Africa. Does this mean that these particular features were transmitted from Spain by way of North Africa to the Cape of Good Hope either as characteristic expressions of a specific race or simply piece-meal? Was it perhaps not a continuous but a simultaneous process, whereby shoots and blossoms appeared on one and the same tree? Or are these associations no more than similarities of style that will not stand up to closer examination?

One of the first links to be discovered was with Egypt, particularly with prehistoric cultures in the Nile Valley. The recent discovery in the south-western Fezzan of a mummified child which goes a great deal farther back than the mummies found in the Nile valley has thrown a new light on the relationship between predynastic Egypt and the desert lands to the west of the Nile. But Lhote copied a number of themes similar to those in the tombs of the Pharaohs and in graves at Thebes. How did such a highly refined and stylised form of art find its way to the rocks of Tassili? Was it the work of Egyptians, who had been taken prisoner by their arch-enemies, the Libyans? Or had Libyan prisoners in the Nile Valley been taught by Egyptian painters? The question is not made any easier to answer by the fact that these Saharan rock-carvings strongly resemble work not only in Thebes and Amarna but also in Assyria and Crete, while some even suggest a negro influence. For several centuries within recorded history the Sahara protected black Africa against the curiosity of the Mediterranean peoples and the Europeans. But at that time, when the desert was green, it was obviously exposed to many outside influences. To identify them and trace each one back to its source—nothing could be more fascinating. But so far all attempts have unfortunately ended in a maze of question-marks.

Until now only the second approach has made appreciable headway: to group the carvings according to motifs. Four groups have been identified which correspond to four periods of time: the hunter, the herdsman, the horse and the camel. The archaeologists are well aware that the net they have cast over their quarry is a very wide one, but this crude classification has so far stood the test.

The hunters portrayed the hunted: elephants, giraffes, rhinoceros, ostriches, and—a characteristic of this period—stag, hippopotamus, crocodile and fish. At this stage there is no attempt at composition; the animals are shown not in herds but for the most part singly. And the dimensions are significant; the animals, even the giraffe, were frequently carved and painted life-size. The treatment is naturalistic. Where the figure is sculpted, the lines are deep, mostly V-shaped, and with a black or at least dark patina. Human figures are rare. When they do occur, they are wearing masks, mostly of animals. They are armed with clubs and crooked throwing-sticks, which were possibly boomerangs. The only domestic animal which appears during the hunters' period is the dog, their constant companion.

In the period of the herdsmen the pictures are smaller and naturalism gradually gives way to abstraction and formalism. Instead of individual figures there are spacious group-formations, the incisions in the rock are U-shaped and less deep, and the patina is lighter, frequently even the same colour as the rock-face itself.

The herdsmen also portrayed game: rhinoceros, ostrich and moufflon, gazelle, wild pig, lion, wild ass, antelope and fish. Only occasionally one sees a hippopotamus. The real star of this period, however, is the ox. Whole herds of oxen are portrayed, accompanied by sheep and goats, driven by herdsmen and dogs, and their mottled hides, ears, hooves and tails are reproduced in the greatest detail. But the most striking feature of these carvings is the enormous variety of horns, some of which even curve forward and downwards like an elephant's tusks. This seems to point to very active and varied breeding.

The herdsmen were nomads. Frequently on the move in search of fresh grazing, the oxen, which served as pack-animals and as mounts, had no chance to grow fat. The cows' udders lie fairly far back, which suggests that they were milked not from the side but from the back.

Men are often portrayed in the carvings and paintings of the herdsmen period, usually naked but sometimes wearing a loincloth. We see them looking after their animals, taking part in ritual ceremonies or engaged in domestic chores. A number of scenes point to agriculture, and it seems a fair assumption that cattle-breeding was combined with nomadic farming. The main weapon is the bow and arrow, which they must have used either to protect their herds against attack or in occasional raids on other herds. Many of the pictures show them fighting. Lhote even found a painting that showed women-warriors, who are depicted with only one breast. The explanation may simply be that the artist had confused the profile and the full-face positions—a forerunner of Picasso but more by accident than design. On the other hand, Lhote suggests that these women may have been such keen fighters that they had one breast removed to give them greater freedom with the bow and arrow. It is not an unreasonable hypothesis, for only half a century ago French soldiers on the Slave Coast encountered two-thousand single-breasted Amazons who formed the redoubtable bodyguard of King Behanzin.

It would be a mistake to imagine that there was a sudden transition from the period of the hunters to that of the herdsmen. The cattle-breeders almost certainly made their way up from the south-east, and they may well have established some kind of *modus vivendi* with the hunting tribes. The herdsmen themselves could not live without hunting, if they wanted to preserve their livestock

and at the same time maintain a fairly varied diet. Moreover the
herds had to be protected against wild animals. It is not unlikely
that the indigenous hunters became the herdsmen's gauchos and
cowboys, especially as about that time the supply of game began to
grow scarce. There is certainly no evidence to show that the herdsmen subdued the hunters by force of arms. There is good reason to
suppose on the other hand that the conflict was decided by the
relative prosperity and security of cattle-breeding as against the
hand to mouth existence of the hunter.

When we come to give a date to the herdsmen's period, we begin
to see daylight. Although we still have a great deal to learn about
the early history of domestic animals it is believed that between the
fifth and the fourth millenia cattle-breeding was introduced, by
way of the Bab el Mandeb at the southern end of the Red Sea, into
Africa and from there to Egypt and the Sudan. This does not, of
course, rule out the possibility that an indigenous species of wild
cattle became domesticated and were the ancestors of the longhorns
in the rock-carvings.

By the third period the elephant, the rhinoceros and the hippopotamus have disappeared. The artists confine themselves to
antelopes, gazelles, ostriches, giraffes, the small berber lions and
moufflons. The men carry shields, lances and spears. Both animals
and men are reproduced almost geometrically, a style that is
characteristic of the third period. But the dominant feature is the
horse and chariot. The chariots have two or four spoked-wheels
and are drawn by two or four horses, which are always at the
gallop. The axle carries a platform to which a shaft is fixed. The
driver stands with the reins in his hand. Most of the pictures show
war- or hunting-chariots but there seems little doubt that they were
also the normal form of transport.

I must refer here to the first known chronicler of the Sahara;
Herodotus of Halikarnassos, better known as 'the father of
modern history.' The first men to explore the Sahara, as far as we
know, were a group of Nasamons, who lived on the Great Plain of
Sirte, south-east of Tripoli. Herodotus records that a number of
Nasamon families had 'very high-spirited boys,' who, as they
grew up, got into 'all kinds of mischief.' The Nasamon 'jeunesse

dorée' one day cast lots and five of them, well supplied with food and water, set off into the unexplored interior. After they had left the coastal belt, they found themselves at first in an area full of wild animals, then in a waterless desert. When they had crossed this, 'which required many days, they finally saw trees again growing in the plain. And they went and picked the fruit which was on the trees and, as they were picking it, little men appeared, less than medium height, seized them and led them away; but they could not understand a word, neither the Nasamons of their language nor they of the Nasamons. And they led them through great swamps and when they had passed through them they came to a town, in which all the people were as small as the leaders and black in colour. And past the town flowed a large river, which flowed from evening to sunrise; in this river crocodiles could be seen.'

The young men of Nasamon were more fortunate than many later desert-travellers: they returned to tell their marvellous tales of black Africa.

Herodotus himself did not enter the Sahara, but shortly before the middle of the fifth century he visited Cyrenaica and learned a great deal about the interior of Libya from merchants and camel-drivers in the Greek trading-centre, Kyrenia. It was on the basis of these interviews that he wrote about the peoples who lived along the coast of 'the midnight sea' from the Nile Delta to Little Sirte.

'Above these, in the interior of the country, is the wilderness of Libya and over the country of the wilderness lies a stretch of sand, which goes from Thebes in Egypt to the Pillars of Hercules. On this stretch of sand, about every ten days' journey, are pieces of salt in great clumps on hills and on the summit of each hill in the midst of the salt a spring of cold and hot water bubbles forth. In this vicinity men also live, the last of them on the side of the desert and beyond the wilderness.'

'Ten days' journey from Thebes live the Ammonites and another ten days to the west is Augila, an oasis in which the Nasamons grow dates.'

'Yet another ten days' journey from Augila there is a further salt hill and a spring and many fruit-bearing palm-trees as in the other oases. And there dwell people who have the name Garamanti,

a powerful and great people. They cover the salt with earth and
then sow corn . . . Here also are the backwards-grazing oxen
which graze backwards for the following reason. Their horns are
bent forward, so that they go backwards when they graze, for they
cannot move forwards because the horns keep striking the ground.
Otherwise they are no different from other oxen, except that their
hide is very thick and tough. These Garamanti chase the Ethiopians, who live in caves, in chariots with four horses. For these
Ethiopians, who live in caves, are the fastest runners we have ever
heard of. But the cave-dwellers eat snakes, lizards and other such
creeping animals. Their language is like no other; they whirr like
bats.'

René Mossu quoted these passages from Herodotus verbatim
and without the slightest need to jog his memory.

'Old-fashioned French education!' he said almost apologetically. 'A lot of learning by heart.'

Later I discovered that this statement was not entirely true. Like
Heinrich Barth and other desert explorers before him, he always
carried a Herodotus with him as an indispensable guide-book to
the prehistoric Sahara.

Herodotus had a weakness for anything that smacked of the
marvellous or the fabulous. As a result his data were for a long time
not treated with the respect they deserve. It is only in recent times
that excavations in the ancient world have vindicated him. When
one sees the oxen with the strange horn-formations on the rock-
carvings in the Sahara, one is almost inclined to accept even his tale
of the oxen that grazed backwards. In any case one feels something
of the astonishment that came over Herodotus's informants each
time they saw the Garamantian cattle. Everything else he has to
say about the Garamanti can be taken literally.

Further sources of information about the Garamanti were the
naturalist Pliny, the historian Tacitus and the geographers, Strabo
and Ptolemaus. The Garamanti served in the Carthaginian army as
mercenaries. They crossed the Pyrenees and the Alps with
Hannibal and marched right up to the gates of Rome. Later, when
the Romans had established themselves in North Africa, Garamanti raids in Tripolitania caused them a great deal of trouble. A

number of punitive expeditions were organized. The Garamanti's
tactics were to withdraw, blocking up the wells behind them—a
scorched earth policy peculiarly adapted to the desert! But in the
course of the first century A.D. the Garamanti surrendered to the
new overlords. Later we find them playing a useful part in Roman
Sahara-expeditions.

The Garamanti capital was in Fezzan. Djerma is the old Gara-
mia. The burial grounds near Djerma-Garama, which are still for
the most part unexplored, contain well over 50,000 graves. In their
heyday the Garamanti controlled the whole area covering Fezzan,
Tassili and Hoggar, and their influence probably extended westwards to the Atlantic and southwards to the Niger. So it is with
some justice that the horse-and-chariot period is also known as the
Garamantian epoch of the Sahara rock-carvings. Strictly speaking,
of course, there is no definite proof that it was the Garamanti who
decorated the rocks with war-chariots. There were other peoples in
Libya who doubtless also travelled through the desert in horse-
drawn vehicles. But as Herodotus speaks only of the chariot-hunts
of the Garamanti, they have become generally accepted as the most
likely rock-artists.

Where the Garamanti came from and where they went we do not
know. The experts are more or less agreed that the Arabs, when
they invaded the territory in the seventh and eleventh centuries,
must have pushed the descendants of the Garamanti southwards
into the heart of the great desert. Today they are called the Tuareg.
There is no such consensus of opinion about their origins. The
only safe assumption is that they came 'from beyond the sea.'
When they came, however, is a mystery. They had the local
inhabitants, the Ethiopians, to contend with. Who were these
Ethiopians? The Greek word means 'sunburnt.' The Ethiopians
were a dark-skinned people. They were not negroes but they belonged to the negroid racial group. Evidence of this is the 'Asselar
Man,' a fossilised skeleton probably from the early stone age. He
resembles a Bantu or a Hottentot. Further evidence is the many
stone tools that seem to be of southern origin and the numerous
negroid details in the rock-carvings.

The Ethiopians of Herodotus undoubtedly formed a representative

section of the Saharan population in the periods of the hunters
and the herdsmen. To the Garamanti, who were white and
obviously keen warriors, this native black population must have
been a godsend. At that time, at least at the beginning of the Garamantian period, the climate of the Sahara was comparatively
humid, and in a hot, humid climate only dark-skinned people can
work on the land. So it hardly seems likely that the Garamanti
exterminated the Ethiopians. Their man-hunts, as recorded by
Herodotus, were probably similar to the slave-raids which the
Tuareg made centuries later into the Sudan. The Italian archaeologist Sergi during excavations in the graveyards of Djerma-Garama
found skeletons of white and negroid people. The latter were
presumably Ethiopian slaves or vassals in the Garamanti capital.

Have the Ethiopians completely disappeared from the Sahara
today? In the Western Sahara stories are still told of a mysterious
people, the Bafour, who were neither white nor black. Anthropologists have suggested that they might have formed a sort of
ethiopoid pocket, and, although again there is no certain proof,
there may be descendants of the Bafour amongst the Imrague
fishermen on the Atlantic coast and the Enaden, who are a caste of
smiths. The movements of the fish and the shortage of fresh-water
springs in that area force the Imragues to lead a nomadic existence.
The Enaden, the smiths, are the pariahs of the desert. Legend has
it that their ancestor watched the Prophet at his ritual ablutions
and had a curse put upon him. To touch a smith is to be tainted; in
some nomadic tribes a woman who marries a smith becomes an
outcast. Yet together with this traditional contempt there is also an
element of fear and almost respect, for the smith, who works with
fire, wind and water, has an obvious association with magic.

Another tribe who may be of ethiopoid origin are the Tibbus
who live in the Tibesti mountains. The Arabs sometimes refer to
them as 'Nas Pharaoun' or 'Sons of Pharaoh', and in the Kufra
Oases, which were once part of the Tibbus' territory, mummies
have in fact been found. This does not mean that the Tibbus are
Egyptians but there is no denying the Egyptian influence in the
rock-carvings and paintings. The Tibbus, some of whom have
mixed with the negro population in the south, have skins of all

shades from caramel to ebony. Their most characteristic features are their aquiline noses and their almost straight hair. They cannot be classed as Egyptians or negroes, as Arabs or Berbers. The inference is, therefore, that they are descended from the Ethiopians. Scholars, who support this theory, naturally underline the fact that the Tibbus are known throughout the desert for their ability to walk fast over long distances and with relatively little food. Herodotus describes them as 'the fastest runners of all men.'

Apart from the Bafour and the Tibbus two other tribes which may be of ethiopoid origin are the dark-skinned inhabitants of the Fezzan oases, although some are probably descended from Sudanese slaves, and the Haratin. The former are more likely to be the descendants of Ethiopians whom the Garamanti conscripted for forced labour in their own fields and palm-groves. The Haratin, who cultivate the palm-groves in the French Sahara, regard themselves as the descendants of slaves who came from the south some time after the Middle Ages. Anthropologists and ethnologists tend on the whole to mistrust this genealogy. The Haratin are at the bottom of the social scale in the oases, even lower than the former slaves who were freed by the French. The Hartani, say the Tuareg, is like a mule, he has no forefathers. His skin is markedly lighter than that of the blacks who were imported from the Sudan.

The Garamantian epoch is, of course, no longer prehistoric. Towards 1700 B.C. the Hyksos, an Asiatic people, invaded the Nile Valley and liquidated the Egyptian Middle Kingdom. It took the Egyptians almost a century and a half to put their house in order again. The Hyksos invasion brought about a revolution in Egypt. The 'Princes of the Strange Lands' had brought horses and chariots with them. Whether and to what extent they found their way westwards into Libya is not known. But it has been established that the Libyans, who were constantly raiding Egypt's western border, were using horses in the thirteenth century B.C. A text of the New Kingdom mentions that Pharaoh's soldiers in a skirmish in 1229 B.C. captured fourteen single-span chariots from a Libyan chief and his sons.

Such evidence as there is suggests that the horse and chariot reached the countries west of Egypt not from the Nile Valley but from the north. In the closing centuries of the second millenium a wave of so-called maritime peoples broke over the Mediterranean from the Black Sea. They probably landed in Cyrenaica and were responsible for pushing the Libyans eastwards against Egypt. It is quite possible that the Garamanti formed part of this invasion. This would explain the Mediterranean features in the Garamanti rock-carvings: the new male and female fashions (tunic for men, short bell-shaped dress for girls, long dress for women), the narrow thighs and broad shoulders of the charioteers, the horses in full gallop. . . .

The one-humped camel is the most characteristic feature of the pictures of the second epoch. Compared with the masterpieces of the hunters and herdsmen, most of the camel-drawings are poor. From an archaeological viewpoint, however, they are extremely interesting.

At what stage the camel first appeared in the Sahara is not known. Camel bones have been found amongst early Stone Age remains, and the patina and vitality of some camel pictures seem to place them in the herdsmen's or even the hunters' period. But in neither case is the evidence conclusive. The champions of the African camel find it hard to explain why there are no references to it in literature. The Egyptian texts and monuments include not a single camel. The explanation that it was treated with religious reverence is not very convincing. Even Herodotus, who would undoubtedly have revelled in descriptions of this strange animal, never so much as mentions it. And the same is true of later historians. Titus Livius and Polybios give a detailed account of the conflict between Carthage and Rome, in which elephants and horses appear but not camels. Sallust in his report on the Jugurthine War in North Africa also makes no reference to them. At the same time none of the ancient authors omits to write about the horse and the part it plays in war and desert life.

The first mention of the camel on African soil is in the account of Caesar's African War. In 46 B.C. at Thapsus Caesar defeated Juba, the ally of his enemy Pompey. Amongst the booty captured by the Romans were 22 dromedaries. In the course of the next few centuries the camel population of North Africa increased sub-stantially. In the fourth century A.D. the town of Tripoli contri-buted 4,000 camels towards a campaign against their enemies.

Emile-Felix Gautier regarded the introduction of the dromedary into North Africa as an historical milestone. In his view the conquest of the black Sahara by white-skinned peoples was carried out on the camel's hump. This view has since been proved wrong. The horse, a full millenium earlier, had fulfilled the role Gautier ascribed to the camel. The horse was gradually superseded by the camel. The chariot appears to have fallen out of use before the camel appeared, but the horse survived for some time after that. There is no evidence that a horse-breeding and horse-riding people was driven out or subdued by camel-riders. Not a single rock-carving so far found shows a 'Meharist' in combat with a horseman. The camel was simply more suited to the desert than the horse.

The rock-pictures of camels frequently carry inscriptions. The symbols belong to Libyan-Berber script systems derived from the Punic-Phoenician script which was in use throughout the Mediter-ranean when Carthage was at the height of its power. Tifinagh, the script of the Tuareg language, is particularly in evidence.

The chronological classification into periods—the hunter, the herdsman, the horse and the camel—is, of course, largely relative. Pictures of horses and chariots are older than camel-pictures and more recent than those depicting cattle. Scholars have also worked out an absolute time-schedule based on the knowledge that the hunters were in their heyday from 5000 to 3500 B.C. and the herdsman from 3500 to 1000 B.C. In the last millenium B.C. horse-driven chariots were racing across the Sahara. The camel appeared about the beginning of the Christian era. The Arab hordes, who invaded the desert in the seventh and eleventh centuries, dealt the art of rock-carving, which in any case was on the decline, its final death-blow. They destroyed, pillaged and converted in the name of the all-merciful God and his Prophet, who teaches: 'Oh, ye faith-ful, forsooth, wine, games, pictures and lotteries are abominable works of Satan.'

Reliable data on the hunters' and herdsmen's periods are almost non-existent. Some archaeologists, including Lhote, believe that

the first rock-carvings date several millenia earlier, but it has now
been fairly well established that they do not go back beyond the
beginning of the early Stone Age. In other words, the oldest of
them are about 10,000 years younger than the paintings in the
Grotto of Lascaux, the 'Sistine Chapel of Ice Age art.'. . . .

I envied Michel Turland his find, a magnificent rhinoceros
carved deep and firmly in the rock. The animal is about a
yard high; from its stubby tail to the points of its powerful,
vicious-looking horn it is two yards high. It is carved on the lower
half of the rock-face in a slanting, climbing position. The hind legs
are like great pillars; whereas the fore-legs are almost like a
piglet's.

The previous evening, shortly before nightfall, I had arrived at
the platinum miners' camp. The dry valley, filled with tents, lies
about 3000 feet above sea-level and takes its name from the black
granite mountains that border it: Oued Tihaliouine. An ordinary
map of the Hoggar gives no indication that there is any human
habitation in this area. The camp only existed on the General Staff
map and at the Headquarters of the Algerian office for Ore Prospecting—as a tiny green flag which now and then was moved a few
centimetres.

Before sunrise Turland, one of the prospectors, woke me up and,
tingling with cold, we walked a short distance up the valley. The
mountains, which a few moments before had been dark and
menacing, were now flamingo scarlet. Strangely enough, the
Tuareg call this the 'dawn of doves.' Turland urged me on and
we arrived at the rock-face just in time. The first rays of the rising
sun were shining through a gap in the mountains on the solitary
rhinoceros.

A closer examination of the rock and its surroundings showed
that the first impression was somewhat deceptive. The rhinoceros dominates its whole environment but it is not alone. At its
feet a second animal is cut in the rock, which is an exact copy but
only a quarter of the size. And between the back of the smaller
animal and the neck of the giant a third is just visible. The body
and legs are barely discernible. The head was obviously carved
then erased, for the rock has been rubbed smooth. This animal,

which is somewhat smaller than the second, is hardly recognizable but is almost certainly another rhinoceros.

Over the stone run vertical columns of Tifinagh script of various lengths, some of them across the outlines of the large rhinoceros. Tifinagh, the ancient script of the Tuareg, has one peculiarity: it can be written and read in any direction, from left to right or right to left, from top to bottom or the reverse, and even in a circle. Presumably the inscriptions on this particular stone are in an archaic Tifinagh, which is mid-way between a conventional script and hieroglyphics. These inscriptions, which are to be found on innumerable rocks in the Tuareg country, are for the most part untranslatable.

Just round the corner, on the north side of the rock, is a camel with Tifinagh symbols. The carving is stilted, small and stylised. Over thin legs and a squarish body, the hump rears up like a pyramid.

There are more carvings in the immediate vicinity. A fourth rhinoceros on a piece of granite is small, beautifully preserved but not particularly graceful; on a stone is an animal difficult to identify, possibly a gazelle or antelope, only lightly cut, barely visible, and obviously the work of an undistinguished artist. There are also a number of graffiti, the meaning of which is not clear, and a further crop of Tifinagh inscriptions.

Michal Turland had found this batch of carvings quite by chance two weeks before while on a brief reconnaissance trip. Since then he had spent every free moment searching the rocks in the neighbourhood. Without the slightest success, he told me. There was no trace of carving implements, only a few remnants of prehistoric pottery, most of them decorated and delicately patterned with bone awl, engraving tool, comb or nails. But no one is interested in such fragments. The Hoggar is full of them. Anyone with the necessary endurance could collect tons of them.

I went back to look at the rhinoceros when the sun was at its zenith. The rock was the colour of honey and the carving could now be seen in all its beauty. I now felt quite certain that originally there had only been this one animal on the rock; all the other works are from later periods and by different hands. The patina of the

outlines of the two smaller animals is much lighter and the incisions
are not so deep. The Tifinagh inscriptions, which also seemed to
have been added later, probably at the same time as the camel on
the North side, are not cut but punched in the rock.

I feel sure that, while the large rhinoceros was the work of an
artist of the hunters' period, the other two were mere slavish
copies and the remaining carvings on the surrounding rocks are
even more inferior in quality.

That evening, shortly before sunset, I saw the rhinoceros from
a new angle and in a new light. I had spent the afternoon, infernally
hot as it was, with the platinum-prospectors. When evening came,
I wandered back to the rhinoceros but not up the floor of the
valley as before; this time I made my way along about thirty yards
above the valley. The granite mountains opposite were reddish gold.
Three black goats, wild and emaciated, trailed gigantic shadows
across the dry flat ground below. A narrow strip in the middle of the
wadi, where the bleached sand still retained some moisture from
the last fall of rain, stood out green and fresh. The orange-yellow
and bottle-green tents under the twisted acacias looked in the clear
evening light like a holiday camp, not a prospectors' base.

With this panorama before me I realised how much is lost if one
only sees the rhinoceros from close at hand. One has to look at it
from a distance to become aware how magnificently it blends with
the landscape.

In the middle of the wadi a sort of rocky plateau rises out of the
alluvial rubble which fills the rest of the valley. This small plateau
is roughly circular in shape and surrounded by large boulders.
From the centre towers the sculptured rock.

The whole setting reminds one of Stonehenge, although here
there is no question of a deliberate arrangement of the rocks in
some artistic formation. Moreover, in the case of Stonehenge the
stones must have been brought from as much as a hundred and
fifty miles away: the island of rocks in the Oued Tihaliouine is an
accident of nature, an example of the artistry of erosion. It is all
that remains of the granite barrier through which the wadi slowly
and relentlessly broke its way. And there is also a considerable
time-gap between the two monuments. Only the oldest parts of

Stonehenge go back to the early Stone Age. If, as I believe, the rhinoceros dates from the period of the hunters, around 1850 B.C., it must have been centuries and possibly even thousands of years old when Stonehenge was erected. But both Stonehenge and the rhinoceros-rock have one thing in common: both are clearly linked with the sun. On 21st June the first ray of the sun falls on the altar stone; in the Oued Tihaliouine the first ray touches the rhinoceros about the time of the winter solstice.

Other signs of sun-worship have been found in the Sahara. Yolande Tschudi speaks of a place called Ti Bedjadj in Tassili, where two footprints are hewn in the rock together with other indentations. Originally this was obviously a place of sacrifice. The Ajjer-Tuareg still pour milk over the rock-face and smear it with butter, which explains why the stone looks so smooth and shiny. Asked to explain this ritual, the natives merely shrug their shoulders. It has simply been practised since time immemorial. But one fact they are aware of: that in summer this particular stone catches the first rays of the rising sun.

Why did the prehistoric hunters and herdsmen carve in rock?

The question was discussed that night by the prospectors in their communal tent. All were agreed that the artists were not working for posterity and still less pursuing their art for art's sake. But apart from that there was a sharp divergence of views.

'Hunting magic, just hunting magic!' said Bernard Guérangé. 'We know that there were hunting rites, in which a picture of the hunted animals played a decisive part. Frobenius once asked a group of pygmies to kill an antelope for his expedition. At first they hesitated, then they agreed on condition that they were given time to make certain preparations. Shortly before dawn the next morning they cleared a piece of ground and flattened it out carefully. Then they drew an antelope in the sand and, as soon as the first rays of the sun touched it, shot an arrow at it. Only then did they set out on their hunt. But, when they got back with the dead antelope, they placed some of its hair and blood on the image in the sand, removed the arrow and erased the image. This, by the way, also took place at sunrise. So I think the artist—and he was an artist even if he was not conscious of it—carved the rhinoceros because he hoped the image would give him some mysterious power over the real animal. These rock-carvings may even have marked a special place where mock-hunts and other ceremonies were conducted before the hunters went out after real game. The artist, in fact, was the witch-doctor or priest of his community. Naturally he also went hunting with them, otherwise he could hardly have produced such an accurate and naturalistic reproduction of the animal. The most important motive behind these rock-carvings was good hunting. Positive, homoeopathic magic.'

'I agree,' remarked Maurice Pinelli, 'but it may only have been indirect. Prehistoric man wanted through his images to acquire for himself the strength and agility of the wild game. Today we shoot anything that takes our fancy. Any Tom, Dick or Harry who has made enough money goes elephant-hunting. It's impossible for us to imagine what hunting with primitive weapons must have been like. It was a trial of strength between man and animal and I imagine the man often came off worst. Drawing or carving can be a particularly intense form of mental preconditioning, of living the part you're going to play. The hunter-draftsman circled round his quarry till he found his weak spot. But above all, in some magical way, he acquired the animal's strength.'

'Most of us know nothing about hunting,' I pointed out. 'Unfortunately. We're not hunters, we're killers. Our weapons have developed in inverse ratio to our reluctance to use them. There was a time when man and nature shared the same destiny. Prehistoric man regarded himself as a child of nature and any interference with nature aroused a sense of guilt. When a tree was felled, the spirit of the tree was frequently placated with a sacrifice. Hardly an animal was killed without some offering being made. Frobenius's pigmy story is an example of atonement. Before the image in the sand was erased, hair from the dead antelope and a calabash of its blood were thrown on it. And this act of atonement probably had a very practical side to it. We mustn't forget that the big-game hunters couldn't survive without game. It was a matter of life and death to them that the game should not die out. Their images were perhaps intended to represent the Lord of the Animals. I certainly don't find it hard to believe that our rhinoceros was supposed to fill that role. So we have appeasement of the Lord of the Animals—and at the same time an element of reproductive magic.'

'Hunting magic, homoeopathic magic, reproductive magic and Frobenius,' Michel Turland broke in impatiently. 'Why in heaven's name do we have to try and probe so deep? Perhaps Papa Hunter was simply giving his young son a few lessons. Or why not assume that the hunter who carved our rhinoceros simply did it for fun? For the good of his soul? I'm not maintaining that he set out to create a work of art. We've all done a bit of sketching, without even thinking of following in Picasso's footsteps. The urge to produce images is something primeval. Portraiture is a kind of self-definition, a way of projecting oneself and yet escaping from oneself. And that is just as true today as it was then. But for pre-historic man this urge to impose his personality on an environment which he felt to be hostile must have been particularly important. Reproducing nature in rock-carvings was, indirectly, a form of self-justification. The beginning of the emancipation you were talking about.'

'You seem to be probing pretty deep!' I remarked.

'Maybe so,' said Turland. 'But at least I stick to psychological motives that we in our century are familiar with. We've been talking as if the only motives that concerned us were the hunter's. I wonder how your theories of magic would apply to the herdsman.'

'No doubt the herdsmen had plenty of rites and ceremonies, in which the rock-carvings played a part, even if we don't know what that part was,' said Guérangé. 'There are many ancient myths showing how the ox, at certain periods and in certain places, was worshipped as a symbol of wealth. Its horns suggested the waxing moon, and the milk also seems to have been linked somehow with fertility. In the pre-Islamic hill-tombs—the sort we have come across so often while we were prospecting—human skeletons and the bones of oxen have been found side by side. In the oases you can often see the skull of an ox over the entrance to a house or on the walls round the palm-groves. It is to protect the inhabitants and the people cultivating the dates against the evil eye. Perhaps these superstitions, which have survived through countless generations, are the last relics of the original semi-magical, semi-religious worship of the ox.'

'I know I've said this before, but we can't take our emancipated attitude to animals as a criterion,' I objected. 'Cattle, in those times, were certainly more than just providers of meat and milk. Even today among the Bororo-Peulh, who breed cattle in the steppes about 600 miles south of this camp, there's still a strong element of mysticism in the relations between the people and their domestic animals. According to Jean Gabus the Peulh give their children two names, one official, the other the name of a young animal. The child is given the second as soon as it is born but is never called by it. This is a secret name which is seldom uttered.'

'But after all the Peulh are not the herdsmen of I don't know how many thousand years ago,' said Turland.

'Perhaps they are,' I replied. 'The prehistoric herdsmen and their cattle must have moved on somewhere. When the land became desert, they may have gone south. The Peulh might well be their descendants. They're reputed, for example, to have introduced the first cattle into West Africa. As cattle-breeders they're certainly superior to any other people in the plain. And Lhote has found human figures amongst the Tassili paintings that date from the time of the herdsmen and show a remarkable similarity to the hair-style of the Peulh.'

The oil-lamps in the tent were running low and the discussion was adjourned. Not surprisingly, it had produced more questions than answers. I took a final stroll in the direction of the rhinoceros. A cricket chirped and glowworms flickered like electric sparks in the darkness. The heat of the day was seeping from the mountains into the valley. The full moon seemed to be floating in milk. Outlined against the translucent sky the great stone was black, silent and mysterious. The message it carries will always remain a mystery.

*   *   *

No one I met had a kind word for First Lieutenant Montagné. 'A gasbag—especially when he has had a drop too much to drink.'

I myself had not yet come across him but I had reasons of my own for believing that he might be better than his reputation. Montagné is the S.A.S. officer in the oil town Edjeleh. The S.A.S. officers I had already met in the course of my journey formed an élite of which France could be proud. Without exception they were 'men against the desert,' cultured, sincere in their affection for the natives, not a military so much as a social élite. S.A.S. stands for 'Section Administrative Spécialisée.' This corps of administrators is, of course, a product of the Algerian war, but it represents France not in a Colonial but in a consultative capacity. The S.A.S. is the advance force in a psychological counter-attack, but I never once had the impression of a calculated manoeuvre, never once heard the word 'propaganda.' In areas with a predominantly peasant population of Fellagha the S.A.S. officers are available, often at the risk of their lives, to render all kinds of services. They are expected to be familiar with the local land-register, to be able to lay out a palm-grove, to deal with irrigation questions and to know all about cattle-breeding. In other words, they have to solve all the problems that arise, day in, day out, in a population that is both sedentary and nomadic.

'. . . especially when he has had a drop too much to drink.'

This remark at least was inappropriate. When it was made, we had all got beyond the stage of quenching our thirst. We had reached the red wine. Several glasses of anisette and white wine had already been consumed, and the champagne was cooling in the ice-buckets, while a black servant armed with a serviette waged a hopeless battle against the red dust that covered the champagne glasses and the cutlery and grated between our teeth. The industrial Sahara was celebrating on the fringe of the paprika-coloured sand-dunes of Edjeleh.

The 'Société-Commerciale de Transport' was holding a special dinner in the barracks, which visitors by polite agreement call an hotel, to celebrate the arrival of two supply-lorries. There was asparagus, chicken, rice, strawberries, ice-cream, chocolate cake, coffee with cream. The asparagus and the strawberries were not out of tins.

'A gasbag. . . .'

Admittedly, First Lieutenant Montagné, who turned up very late, clearly enjoyed talking. Presumably no-one would have held it against him, if he had been on the same 'wavelength' as the others. The conversation was about lorries, air-conditioning plant and the growing competition on the roads and tracks of the Sahara. Lieutenant Montagné, however, was obviously not very interested in the two Berliet lorries, Type G.B.O. He consumed his ice-cream in thoughtful silence. Perhaps he was thinking of his shells, bones and carvings. He talked of them with passionate interest, his eyes glowing in his taut, deeply-tanned face. He would plunge into his pet subject in front of people who were not remotely interested. That was his failing.

That Sunday morning at Edjeleh, Lieutenant Montagné was anxious to show me his treasures. Yet when we set out it was not in the direction of Gour Laoud, twenty-five miles away, where the rock-carvings had become a permanent attraction for visiting oil-men. Instead, the jeep clambered up through the rocky hills behind the camp. The sandstone ridge is broken every now and then by a long tongue of sand that runs down like a glacier. We made our way up one of these, higher and higher into the mountains. The weird shapes of the sandstone, each one a fresh source of surprise, are mostly wrought by the wind. I got out and examined two rocks which were so close together that they looked like the walls of a huge tunnel. For thousands of years the wind has whistled through this cavity like water through a spout. A column of rock immediately in front has been polished as smooth as a billiard-ball by the action of wind and sand.

But we did not spend much time on these quirks of Nature. 'Just round the corner' (my companion had his own peculiar method of finding his way about the desert) we would come upon the first carvings. I was excited. Apart from the fact that Lieutenant Montagné had found the carvings only a few weeks before during one of his solitary excursions, I had so far seen only one rhinoceros, not a collection of rock-carvings. Hence my sense of excitement, as if the curtain was just going up on a première.

There are, in fact, two collections, about two minutes apart by car, but otherwise identical. A long reef, corroded by wind and weather, rears up from the ocean of sand. It is covered with carvings. There must be hundreds of figures cut into the rock, without order or pattern: oxen, many oxen, antelopes, gazelles, a small lion, ostriches, and little men, about the size of dinner plates, with round heads hunting the ostriches. Some of the animals, an elephant and a rhinoceros amongst them, are unfinished. In size, line and artistic merit they vary, but none of them reaches monumental proportions. Most of the carvings are of medium size and there is no patina; the incisions are the same colour as the rock. It is just as if these rocks had been used as a sort of communal sketch-book by a large group of herdsmen-artists. One of the sculptors, however, has a style of his own: in carving animals he turns the hindlegs, sometimes even all four legs and the tail, into wind-blown flags—a mannerism not without elegance and grace.

One feature of both collections that particularly struck me was the remains of an overhang of rock. Both cave-dwellings, for that was almost certainly their original function, lie rather surprisingly on the windward side. The wind, which always blows from the same direction, has played havoc with the carvings and the overhang has been whittled away to a mere stump of rock. I was immediately reminded of the southern façade of the Roman triumphal arch at Orange in the Rhone valley; there too the relief-work has been sadly worn by the moist sea wind.

Could it be that when these rock cavities were inhabited, the prevailing wind came from another direction? Or were the Stone Age people forced to make do with any shelter, however uncomfortable, that Nature provided?

After I had located the direction of the wind, I noticed that on the leeward side of the rock there were no oxen. Most of the sculptures were of gazelles, antelopes and ostriches, which did not appear on the windward side. It is naturally pointless to speculate whether this has any special significance. There is, in any case, nothing to suggest that the two sides belong to different periods. The artist who gave his animals elongated legs worked on both the leeward and the windward.

On a spur of rock at the second site I came on one carving which

must surely take a special place in the Sahara's stone visitors' book:
a girl, and without even a bikini.

Lieutenant Montagné had left me to satisfy my own curiosity
and begun to burrow in the sand a short distance from the cliffs.
Suddenly he called me over. An enormous skull had appeared,
bleached and corroded. We spent the next half-hour tracing the
backbone. It was a good twenty yards long.

'A whale-fossil,' he said unhesitatingly. It sounded ridiculous.
A whale in the middle of sand which in two hours' time would be
too hot to touch with one's bare hands? And yet before long I found
myself accepting the idea.

During the millions of centuries of the earth's history the desert
has several times been flooded, either partially or entirely, by the
sea. For a long time the Sahara was, in fact, considered to be a
dried-up ocean-bed, a theory based on the association of desert
sand with a sea-shore. The salt lakes and swamps in the desert—
so-called Chotts—were taken to be the last remains of the sea,
which the sun had not yet evaporated. The modern geologist will
laugh at you if you come out with this 'old wives' tale' yet as
recently as thirty years ago reports of a 'sea of Timbuctoo' were
being seriously investigated.

In 1899 the botanist, Auguste Chevalier, was wandering round
the Timbuctoo area when, to his surprise, he found a snail's shell
in the sand. His surprise was understandable: this particular
species of snail lives only in the sea. The natives were completely
baffled by the foreign visitor's excitement. They showed him
places where he found other shells, some of which belonged to a
second maritime species. Chevalier published a report of his
discovery in 1901 and came to the conclusion that in the Quaternary period less than 800,000 years ago, the sea had advanced as
far as Timbuctoo. As Timbuctoo today is almost a thousand miles
from the Atlantic Coast, this theory caused a considerable sensation. Other scientists, who regarded Chevalier as a charlatan and
made on-the-spot investigations, also found snails' shells of the
same species but the sheer quantity of them strengthened their
suspicion that this was not the work of Nature.

It was not until 1935, however, that these suspicions were finally confirmed. Theodore Monod collected 10,133 shells and examined each one separately. The result: these shells were a form of currency brought by caravan from Mauretania to Timbuctoo. Oddly enough they show no signs of wear; presumably they were only exchanged in bulk. The exchange-value of each shell seems to have been very low and on the Atlantic coast they were passed from hand to hand in quantity. Towards the end of the Middle Ages they went out of circulation, when caravans from Morocco started trading in cowrie-shells, a porcelain-snail from the Indian Ocean which the Venetians had built up to one of their major exports. Timbuctoo adopted the new currency and joined the cowrie-area. And one result of this currency-reform was that the old coinage was buried, though whether spontaneously or on the orders of some Finance Minister is not known.

Once the myth of the 'Sea of Timbuctoo' was exploded, all hope of tracing a Quaternary Sea in the Sahara disappeared. The last time the Mediterranean and the Gulf of Guinea formed one ocean across the Sahara was in the Upper Chalk Age, perhaps seventy million years ago, when the primeval rocks of the Hoggar mountains were washed by its waves.

Lieutenant Montagné's whale may, therefore, have had its place in the prehistoric desert. That it lies, so to speak, on the doorstep of Stone-Age man is a rather whimsical trick of Nature—a joke without any real point. The whale had been dead about eighty million years when a Neolithic flint made the first incision in the rock. We searched the area round the skeleton and unearthed gigantic fossilised mussels and fins.

'This makes me feel like a plate of bouillabaisse,' said Lieutenant Montagné ironically but not without a certain nostalgia. For a moment the man of the Sahara had become a Frenchman from the Midi again, whose mouth watered at the very thought of sea fish in saffron sauce.

I returned to the 'hotel' Edjeleh with my knapsack full of bones, fins and shells. The others admired my treasures but somewhat scornfully and briefly. The Foreign Legion had invited us to champagne cocktails in return for the gargantuan meal of the night before.

The officers of the Legion did the honours, their pleated trousers and their sandals as white as snow. Within half an hour the desert landscape completely changed. A hot wind swept down the road to the camp, whipping the sand in countless little whorls, filling the air with fine dust. The *tricolore*, the machine-guns on their self-propelled gun-carriages and the small-arms of the sentries were all swallowed up in the reddish mist. It was as if the sandstorm had dropped a curtain on the unforgettable Sunday morning I had spent with Lieutenant Montagné.

4. The Green Desert

EVERYTHING that has been written on the Sahara—the myths and the legends, the lies and the truths—is recorded in the 'Institut de Recherches Sahariennes.' Yet, although it is called a Research Institute, its basic or at least its primary function is not research but something much more important: it is an exclusive club for students of the Sahara, where any scientific research into the problems of the great desert can be co-ordinated.

The Institute is on the ground floor of one of the enormous buildings which keep shooting up like mushrooms in Algiers. It is loosely connected with the University; its Secretary-General, Professor Robert Capot-Rey, is also the Director of the Geographical Institute at the University.

My conducted tour of the Saharan Institute with Professor Capot-Rey was a somewhat ghostly experience. The Professor had his own special method of closing doors. As we left each room, he would pause for a second with his artificial leg still just inside it, then use the final heave at the door-handle to propel himself on his way. I don't mind admitting that at first this ingenious way of overcoming a disability seemed to me almost eerie, but I then found myself wondering if, without it, Professor Capot-Rey's scientific achievements would have been humanly possible. His book on the French Sahara, which is known throughout the world, is not only a careful and accurate survey of the outstanding foreign contributions on the subject, it also gives an account of innumerable investigations and expeditions he himself made in the Sahara.

Although his official title is Secretary General of the Institute of Saharan Studies, the Professor, who entered his sixties in 1957, is in reality the uncrowned king of Saharan geographers.

We talked, to begin with, about oil, about the platinum-deposits and diamond-prospecting in the Hoggar. I had a feeling that Professor Capot-Rey, at this particular stage in the conversation, was merely being polite. In fact, when we discussed the industrial potentialities of the Sahara, a certain stiffness crept into his voice. The 'air-conditioned' desert is not the desert that has revealed so many of its secrets and wonders to him.

His whole manner changed when I began to ask questions about the prehistoric Sahara. Its humidity! In Tassili, more than six thousand feet above sea-level, Lhote copied an unusually significant hunting-scene: three canoes made of rushes are circling round three hippopotamus. Today, however, the hippopotamus, like the elephant, giraffe, rhinoceros and antelope which are portrayed on thousands of rock-walls in the Sahara, is only found much farther south in the savannah or in the equatorial jungle. The herds of cattle have also moved south. During the Ice Age, from about 800,000 to 10,000 B.C. the Sahara appears to have had a distinctly humid climate.

Today the air-conditioning plant and the refrigerator are symbols of an invasion. Industrial combines and towns are already on their way. The desert is at last being colonised. Yet the traces left by prehistoric man suggest that the Sahara was once more densely populated than it is likely to be in the foreseeable future. Apart from the rock-carvings and the countless fragments of pottery, the stone-axes, the flint arrow-heads, the pestles and mortars, the bone bodkins and harpoons, the beads made of ostrich-egg shells, all of which were produced and employed by the people of the rock-carving period, there are also relics from previous millenia, which may even be hundreds of thousands of years older—from the Early Stone Age—which point to an astonishingly dense population in the desert. Incredible quantities of scrapers, knives and stone wedges have been found in some places. In the heart of Tanezrouft and Tenere, which today are completely desert, fishermen and shell-collectors once lived. Not only have stone implements, the remains of ashes, the bones of hippopotamus and elephants and turtle and mollusc shells been found but whole lorry-loads of fish bones.

When prehistoric artists were filling caves in southern France

and northern Spain with their carvings and paintings, Central
Europe, or at least those parts which were not under glaciers, was
swept by the icy winds from the Scandinavian and Alpine ice-cap.
Lichen, heather, moss, reeds and cotton-grass, Alpine violets,
dwarf willow, crowberries, bilberries and dwarf beeches were the
main features of a tundra-like vegetation. The animal life: mam-
moth, rough-coated rhinoceros, silver fox, reindeer, musk-ox,
cave-bear, lemming, ibex, chamois, marmot, saiga antelope, wild
ass, wild horse, wild boar and whistling hare. Long, severe winters
were followed by short, arctic summers. In spring and autumn
there were violent storms which whipped up great clouds of fine
dust from the steppes and deposited it in more sheltered places.
These storms would sometimes bury whole herds of exhausted
animals under massive funeral-pyres of dust.

It was a topsy-turvy world, in which Central Europe was a desert
waste swept by dust-storms, while rain was pouring down on the
Sahara! For the view is gaining ground that the rainy periods in
the Sahara coincided not with the glacial periods in Europe but
with the more temperate intervals when the ice-cap of the northern
hemisphere was melting.

The Sahara is not a desert in relief. In other words, its barrenness is not a mere surface phenomenon. The Atlas mountains, it is
true, act as an umbrella but they are not responsible for the desert.
The Sahara is a product of the climate. Over the equator, where
the sun's angle of incidence or the range of its rays is at its widest,
massive currents of air are generated, which condense the moisture
in heavy clouds, flow northwards and drop in the region of the
thirtieth and thirty-fifth parallels. Deprived of their moisture and
becoming even drier as they sink, they flow back over the surface
of the earth, like hot air from an oven, to the equatorial low-
pressure area, sucking the soil and the atmosphere dry of moisture
and leaving them exposed to the blazing sun.

'The relationship as we see it between the rainy periods in the
Sahara and the inter-glacial periods in Europe is still far from
clear,' said Professor Capot-Rey. 'It seems unlikely that the
northern and southern areas of the desert underwent the same kind
of climatic change. A deterioration of the climate in one part may

very well have been accompanied by an improvement in the other. North and south were subject to quite different climatic conditions. Even today the north is an area of winter rain, while the south is dominated by the summer monsoon rains. It's very important to bear this in mind. Let's assume that the desert retreated in the south and that the Sudanese monsoon rains moved northwards. Then it's quite likely that the desert advanced towards the foot of the Atlas mountains or even into the Algerian plateau. And vice versa. At the Congress of Prehistoric Studies in Zurich, Lionel Balout put forward a theory that aroused a great deal of interest. He suggested that as the cold air front receded in the interglacial periods there was a corresponding movement of the monsoon rain northwards, whereas, on the other hand, the growth of the ice-sheet in the glacial periods had driven the monsoon rains back but had led to increased rainfall in the northern Sahara.'

'It is an attractive theory, all the more attractive because it would explain why relics from different Stone-Age periods are so unevenly distributed. Balout's theory has, however, met with opposition among meteorologists. Obviously no final answer has yet been given either on this or on the question of the Sahara's prehistoric climate.'

The most lasting impression one can have of the part played by rain in the Sahara is from the air. In the evening as the shadows lengthen and the desert becomes a gigantic relief-map one sees the corpse of a once well-watered landscape, deeply-scarred by stream- and river-beds. Throughout almost the entire year they are dry; only for a few days or even hours are they in spate. Then they are filled with a yellow, racing torrent. But before long it dies down and evaporates in sun and sand. These brief torrents have not created the valleys but merely made use of them. Most of the wadis are relics of the prehistoric rainy periods, when the mountains in the heart of the Sahara were the source of great rivers. The Hoggar Massif in particular sent its waters far to the south and north. The Oued Igharghar, for example, which today is littered with sand-dunes that diverted the streams, rose in the Hoggar and flowed into a lake near Biskra.

'In oceans of sand, which today are completely windswept,'

Professor Capot-Rey continued, 'there were once extensive stretches of water surrounded by sandhills. In the hollows and gulleys between the dunes you will frequently find grey or black sand. The colour depends on the mixture of organic substances. The sand is peaty and contains decomposed matter from reeds together with mollusc- and snail-shells such as you find in stagnant water with luxuriant vegetation. The same varieties are to be found today in the sweet-water pools of North Africa and French Sudan. Quite a common feature of those particular areas is rods of quartz-glass, so-called lightning-rods which were produced when the lightning struck the sand and smelted it. Some of these rods are several yards long and obviously indicate severe thunderstorms. Significantly enough they are not to be found in sandhills of more recent formation.'

'There are quite a few indications that the rainy periods in the Sahara were by no means all equally humid but that more rain fell on the early stone age peoples than on the hunters and herdsmen of the late stone age. The fishermen of the early stone age were sedentary, while the hunters and herdsmen were compelled to lead a nomadic life. Some archaeologists regard the geographical position of the various collections of rock-pictures as an indication that, when the herdsmen's period began, large tracts of the desert were already inaccessible to cattle. This can, of course, be no more than speculation till a complete inventory of the rock-pictures has been made, but there is a great deal to be said for the view that these art-collections concentrated in a small area represented some kind of prehistoric oases, the inhabitants of which were surrounded by a wide expanse of dry and even hostile country. This would explain why so many different styles are to be found comparatively close together. Amongst the Tassili frescoes, for example, some are as different from others in style as a fresco by Giotto is from a picture by Picasso, although they may all belong to the same period.'

'A further significant pointer to the late Stone Age climate is the fact that many of the early Stone Age implements found are in parts of the desert which today are uninhabitable even by nomads. Tanezrouft, where fishermen and shell-collectors once lived, is not called the Land of Fear for nothing. On the other hand the majority of the rock-carvings are within reach of a spring, a guelta (rain-pool) or a water-point of some kind. Moreover those found on the walls of a dry valley are often well below the high-water mark reached by the Oued tens and hundreds of thousands of years before and just above the present flood-level. The volume of water that passed through these wadis seems, therefore, to have dropped very little with time, otherwise the pictures would not be in such a good state of preservation. That naturally applies much more to the paintings than to the carvings.'

'But doesn't this mean,' I asked Professor Capot-Rey bluntly, 'that the green desert of the rock-carvers and painters was a mirage, a chimera? Perhaps the giraffes, elephants, hippos and other animals never existed in the Sahara. Perhaps it was big-game hunters, who had been on safari in the Sudan, who came north and carved them from memory.'

'Of course they existed,' the Professor assured me. 'The pictures are much too numerous and too lifelike to have been drawn from memory. Besides, we know that many of these animals were still living in the Sahara in historic times. As for the green desert . . . that too certainly existed.'

Before we parted, Professor Capot-Rey gave me an introduction to Pierre Quézel.

* * *

Professor Pierre Quézel is a rather unimpressive figure, who looks like a typical civil servant. When I eventually found his room, after wandering through the maze of corridors in Algiers University, I committed the faux pas of taking him for his assistant. With the same diffidence that any scientist must feel when he is called upon to show a foreign visitor into a laboratory which he knows is antiquated and poorly equipped, Professor Quézel led me into a somewhat shabby attic-room.

Appearances were deceptive. His workroom may be as remote from the popular conception of a modern scientific laboratory as Professor Quézel himself is from that of a brilliant scholar, but the significance of the work being done there is beyond question.

Towards the reconstruction of the green desert Professor Quézel has provided the most recent and in some respects the most vital clue so far. It is not based on supposition or more or less bold deductions. It is a relic of the green desert itself.

The male germ-cells of plants, the pollen-seeds, are barely visible, and sometimes even invisible, to the naked eye. It takes not merely hundreds of thousands or millions but billions of them to fill a thimble. But under a microscope one can distinguish the pollen of one plant-species from another. By analysing a single pollen-seed the expert can usually identify the plant from which it originally came. By examining the pollen in honey, for example, he can tell from which flowers the bees extracted it.

The study of pollen as such is more than a century old. But it was not until 1893 that a scientist in Bremen, C. A. Weber, realised its potential significance as an aid to prehistoric research. Trees pollinated by the wind produce enormous quantities of pollen and the wind scatters it over a wide area. Sulphur-rain, for instance, is quite a common phenomenon; a storm brings down pine-pollen which is absorbed as a yellow powder in pools and puddles. The astonishing fact is that these tiny seeds may survive for thousands of years, in exceptional cases even for millions of years. Various species of pollen have been discovered in brown coal from the Tertiary or third geological period.

Such discoveries, together with implements, ash remains, animal bones, and parts of human skeletons, are naturally of the greatest interest to the student of prehistoric times, for they tell him what the vegetation looked like and from this he can deduce with a high degree of certainty what the climate was like. But the different species of pollen not only provide a general picture of prehistoric vegetation, they also reveal a wealth of detailed information. Where pollen species from different periods but from the same area can be listed, they are diagrammatised to give a complete picture of the vegetation in that area. To take the stock example, what we know today of the past history of the forests in Northern and Central Europe we owe to a considerable extent to pollen diagrams.

'Until recently,' Professor Quézel explained to me, 'scientists held very pronounced views about the kind of environment in

which pollen can survive. One condition seemed to be lack of
oxygen. So peat bogs or the mud in stagnant lakes are veritable
pollen museums. And, not surprisingly, the first analyses of pollen
were confined to peat and mud. But these are two natural deposits
which are completely lacking in the Sahara. It simply did not
occur to biologists, therefore, to try pollen-analysis as a means of
determining the prehistoric vegetation and climate of the Sahara.
Then it was discovered that in certain conditions pollen-seeds
survive even where a small amount of oxygen is present. This is
particularly true of soil rich in humus, of so-called bleached earth
or pod-soil, and of fine sand.'

Professor Quézel carried out his research in collaboration with
Armand Pons. In his report to the Academy of Sciences he
modestly concealed his own pioneer-work behind the anonymous
pronoun 'we'. Even during our conversation he studiously avoided
any reference to the first person singular that might reflect on his
collaborator. But there is no doubt he was the brains of the
operation.

In March 1956 he went to the Central Sahara to investigate the
alluvial terraces, the finest of which consisted of five terraces on
top of one another. In all probability each one corresponded to a
different period of rain or humidity. The total thickness at some
points was as much as a hundred yards. For the most part the conditions were not favourable for the preservation of pollen-seeds, but
in the upper part of one terrace a grey, powder-like layer was found.

'We examined it under the microscope and there was no possible doubt: this was a genuine fossil deposit. You can imagine our
excitement at discovering this unprepossessing grey powder, for
here we could expect to find pollen.'

Professor Quézel took samples from three different places: in
the heart of the Tefedest mountains, at Tin Tessandjelt about
4,000 feet up on the eastern slopes of the Tefedest, and at In-Eker
on the Hoggar 'highway' between Tit and Tesnou. Some of the soil
was found to contain remains of plants, while in other parts there
were traces of human implements, which in one case enabled
Professor Quézel to identify the soil-layer as belonging to the later
period of the Early Stone Age.

'Don't forget,' he warned me, 'that an examination of fossil pollen can only produce results if we have a list of pollen species of living plants, for only then can we trace the origin of fossil pollen. For Northern and Central Europe the pollen catalogue is fairly extensive. A whole generation of Scandinavian and German biologists have worked on it. But similar information about Mediterranean vegetation was almost completely lacking. We had to collect it very laboriously before we could even begin to identify the pollen of the Sahara.'

Professor Quézel showed me pollen-seeds under the microscope. Most of them were more or less round in shape, but some came to a point and in fact no one seed was the same as another. Professor Quézel sounded almost like a sorcerer when he explained that one was from an Aleppo pine, another from an evergreen oak.

He found pollen from the following species and varieties of plants: cypress, sandarac cypress, juniper, Aleppo pine, Atlas cedar, corn, black or grey alder, evergreen oak, southern nettle tree, Italian daphne, lime, and possibly winter-lime, French tamarisk, the jujube tree, ash or jasmin, and olive.

This list means little or nothing unless one realises where the pollen-seeds come from: the heart of a desert which more than any other on this planet comes nearest to being completely barren.

'Such evidence as we have,' said Professor Quézel, 'is too slight to warrant any far-reaching conclusions but it does seem a fair assumption that in the top strata, which means the most recent periods, conifers and particularly cypress predominate. On the other hand, we can trace an extremely interesting qualitative change in the general picture. Lime and alder are essentially northern trees. There are no limes in North Africa today and the black alder is only found in certain well-watered areas of the Riff and Eastern Algeria. We found traces of lime and alder pollen only in the lowest stratum, which, to judge by the early palaeolithic stone implements it contained, goes back some eight to fifteen thousand years. And this pollen is mixed with typical Mediterranean plants, Aleppo pines and evergreen oak. This seems to me to indicate a humid but changeable climate. Trees fond of warm, dry weather—olive, jujube and cypress—are only found in the topmost stratum, which is certainly no more than five thousand years old.'

'Am I right in thinking that you showed me corn pollen?'

'Yes, but that was only found in the two lowest strata. Whether this means that cereal cultivation was abandoned because of a deterioration in the climate remains to be seen. As I said before we haven't enough evidence to allow us to draw that kind of conclusion.'

'You mentioned five alluvial terraces, each of which must be connected with a period of humidity. But from what you said I gather they might all date back to one single period.'

'They undoubtedly do. They all belong to the last Saharan rainy period. They were designed to strike a balance between wet and dry. It's significant that pollen of Aleppo pine, southern nettle tree and evergreen oak is found at all levels. These trees like a moderately dry climate, such as you have today in North Africa, Spain and Sicily. It appears to have lasted throughout the Early Stone Age and only taken a radical turn for the worse about 1000 B.C.'

The results of this pollen research were received with great excitement by Saharan specialists. For Professor Quézel they were no more than an encouraging beginning. He had set his mind on continuing his pursuit of the green desert. And as the scientist only gathers information by looking for it, the Professor set himself the not very appetising task of examining fossil manure. A prehistoric rock-dwelling hoof animal about the size of a rabbit, closely related to the elephant and the rhinoceros, had bequeathed it to science several thousands of years ago. It was found under an overhang of rock on a peak in the Taessa Massif of the Hoggar mountains about 6,000 feet up by Henri-Jean Hugot.

Fossil guano is not uncommon in the Hoggar mountains. My own experience of it was not particularly pleasant:

There seemed to be no end to the loose, coal-black rubble over which we rode that day and there was not a breath of air. It was like riding in an oven. Even my guide, a solemn, taciturn Targi, who had been leading his camel, found the heat of the ground intolerable and took refuge on the swaying back of his mehari. Vaguely the square blue Akar-Akar peak loomed up on the horizon. It had once featured in a film as Antinea's castle. We planned to take shelter from the midday sun in one of its caves. Hennon ag Amanrassa, my companion, saw to the camels while I tried to make myself comfortable in the shadow of the rock. I paid no attention to the deposits of manure which were lying around and which were undoubtedly very old. They were not the first I had seen. But Hennon shrank back with an expression of horror. Normally a very sensible person he refused on this occasion even to listen to reason. As his French vocabulary consisted of one word, 'Mossio,' he spoke in Tamahaq, the dialect of the Hoggar-Tuareg. I used Swiss-German. So far we had got along famously. But these deposits of fossil manure completely changed the atmosphere of friendly understanding. Hannon was deaf to all my appeals. He saddled the camels. Willy-nilly I had to pack my goods and chattels again and we set off as if pursued by bandits. I was completely mystified by Hennon's peculiar behaviour, but the midday sun, which was beating down mercilesssly, soon killed my curiosity.

This prehistoric guano reminded me of that incident. Professor Quézel laughed: 'The answer to the riddle is in the folklore and legends of the Tuareg. Your guide took the guano in all seriousness for remains of the body of Elias. Elias and his uncle Amamellen, from whom all rock pictures are said to originate, play an important part in the mythology of Hennon's people. Hence his panic at the very thought of entering the cave or even remaining near it.'

Professor Quézel was not thinking of Elias, when he examined the pollen-seeds which had been preserved in the fossil manure. He was interested in the animal's menu. And he was able to establish that, in addition to some ferns, the following plants were represented: crucifers, heather, grasses, sumach shrubs, compositae, olive, umbel plants, nettles, clove, goosefoot, walnuts, labiates, reeds, knot-grass, willows, maples, woodbine, beech, milkwort, lime, reedmace, and—representing the gymnogenous plants—pine, cypress and sea-grape.

'This list,' Professor Quézel explained, 'is so arranged as to record the relative position of each species in the total number of pollen-seeds examined. But here too it is naturally not possible to deduce what the position of each species was in the actual vegetation of the area. The prehistoric rock badger was not interested in botanical statistics. He ate anything that tickled his taste-buds. But even so he is an extremely useful collaborator. His food obviously had a strong Mediterranean flavour. Crucifers, sumach, heather, olive and umbel plants are its main features. Of course, it is often difficult to pin down the individual pollen-seeds to a particular genus or variety. It's only with trees and bushes that the picture becomes fairly clear. The guano contained the following: Atlas cedar, cypress, large sea-grape, Aleppo pine, three-lobed maple, the terebinth or turpentine-tree, the mastic or gum tree, juniper, briar, oak, royal walnut, bay lime, willow, the large-leaved lime and the mountain ash.'

The manure, incidentally, like all matter that has once been living, also contained a clock. Throughout countless centuries the proportion of 'dead' to live carbon atoms has been changing in accordance with an inviolable law of nature. By ascertaining this proportion at any given moment the atomic physicist can establish when life ceased in the organism under examination. Guano is the ideal substance for this so-called C14 Test. The carbon clock of the excrement in question registered an age of 4680 years with a margin of error of 300 years on either side. In other words, our rock-badger had his orgy sometime between 3022 and 2422 B.C.

3000 B.C. marks the dawn of history. Jericho, the oldest known town on our planet, had been inhabited for at least 5000 years before that. The Nile Valley was on the point of being united under one Empire. In Uruk, the leading Sumerian City State, brick-making and the brewing of beer were already common practice, and a monetary system was introduced. The priests of the temple, which served not only as a place of worship but also as a court of justice, a royal residence and a supermarket, devised a script, which is probably the most important invention in the history of the human race. Significant is the fact that it was obviously not devised for the greater glory of the gods but to safeguard the divine ministers against sharp practice when the corn, oil, dates, vegetables, hides and skins were delivered to the temple.

By the year 2400 B.C. the great pyramids had already been built in Egypt, the Sun God Ra was about to occupy the place of honour amongst the Egyptian Gods, and Pharaoh's doctors were laying the foundations of Egypt's fame as a world-centre of medicine. In the valley of the Indus great cities flourished. King Sargon of Akkad, the first Mesopotamian Prince with any claim to be a world conqueror, overran the Sumerians, adopted the title "King of the four continents" and maintained a standing army of 5,400 men. The solid disk wheel was superseded by the spoked wheel.

This is the general historical background to the first Saharan 'menu' known to us in detail. During the lifetime of the rock-badger conditions in the desert were still those of the early Stone Age. But above all it was green.

'Less than 5,000 years ago,' said Professor Quézel, 'the Hoggar mountains were covered with rich Mediterranean vegetation. Even lime and walnut trees, both no longer indigenous to North Africa, were quite common. The flora indicated by the Meniet pollen must have bloomed about the same time. The fact that they include varieties that prefer a warm temperature probably has something to do with the altitude. Meniet is about 3,000 feet below the place where the guano was found. The result of our investigations is staggering: for the first time we have some conception of the extent and the rapidity of the climatic change which brought the desert in its wake.'

Under the rock overhangs of the Meniet Hugot also came upon fossilised grains of seed, which originate from the fruit of the edible jujube tree and the southern nettle tree. The latter only flourishes where the annual rainfall is more than twelve inches. Today it grows in Algeria but only in the coastal Atlas mountains and in certain parts of the Saharan Atlas which have a favourable climate. Furthermore, it is usually to be found together with the evergreen oak. The seeds of the jujube, which Hugot unearthed at Meniet, are indistinguishable from the subspecies which grows today on the northern fringe of the Sahara, in the Daya area between the towns of Ghardaïa and Laghouat. So the climate in the later Early Stone Age was undoubtedly very similar to that in the Saharan Atlas today.

Professor Quézel pointed out that it would be a mistake to visualise the history of the Sahara's vegetation in too simple terms. In the Hoggar, Tassili and Tibesti mountains the indigenous Saharan plants grow side by side with some varieties which are more at home in the north, on the Mediterranean, and others from the south, the Sudan. They are botanical evidence of the climatic tug-of-war between North and South. The periods of tropical, monsoon rain brought Sudanese plants northwards, while the Mediterranean type of rain brought Mediterranean plants southwards. When these climatic waves finally receded to make way for the desert, they left behind on the watershed of the Sahara mountains plant species which gradually succumbed to the encroaching desert or, in spite of the hostile environment, managed to eke out a miserable existence until the present day. The conception of plant migrations from north and south is not a new one, but Professor Quézel was the first to decipher the language of the pollen and thereby to gather invaluable evidence as to the time, duration, intensity, origin and progress of the climatic waves and the movement of vegetation in the Early Stone Age.

A very deep shaft is dug, the walls of which are
carefully reinforced and this work is continued
till a layer of very hard rock is reached.
This layer is assailed with picks and
mattocks to make it thinner. Then the
.workmen climb out of the shaft and
hurl a piece of iron to the bottom. The layer
breaks and the water beneath it is released.
The shaft fills up with water, the water
overflows and forms a stream on the surface.
Sometimes the water rises with such speed
that nothing can escape it. This pheno-
menon occurs in the Ksour of Touat and
Gourara, of Ourgla and the Rhir. The
world is the mother of miracles and
God the all-knowing is its creator.
IBN KHALDUN

5. Water: Public Enemy Number One

'THE sun?' I cried. 'Or the wind?'

Bulldozers and scrapers, like gigantic mechanical beetles, tore up the landscape and filled the crystal-clear desert air with a hellish tumult. My question was directed at young Razel, under whose supervision a hundred and fifty miles of asphalt road were being built between the Mozabite town of Ghardaïa and the oasis of El Golea. Which is the Public Enemy Number One of the Sahara's communications, the blazing summer sun that turns the road surface to a bubbling mess or the wind that drives the dunes before it and covers the roads with sand-drifts?

Claude Razel pointed to a group of black labourers, who were hammering two sections of drain-pipe together. So great was their diameter that once they were built into the embankment they acted as an underground tunnel. Our jeep could have travelled through it comfortably.

'Public Enemy Number One?' Razel shouted back. 'Water. It will wash away the entire road if we don't take steps to prevent it.'

When the din of the bulldozers and scrapers and winches died down for a moment, he added:

'It's one of the terrible ironies of the Saharan climate that water, which is so priceless, can often lead to disaster.'

Water is the key-word in the language of the Sahara. Without it there is no life, yet it can also be a deadly threat. Cloudbursts turn the mud-brick houses of the oasis into liquid mire. Large sections of a desert-settlement may disintegrate like chocolate in the sun. So the joy of the natives at this unexpected shower bath is always tinged with fear for their homes. In 1958 in Ouargla, where there is the same housing-shortage as in Paris or any other European city, I found that 427 dwellings had been either destroyed or damaged by rain. And when I reached El Golea I could hardly believe my eyes. Was it a mirage? Or were the arcades of the bazaar, the palms and cypresses, and the high walls of the fort really reflected in a small lake? My last doubts were dispelled when I saw the Foreign Legion's jeeps and the oil company's Land-Rovers performing a sort of motorised water ballet in this un-expected pool. A week later, however, it had disappeared leaving a thick crust of salt. And amongst other unromantic consequences of the sudden downpour of rain I noticed dozens of ruined huts reduced to heaps of unfired mud-bricks, so-called Toub, which had been reduced to pulp. Monsieur Jacques, general administra-tor and manager of the headquarters set up by an oil company in El Golea, took me for a drive on his trolley through the oasis. He stopped at a spot where three 'Haratin' or dark-skinned peasants were laying the foundations of a house, without so much as a glance in our direction. With understandable pride he said:

'It is not true that the natives only spend the money they earn from us on knick-knacks. This spot is where Ahmed's hut stood. Like many others it was demolished by the rain. Ahmed will re-build it. He is not even particularly unhappy about the disaster. To begin with his goats and his wife were able to reach a place of safety but apart from that the rebuilding of his house enables him to make it more secure by using sandstone. This, I think, is an improvement on which we and Ahmed can congratulate ourselves, not only because we advanced him the money to buy the expensive sandstone but still more perhaps because we have done something to counteract the sweet poison of fatalism which has been in his blood ever since he was born. For he has realised that he can't just leave it to Allah to decide whether the next cloudburst is to bury his livestock and his family under the ruins of his hut.'

The effect of cloudbursts in the open desert is even more shattering than in the oases. An unsuspecting caravan pitches camp in a bone-dry Oued or wadi, which can change in a matter of minutes into a raging torrent. In October 1957 the Seguiet el Hamra in Mauretania claimed fourteen victims.

The fact, however, that more people die in the desert by drowning than from drought does not mean that water is not scarce. Over the 1,800,000 square miles of the Sahara the average rainfall is $1\frac{1}{2}$ inches. The layers of dry air, which lie like enormous sheets of blotting-paper over the desert, can absorb each year a lake hundreds of times their own depth, a Saharan inland sea between twelve and fifteen feet deep. Meteorologists have tried to analyse this discrepancy between supply and demand, which is fundamental to the desert. Jean Dubief, for example, worked out how many days it would take the sun to consume the average annual rainfall in one given place. Any such calculation has, of course, only theoretical value, for water is lost not merely through evaporation but also through absorption in the soil and lack of storage. Nevertheless the value of Dubief's drought index is considerable. In Ouargla where the average rainfall is $1\frac{1}{2}$ inches the potential condensation rate each year is around 10 feet. So in this oasis evaporation is about a third of an inch a day, which means that in Ouargla the total precipitation for the year should evaporate in precisely five days.

Dubief has given El Golea the same index-number as Ouargla: 5. As one penetrates further into the desert where rain is still less frequent and the rate of condensation still higher, the index-numbers grow smaller. At In Salah it needs only one day, at Aoulef little more than half a day to turn the precipitation of a whole year into vapour. On the other hand, where the desert and the steppe country meet the index figure is 28, and the borders of the North African agricultural area, which needs no artificial irrigation, have the index-figure 100.

Figures of this kind are naturally popular in the schoolroom but

they are considerably more important for the drawing-up of
weather and climate charts than, for instance, to the peasant cultivating dates. The latter is not seriously interested in meteorological
averages but in whether precipitation takes the form of winter or
spring rain, of heavy rain which will penetrate deep into the soil or
of light showers which merely moisten the surface. And how high
is the rate of condensation at the time of the rainfall? At times the
clouds may empty themselves of moisture but it still does not rain.
The heated air over the desert, thirsty for moisture, acts as a kind
of umbrella. Each drop of water evaporates before it reaches the
ground.

The data provided by the meteorologists do not cover the most
essential factor: the irregularity of the rainfall. Systematic observation over a period of ten years revealed that there is one point in
the Sahara with a yearly average of 2 inches. This does not mean,
of course, that at this point it will only rain once this year or next.
During the ten-year period of observation three were completely
rainless while five others produced only a bare minimum. All in all
these eight years accounted for less than an inch of rain. The
remainder—some 19 inches—came down in the space of two
years and in certain very limited areas, usually with catastrophic
results.

The rainfall in the Sahara as a whole is too irregular and too
restricted to make possible a settled population. The relatively
small number of nomads or semi-nomads with their camels, goats
and sheep can only adapt themselves to the small quantity of water
by leading extremely frugal lives and to its irregularity by remaining permanently on the move. Yet, surprising as it may sound, the
Sahara is not without a natural supply of surface water, some of
which is even permanent. I remember the murmuring springs at
the foot of the steep wall of the Tassili and the Great Gueltas of
Im-Laoulaouen in the Hoggar Massif. A Guelta, sometimes called
an Aguelman, is a rainwater pool in the bed of a wadi, usually of a
deep canyon. The rocky bed prevents the water from seeping away,
while the steep walls reduce evaporation. The Great Gueltas,
which are divided by the rock into two basins, are amongst the
attractions of the Sahara. The granite walls shimmer with all the

colours of the rainbow and in the deep blue water the mountains
are reflected as in a great, mysterious eye.

When I visited Im-Laoulaouen I was met by a cool, damp
draught of air, and for a moment I could almost imagine myself in
an Alpine ravine instead of the Sahara. I was told, however, that
these small mountain lakes cannot always survive the fiery breath
of the desert. They dry up temporarily, sometimes even for several
years. Occasionally the natives convert these gueltas into cisterns
and cover them to reduce evaporation. They are a godsend to
exhausted caravans. Henri Lhote and his companions spent weeks
in the Tassili drawing on gueltas for drinking and cooking water.
But the supply is too small for irrigation purposes and there is
seldom any cultivated land near the gueltas.

What of the natural spates that arise in the dry wadis? They
only last for a few hours or at most a few days in the year, and the
wadis in the interior often remain dry for years. But is there no
way of storing-up even these short-lived spates?

Before and within the palm-groves of the Mozabites, a Berber
people who inhabit the deep network of valleys on the Mzab
plateau, dams have in fact been built. The oldest are between seven
and eight hundred years old. Their purpose, however, is not to
create reservoirs. Those that lie at the head of the wadi divert the
flood-water towards the palm-groves, while those lower down
cause the water to spread over the entire bed of the valley and so
feed the wells in the groves. The Mozabites are a resourceful
people. As they can only reckon with flood-water in their wadis
every second year, they have set up multi-purpose devices. The
dams serve as refuse-dumps, the sluice-gate is surmounted by a
bridge with arcades and between floods the large discharge-canals
are a means of communication.

Special conditions naturally prevail on the southern and
northern fringes of the desert. It is possible that one day rivers like
the Shari and the Logone, which at present evaporate in the
cauldron of Lake Chad, will be utilised to irrigate the southern
fringe. In the Niger bend and in Lower Senegal there are other
streams which could fairly easily be used for irrigation farther
north. No detailed plans have yet been worked out. Up till now

the peasants have always looked northwards in their search for water. The wadis in the northern desert have the advantage of emanating from the Atlas mountains or their foothills, the so-called Piedmont of the Sahara. Below them lie the giants among the Saharan dry wadis, at least as far as the volume and extent of the flood-water is concerned. The Saoura, the first section of which is called Guir, holds the record. Once every twenty years it carries floods southwards for five hundred miles, a distance that has remained substantially the same since prehistoric times.

In the Laghouat district, thanks to the dams at Tadjmout and El Fatha, the frequent floods in the Wadi Mzi leave a rich deposit of mud over wide cultivated areas. These two dams, which also form a reservoir, service about fifteen thousand acres of cereals, vines, fruit trees and clover. Of the many plans that have been drawn up for storing the flood-water, only one has so far been realized: the 200 feet high dam at Foum el Gherza east of Biskra. It is built in a narrow gorge of the Oued el Abiod, which starts in the Aures mountains. The reservoir supplies water to Sidi Oqba and four smaller oases. Of the other major projects the most advanced is on the Guir, where water is stored up on the slopes of the High Atlas in Morocco and flows in its upper reaches throughout the year. At Abadla where it enters the Sahara there is a flow of water for eighty-two days. At Beni Abbes, only a hundred miles to the south, the flow of water drops to thirteen days a year. The Road of Palms, the chain of oases between Adrar and Reggan, only has water from Saoura once in a generation.

The Guir project is to have two dams, one underground to catch the subsoil water and help to establish an industrial area at Colomb Bechar which is to be the biggest in the Sahara, the other an above-ground well down the wadi some thirty miles north of Abadla, which should provide more than 250 cubic yards of water and supply 1500 new oases, each with 200 families. The planners have visions of an inland Guir Delta, an irrigated area of 75,000 acres which would be a pocket-edition of the Niger Delta between Njasso and Timbuctoo. It sounds exciting but there are drawbacks.

'The whole project is madness,' an expert on tropical agriculture told me bluntly. He was an Israeli who was travelling through the Sahara in search of ideas for his own country's battle against the desert. 'This is not the place to erect a modern dam. Heaven knows I'm not entirely blind to the beauty, one might almost say the poetry of a dam. But the French won't find much more than poetry in this particular spot. The reservoir will simply silt up with the mud from the Guir, which the fields need even more than water. This mud is their main source of fertility. A series of smaller dams on the native pattern would be much more to the point. Flat reservoirs collect the mud-deposits and gradually become fertile soil. Then the course of the river is changed, a series of new small dams are set up and fresh reservoirs are created. So it goes on until the Abadla plain becomes unrecognizable.'

For the time being, however, it looks as if much water will flow down the Guir before the Djorf Torba dam is built.

It is only in exceptional cases that the date-palm cultivators of the Sahara can draw on surface water supplies. From times immemorial, therefore, the inhabitants of the oases have pinned their hopes on subsoil water. Ever since man first began the grim struggle against the desert climate he has employed all his ingenuity to exploit these subterranean water supplies, often with bitterly disappointing results. Today the traditional methods are dying out.

I shall never forget the spectacle of the crumbling, sand-filled foggaras. Nor that of the peasant whom I saw, at the risk of his life, planting a full-grown date palm a yard and a half deeper in the ground.

The foggaras are underground galleries, which can be up to ten miles long and which draw off the precious moisture from a watery subsoil very much as we in Europe drain the water from marshy ground. Each foggara forms a regular pattern on the surface where shafts have been dug for ventilation or for entering the gallery. Seen from an aeroplane these networks of shafts look like molehills or some mysterious hieroglyphic in the sand. The real home of the foggara is Tidikelt, Touat with its Road of Palms and Gourara with its flaming red oasis town Timimoun, all three at the foot of the high Tademait plateau. Nowhere is the climate better designed to create a desert in the desert. There is no air-moisture;

rainfall of any kind is extremely rare; even in the so-called rainy
period, which often comes after years of complete drought, the
wadis are only in spate for a matter of hours; a temperature of 120
in the shade is not uncommon in summer; sand and dust storms
are as frequent as they are violent. Anyone careless or rash enough
to venture into the desert in the summer months without water
dies a horrible death after a few hours. Yet it is precisely here that
an archipelago of lush oases has been conjured up from the desert:
thanks to the foggaras. In Tidikelt, Touat and Gourara there are
more than a thousand of them covering altogether about two
thousand miles. Their total yield of water is around 600 gallons
per second but the average varies considerably from one district
to another. In Gourara it is about half a gallon per second, in
Touat nearer a gallon and in Tidikelt one and three quarter gallons.
The difference is even more marked when one compares individual
foggaras. The weakest produce less than a quart of water per
second, whereas the most productive—in the Aoulef Cheurfa oasis
—yields more than 10 gallons a second. When one considers the
enormous work involved in building such a canal-system, these
figures seem very modest. But one must remember that they provide a water supply which is not dependent on the whims of the
weather and which continues day and night, year in, year out. And
a further advantage of this system is that the water flows of itself
from the sloping galleries into the palm-groves. For people who
are by nature averse to hard work this seems to be the ideal form of
irrigation. Capot-Rey even maintains that but for this labour-saving
system the white cultivators in Gourara would be unable to keep
going. In the oppressive climate of Gourara only the blacks are
capable of doing agricultural work.

The people in the foggara country have found the boldest, while
the people of the Souf have found the most original solution to the
water problem. The Souf lies in the northern offshoot of sand-
dunes from the Great Eastern Erg and seems condemned to be an
eternal desert, yet again it is here that man has succeeded in estab-
lishing an astonishing number of oases. They catch the eye first of all
by the charming and unusual style of their houses. If in El Oued, the
capital of the Souf, you accompany the muezzin up to the minaret

of the leading mosque you find yourself looking down on a landscape of grey domes and barrel vaults. It is as if the town were inhabited solely by marabouts and pashas. Domes and vaults are generally confined to religious buildings and palaces. But in El Oued unbelievers and paupers also live under domes. The terrace-houses of clay and palm-wood which are so common elsewhere in the Sahara would be an unnecessary luxury. There is no clay in the Souf but under the sand is a thick crust of gypsum which is mixed with sand to make bricks or burnt to make mortar.

The eternal glory of the Souf is its palm-groves. Flying over the town is like flying over the moon. The Souafa have dug troughs in the dunes and ten, twenty even several hundred palm-trees grow in craters of widely differing sizes. Some of the craters are so deep that the crowns of the palm-trees are below ground-level. In almost all troughs there are draw-wells from which vegetables and tobacco-plants are irrigated. They are not used, however, to water the palm-trees, for the Souafa have planted the trees so deep that their roots are in subsoil water. The healthy state of the palms shows that there is an underground river, for stagnant water would kill the trees.

The Souafa are generally considered to be a clever and even cunning people. Theft, it is said, is unknown amongst them because their ability to pursue even the faintest of human or animal tracks in the sand is so uncanny that no criminal can hope to escape. This may be something of an old wives' tale but the investigations made by the Algerian water authorities have shown that the Souafa are even smarter than their trick with the palm-trees suggests. For the sand-embankments serve as watersheds. Two samples of sand which are equally porous and roughly equal in grain react quite differently to rainfall according to their humidity. Sand with a water content of one per cent, for instance, will absorb the same quantity of rain in five minutes that a similar area of sand containing only one-tenth per cent water will take five hours to absorb. So the sand barriers in the Souf act as funnels through which the rain flows into the palm-groves.

Compared with the palm groves of the Mzab where for centuries camels, donkeys or mules have paced back and forward on a ramp, drawing up the full skins of water, the foggaras and palm-groves of the Souf seem designed for comfort. So, at least, I thought until I saw for the first time a foggara that had caved in. Then I flew over the dunes of In Salah in which one foggara-shaft after the other is dug. I heard the gasps of the men and the screams of the donkeys as they toiled up the twisting path from the crater with palm-leaf baskets full of sand. And I saw a Souf peasant lowering a palm tree. It was a tree in full growth, which had been fastened with ropes to surrounding trees. The owner and his son had dug a deep hole round the roots and were waiting for five men to arrive from a nearby garden to help them with the final stage, the actual lowering of the tree. But the tree did not wait. It dropped by itself, a piece of the root whipped up and gashed the boy's right calf, and the father, who was still in the hole below, was nearly crushed to death.

Oases which are watered by foggaras lie in a hollow. From the mouth to the source of the subterranean galleries the ground-level usually rises fairly sharply. The deepest ventilation shafts are between sixty and a hundred feet. They were hewn out with nothing more than a short-handled mattock and a basket. With the same primitive tools a tunnel was bored from the base of one shaft to the next. Hundreds of men must have died—buried alive, suffocated or simply exhausted. To build a foggara two and a half miles long at an average depth of forty feet with ventilation shafts every ten yards takes about 48,000 working days. In other words: a hundred and fifty men worked a whole year for a few pints of water per second.

But the maintenance of these water-galleries is almost as laborious as their erection. They must be cleaned out regularly. And they are constantly threatened with thrombosis. If the water-supply drops, then the foggara must be extended, deepened or provided with side-galleries or "feet." The upkeep of the foggaras at In Salah in 1947 cost the administration 115,191 working days. The 'foot' which was added to one foggara between May 1948 and October 1949, after the main gallery had caved in, cost the equivalent of 13,574 working days for a mere output of half a gallon of water per second.

The foggaras, like the Pyramids, are only conceivable with slave-labour. 'The slaves of the Moors of Djenne are not unhappy; they work little and from time to time receive a few cowries. Their lot is preferable to that of many European peasants.'

This observation was made by an unimpeachable witness, René Caillé, who on April 20th 1827 was the first European to reach Timbuctoo (and who, in spite of the umbrella he took with him, was a Frenchman!). He was the son of a chain gang convict who had himself suffered enough humiliation and insult to be able to speak with some authority on the treatment of slaves. But Caillé can hardly have been thinking of the foggara slaves who were no better than galley-slaves.

With the emancipation of the slaves by the French the foggara gradually became a thing of the past. The slaves became part-tenants of their former masters, looking after the gardens, tending the trees and gathering the dates. From 1900 onwards no new foggaras were built and the upkeep of the existing ones was more and more neglected. Today not only the funds but the manpower is missing. In Tidikelt the number of disused foggaras has risen since 1904 from 51 to 86.

The advance of civilisation has not only destroyed the foggaras, it has even threatened the Souf oases. Here everything revolves round the artificial basins, which are constantly being dredged. Yet those who draw a parallel with Sisyphus assume quite wrongly that as the peasants remove the sand the wind blows it back again. It is true that in districts in which, for some reason, these sunken gardens were abandoned, the palm-trees were soon completely engulfed in sand. But the people of the Souf have an ingenious and effective method of breaking the wind by a system of palm-leaf hedges. The arrangement and tending of these wind-breakers is a considerable science, in which the fellaha are experts. If the wind-breakers are properly erected, then the sand-basins are safe.

The real anxiety of the Souafa lies elsewhere. Inevitably the ground water-level sinks. So long as it does so within reason draught-wells are not seriously affected. It simply means more work. But in the Souf this is a catastrophe. A drop of three feet and the palms cease to bear any fruit. Six feet and the trees will die if they are not lowered. So the Soufi is condemned to a life of eternal drudgery, making his irrigation-basins deeper and deeper to keep pace with the falling water-level.

The main if not the sole cause of the drop in the water-level, however, is progress. The French put a stop to the feuds between families and tribes which were decimating the population. They protected the weak against the strong. They made hygienic and sanitary innovations, built hospitals, fought epidemics, and distributed grain if the date harvest did not last out the year. There are oases in the Sahara where the population can only support itself for at most three months in the year.

These humane measures produced repercussions which spread into the most remote corners of the desert. A proletariat grew up in the oases with the result that today, if one compares population with cultivated land, the enormous area of the Sahara is terribly over populated. In the French Sahara 870,000 people are living on half a million acres of cultivated land. The desert oases are like lumps of sugar at which swarms of ants are sucking and licking. Experience has shown that overpopulation of this kind leads to ruthless exploitation of the soil and the Sahara is no exception.

The Souf with its 115 square miles of cultivated land is a case in point. In 1887 21,000 people lived there on the produce of 160,000 date-trees. By 1930 the population had more than trebled and the number of palm-trees had increased nearly two and a half times. At the moment the population is estimated to be 100,000 and the number of trees 450,000.

Nature did not fail to take her revenge for the over-exploitation of the surface water-supply. Since 1930 the water-table has been dropping steadily.

'If it goes on like this,' I was told by one of the fellaha, a dignified, slightly stooping figure whose shoulders seemed weighed down by thousands of baskets of sand, 'in a hundred years the Souf will be desert.' And he added with a note of bitterness: 'Except, of course, for a few domes and camels for smart tourists.'

Before closing this chapter I would like to recall one personality whose fate is closely bound up with the Souf. It was here that the strangest of all Sahara explorers first felt the call of the desert. Si

Mahmoud's billowing burnous, the high white muslin turban held in place by a brown camelhair cord tied across the commanding forehead, the slightly husky voice—these have all become part of the legend. There was a time, however, when they were part of a scandal. For Mr. Mahmoud was a woman. Her mother was a Baltic Baroness who had left her husband, a Russian General, together with her three children; her father was a Russian exile with whom she lived in Italy and Switzerland after abandoning her husband.

Isabelle Eberhardt was born in 1877 at Meyrin near Geneva, where today the European Atomic Research Centre stands. Her family does not seem to have been a very happy one. Isabelle's half-sister, who found her 'uncle's' revolutionary intrigues too much for her, fled back to Czarist Russia. One half-brother took his life, and the second, after a brief period in the Foreign Legion, also committed suicide. The father died of an overdose of sleeping-tablets.

After the death of her parents, Isabelle Eberhardt, who had inherited a very small fortune, started at the age of 22 on her travels through Tunisia, Eastern Algeria and the northern Sahara. She travelled alone, on horse-back, dressed as a male Arab. Si Mahmoud, the Tunisian scholar, was naturally a Moslem. This at least was no pretence. In Geneva Isabelle had learned not only German, Russian and French but also Arabic. Her father, who had begun as a priest and ended up as a disciple of Bakŭnin, had at one point practised as a Moslem. In Algeria Isabelle was converted to Islam. Even her mother, the proud Natalie Dorothea Charlotte von Eberhardt, was buried in the Islamic cemetery at Bone under the name Fatima-Manoubia.

In 1899 Isabelle Eberhardt caught her first glimpse of 'the city of a thousand domes.' In her diary there is this brief and somewhat ominous entry: 'Arrived at El Oued about seven. Ran into a Moslem funeral.' A year and a half later she made this entry: 'As I was carried on a stretcher to the hospital through the villages around El Oued, the inhabitants, both men and women, came out into the street and uttered those cries and shrieks which are usually reserved for funerals.'

Unable to forget that first glimpse in 1899 she had returned the
following year. She contracted a marriage there by Moslem religious
law with Sliman Ehnni, a Spahi N.C.O., joined the Kadriya
Brotherhood and in January 1901 was severely wounded by a
member of the Tidjanya brotherhood. She only escaped with her
life because a washing-line over her head broke the force of the
blow. The would-be assassin, who could give no other reason for
this near-fatal sword-thrust than that he had been 'inspired by
Allah,' was condemned to twenty years' forced labour. His victim,
on the other hand, who had become a thorn in the flesh of the
Algerian authorities, was expelled for life. This deprived Isabelle
Eberhardt of her adopted homeland. She demanded to be told the
reasons for expulsion, but in vain. She appealed to the Russian
Consulate in Algiers. 'You wore the clothes of a male Arab', came
the reply, 'which, you must admit yourself, ill becomes a Russian
maiden.' The use of the word 'maiden' was deliberate: the
Algerian authorities would not recognize her Moslem marriage to
the Spahi but at the same time refused to carry out the civil
ceremony.

In Marseilles Si Mahmoud managed to subsist as a port-worker
till Sliman Ehnni arrived and they were able to go through the
civil ceremony which had been denied them at El Oued. Now a
French citizen Isabelle had no difficulty in returning without
further ado to Algeria. As Si Mahmoud she camped with the
nomads, rode on a milk-white mare called 'Souf' at the local
rodeos, slept in the sand under the sky, visited Mohammedan
monasteries and wandered about the Souks and the oasis villages.
Everyone knew who Si Mahmoud really was but no one gave her
away. She was even allowed into places where women are forbidden. The one concession made to her sex was that, whenever
she appeared, the obscenities in which the Arabic language is so
rich would die away—a sign both of respect and shame.

Her accounts and observations of Moslem life were widely
appreciated. Lyautey, who was subsequently to create modern
Morocco and to become a Marshal of France, was one of her
admirers. Many, on the other hand, were highly suspicious of this
Moslem Russian woman with a German name, who wore men's

clothes. She was suspected of anti-French activities, particularly as she did not conceal her dislike of certain symptoms of European Colonial policy. She acquired the reputation of being a new Kahena.

Kahena, a Berber queen of Jewish stock, had mobilised the tribes of the Aures mountains to fight the Arab invaders; the second wave was held up at the Gulf of Gabes, but the third swept her and her tribes away. The spell she had cast had not been strong enough to win her subjects over to a scorched-earth policy. The tribes deserted her, and towards the end of the seventh century Kahena, at the head of a small loyal band, was defeated and killed.

Isabelle, like Kahena, was an Amazon, and like her famous predecessor—so said her enemies—she was trying to mobilise the natives against the invader, this time against the French invader, if for no other reason than revenge for the way she had been treated at El Oued.

She herself denied that she had any political ambitions, and there is no doubt that, although she was the daughter of a revolutionary and an anarchist, she was no bomb-thrower. Her sole motive was a lust for adventure, which was fanned by the endless waste of the desert, by the undulating horizon and by the long, solitary rides she took.

In 1904 she was at Ain Sefra on the northern fringe of the desert. She was to report to Algerian newspapers on Lyautey's campaign in the Moroccan-Algerian border areas. On October 27 the Oued Sefra suddenly and unexpectedly burst into flood and swept through the small town. Si Mahmoud, who had come out on to the terrace of her house to see the flood, was swept away by the torrent.

6. Savornin's Sea

THE 'Jardin d'Annexe' at El Golea is a kind of shop-window for all the French have achieved in the desert. It is a veritable paradise with head-high rose hedges, palm, cypress and eucalyptus, and every species of fruit tree: orange, lemon, mandarin, clementine, pomegranate, apricot and peach. Amongst the palms one hears the cooing of doves and smells the scent of violets. There is a network of tiny streams which are the life's blood of this lush garden. For some time after sunrise, while the air is still fresh, a thin veil of mist rises from those streams, for the water, which is artesian and rises to the surface under its own pressure, is warm.

I could well understand the note of pride in Captain Barba's voice, as he spoke to me in his cool, shady office near the exit.

'El Golea is a French creation. When we occupied the oasis in 1891, it consisted of 6,400 palm trees which survived as best they could on the water that lies between three and twelve feet below the surface. There are also a few foggaras. But with such a limited supply of water there was no chance of increasing the number of palms. Then in 1892 our engineers discovered a fresh source deeper down and ever since then we have continued our search. Today there are twenty artesian wells producing about seven thousand gallons a minute for the 30,000 inhabitants and their 125,000 date-palms.'

Captain Barba spoke with a bitterness which was not difficult to understand. Only a few weeks before Algerian fellagha had murdered a fellow Moslem at El Golea and severely wounded another. Barba declared a state of emergency: the population were forbidden to leave their houses between eleven at night and five in the morning, to gather in groups in the street, or to sit down in the street, and both hands must be plainly visible and clear of the body. . . .

I felt like pointing out to the officer, who carried the civil and military responsibility for the oasis and the administrative area around it, that "colonialism" is a problem that has arisen not from what has been done for the colonised peoples but from what has not been done yet could have been done. I suppressed the impulse, for it would only have led to fresh misunderstandings. And I would not be doing justice to the benefits France has brought to the inhabitants of the Sahara if I did not admit that she consistently played the part that Moses played in striking water from the rock. Barely had the soldiers occupied the oases when the engineers moved in and under their orders the soldiers frequently excelled themselves in discovering subterranean water-supplies.

The story Captain Barba told me applies not only to El Golea. At the end of 1854 the French marched into Touggourt, and the Souf and Oued Rhir areas also surrendered. The Oued Rhir is the valley that borders the Souf and stretches northwards from Ouargha by way of Touggourt to the salt marsh at Melrhir. In the rainy period the Wadi Igharghar, which came from the Hoggar, and the Oued Mya had poured their floods through the Oued Rhir into the lakes where the salt marshes are situated today. Bit by bit, however, as the rainfall decreased, their dry beds were filled with rubble, till the Oued Rhir ceased to look like a valley and became what it is today, a rather boring, flat landscape, a loose succession of palm groves and salt-water pools like glass-beads strung on a thread of white dunes.

Date-lovers will probably resent my use of the word 'boring'; for many decades the Deglet Nour, which are usually sold in Europe as muscat dates and are the delight of connoisseurs, came almost exclusively from the Oued Rhir area. Until recently the French regarded it as the only 'productive slice' of the Sahara, which actually earned a little more from its dates than it cost.

This special position was due to the existence of fresh water in several layers of subsoil. It was under such natural pressure that from time to time it would erupt like the lava of a volcano and shoot through the surface in the form of geysers. Herodotus was told of these natural springs and similar eruptions must have led to the construction of the foggaras in the Gourara, Touat and

Tidikelt. Legend has it that the irrigation of the Rhir district began
in 1341 but it must in fact have started several centuries earlier.

Ibn Khaldun, born in Tunis in 1332, was the first of the water-
chroniclers. At the age of twenty-four he launched out on an active
political career which was as adventurous and unpredictable as a
penny dreadful. At different times and sometimes even simultaneously he was a Minister, conspirator, Deputy of the Sultan,
revolutionary, courtier, plotter, general, bandit, sycophant, Kadi,
scientist, deserter, ambassador, traitor, perjurer, favourite—and
with all the skill of a notorious opportunist he played these parts in
practically all the Islamic States from Syria to Andalusia. No less
bewildering than his life, of which he himself gave a full account,
is the history he wrote in an attempt to ascertain why he was a
political failure: 'The Book of exposition and compilation of the
origin and the report on the battle-days of the Arabs, of the non-
Arabs and Berbers and on the contemporary holders of great
power.' This work, which proved to be as ambitious and baroque
as its title and often as unpredictable as the author's career, brought
him fame while he was still alive. Since Ibn Khaldun's historico-
philosophical and historical work also became known in the non-
Arab world, the number of his admirers has increased. 'The
Herodotus of the Arabs,' 'The Father of Sociology,' 'the Arab
Montesquieu,' 'the Hegel of North Africa,' 'Oswald Spengler 550
years before "The Decline of the West" '—these are some of the
tributes that have been paid to Ibn Khaldun. But in their very
complexity they reflect some of the embarrassment that Ibn
Khaldun's achievement has caused in cultural circles in Europe.

In that part of the complete works which relates the 'History of
the Berbers and the Moslem Rulers in North Africa,' Ibn Khaldun
describes how the natives proceed to sink an artesian well:

'A very deep shaft is sunk with carefully supported walls and
this work is continued till a layer of very hard rock is struck. This
layer is assailed with pick and mattock to make it thinner. Then the
workers climb out of the shaft and hurl a piece of iron down to the
bottom. The rock-layer breaks and lets the water through. The
shaft fills up with water, which overflows and forms a stream on
the soil. Sometimes the water rises with such speed that nothing

(1) Prehistoric rock-carving near Edjeleh, probably representing a black antelope.

(2) The Sun Stone in the Oved Tihaliouine, with prehistoric carving (3) of a rhinoceros.

(4) Air view of ventilation shafts of a foggara near In Salah.
(5) Draught wells in the Mzab.

(6) El Oued, "town with
the thousand cupo-
las." In the back-
ground: palm-plant-
ing basins character-
istic of the Souf. (7)
Chimney of an ex-
tinct volcano: the
basalt "organ-pipes"
of Ikadelout in the
Hoggar.

(8) Meharists and their animals. (9) Guerrara's artesian well: symbol and guarantee of the fertile desert.

(10) The mountainous landscape Charles de Foucauld saw from his hermitage on the Assakrem. (11) The Iharem ("Laperrine Peak") in the Hoggar.

(12) The dunes of the Great Eastern Erg. (13) Storks forced down by a sandstorm on the oilfield at Hassi Messaoud.

(14) Robert Pieuchot with M'Kratta's camp mascot, the vicious desert fox.

(15) Native worker laying cable for geophysical investigation.
(16) Oilmen at their favorite sport—dune-hopping.

(17) Tauregs using rocks to break tamarisk branches for firewood. (18) The tent of Mekhadina nomads in a walled courtyard marks transition to a sedentary life: when the tent falls apart, they move into the house.

(19) Out for a stroll in the Ouargla oasis. (20) Reed mats shading the camp streets at Hassi Messouad.

(21) Giants of the Saharan road. (22) LD 101, the historic oilwell at Edjeleh, where the first oil gushed from the Sahara in January, 1956. (23) Despite the mechanization of the Sahara, Allah still calls the faithful to prayer.

Nomads taking examinations in drawing (24) and in skill and perseverance (25). (26) Two Ouled Nail, favored children of the Saharan miracle.

(27) Inspecting washed and sifted sand for diamonds. (28) The Bishop of the Sahara visits a training school.

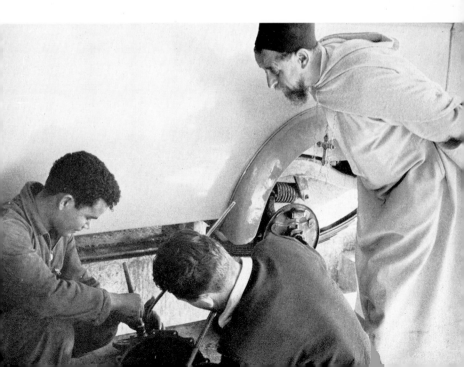

(29) "The Sahara possesses only one source of wealth that is steadily increasing: its young people."

can escape it. This phenomenon occurs in the Ksour (oases) of
Touat, Gourara, Ouargla and Rhir. The world is the mother of
wonders and God the omniscient is its creator.'

All the experts I have consulted believe that the Oued Rhir,
including Ouargla at its southern end, was the only area in the
Sahara in which the inhabitants had put down artesian wells before
the arrival of Europeans. Ibn Khaldun, who for some time was
hatching his plots in Biskra, must have known the springs in the
Rhir district at first-hand, those of Touat and Gourara only from
hearsay. At the same time he probably confused the natural
eruptions of water which had contributed to the building of the
foggaras with artificially created wells.

About the middle of the last century the situation in the Oued
Rhir was critical. Either existing wells were silting up or the badly-
supported walls were caving in. The natives found themselves
compelled to sink new wells in less favourable conditions than their
ancestors had enjoyed. The simple method described by Ibn
Khaldun was no longer sufficient. There is no record of iron bars
being used to break the thin layer of rock but rather of workers
standing on the floor of the shaft and laboriously picking their way
through the rock, all too often to drown in the sudden upsurge of
water. In many cases, however, the natives failed even to reach the
water-table. To dig a perpendicular shaft of more than two hundred feet deep required a stupendous amount of human effort.
Sometimes the entire operation was paid for in grain, but many
shafts had to be abandoned at a depth of 120 to 150 feet, when the
pickaxes struck solid rock. Then the palms died and the population
moved elsewhere.

The French appeared on the scene like magicians. A deposit of
gypsum, on which the primitive native instruments had made no
impression, was child's play for the French technicians. Moreover,
instead of the Arab type of well which was always threatened by a
cave-in they put down the much more productive piped well.

In June 1856 the first strike was made at Tamerna to the north-
east of Touggourt; 1,000 gallons of water a minute poured out
into the sand. In February and March of the following year further
and equally successful borings were made at Tamelhat, south of

Touggourt, and at Sidi Rachid, to the north of it, where French soldiers under the supervision of engineers took four days to pierce a layer of rock, which had caused a previous project to be abandoned. Again 1,000 gallons per minute gushed out. These three piped wells alone produced almost a quarter of the total output of three hundred 'arab' wells. News of this water magic spread rapidly southwards, and France's pioneering work did not go unacknowledged in Europe.

From the beginning her major task in the desert has been—and it is still—to rescue one oasis after the other from drought. I have already referred to the dying foggaras and the falling water-level in the Souf. Here too the French were not entirely inactive. Between 1910 and 1920, when it was already clear that the foggaras were doomed to destruction, twenty-four artesian wells were put down in Tidikelt, but unfortunately it was not possible to find water in Gourara and Touat which would rise to the surface under its own pressure. So in both these areas the foggaras have continued to play a predominant part. Strangely enough it was only towards the end of the war that the administration in the Souf became aware of the dropping water-level. So the Algerian Water authority began a somewhat belated search for fresh supplies of water. To judge by the first five artesian borings, all of which were successful, there is enough water under the Souf to irrigate extensive new palm-groves. In fact the Algerian Sahara as a whole is one of the richest areas in the world as far as subsoil water is concerned.

In conversations with hydrologists in the Sahara one word constantly crops up: Alb. Anyone who has no Alb to draw on feels that Nature has let him down. Anyone who has Alb at his disposal knows how privileged he is and guards it with his very life. I heard even simple 'Ksouriens' and date-peasants use the word. For them 'Alb' is as magical as 'petroleum'. Alb means hope, and end to years of anxiety, a blooming garden, fruit-bearing palms—the conquest of the desert.

I am afraid the following explanation must sound prosaic. To the geologist Alb, or the 'Albienne Nappe', as it is technically known, is a stratum that belongs chronologically to the lower chalk-formation. In the Sahara the Alb stratum consists mainly of

loose sand and a series of porous sandstones. These are deposits
left by streams and rivers perhaps fifty million years ago. In the
early chalk period, which preceded this continental epoch, these
deposits were sealed in by marl and clay left by a sea. This is the
geological explanation for the subterranean Saharan lake or
'Albienne Nappe', which stretches nearly 650 miles southwards
from the southern foothills of the Atlas, is bounded on the west by
the Saoura valley and on the east by Tunisia and the Libyan
Fezzan.

The French geologist Justin Savornin called the Alb the finest
hydraulic device in the Sahara and, because he did more than
anyone else to explore it, it has become known as Savornin's
Sea. It is only exceeded in size by the great artesian basin in
Australia.

Savornin's Sea covers an area of about a quarter of a million
square miles, which is larger than metropolitan France. The word
'sea' can, of course, only be used figuratively. Savornin's Sea is not
a stretch of water but a gigantic sandy sponge, which in some
places is only 300 feet thick, but in others anything from 1500 to
6000 feet.

Savornin's Sea also draws water from outside the Sahara. It is
fed by the winter-rains which thunder down on the southern
flanks of the Atlas. Here in the north-western sector much of the
sandstone of the Alb runs obliquely and acts as a funnel for
channelling the water southwards. On its subterranean journey
southwards, with only the motive force of gravity, the Atlas rain
takes centuries. The proprietor of the 'Dal Piaz' hotel at El Golea
was not exaggerating when he offered me a glass of clear water with
the words: 'I hope you enjoy it. It wasn't exactly made yesterday.
It probably fell on the Atlas as rain in the time of Charlemagne. . . .'

The reaction of my gums was not to the age of the water, which
according to recent research probably goes back several thousands
of years before Charlemagne, but to its salt content. Since there is
no normal water circulation in the desert, salts accumulate in the
soil and all the water in the Sahara is more or less salty.

One of the stock stories told by the oil-drillers over their pâté de foie and champagne or by the Meharists over a handful of dates is the account of André de Meyendorff's death and the strange survival of one of his companions. I have often heard it; each time a few of the details were different, as is only right and proper for any anecdote which is fast becoming a legend.

In 1941 it was decided, somewhat hurriedly, to build a trans-Saharan railway from the Mediterranean to the Niger. Six hundred miles of track were to be laid each year. Amongst the geologists who flocked into the desert to reconnoitre the country to be crossed by the railway (in which, incidentally, none of them believed) was the twenty-four year old Meyendorff. In 1942 with two natives he explored the area of dunes known as the Erg Shech. The only well in the area known to the guide had filled with sand. Having reached the end of their water-supply, exhausted and tormented by thirst, Meyendorff and the guide drank brackish water with a strong content of magnesium salt from a nearby pool. Both men died that same evening in appalling agony. The third member of the party, who managed, in spite of his thirst, to resist the temptation to drink, filled all his gourds with the deadly water, tied himself to the saddle of his camel and let the beast go where-ever it chose. From time to time he summoned enough strength to pour water from the gourds over his head and body. Two days later a dying white camel appeared in one of the Touat oases. On its withered hump was a pillar of salt, which sparkled and glistened in the sun a long way off. The frequent douches of water had covered the Chaambi with millions of salt crystals which the doctors in the local military hospital were able to remove. The native who had refused to slake his thirst lived to tell the tale.

The water in Savornin's Sea harms neither plants nor animals, and it is even safe for humans to drink. If you allow a pint of it to evaporate, you will only find about twenty grains of salt. By European standards this may be much too high for drinking-water, but in the Sahara one is not so particular. The water from the Alb is considered good, even excellent.

The two chief virtues of Savornin's Sea are the quantity and the quality of its water. There is a third, which is perhaps the most important and which I have so far mentioned only in passing: the Alb deposit forms a gigantic trough covered by a watertight layer of marl. As it lies below the level of the 'funnel' in the Atlas through which the water flows in, there is a natural pressure. It is sufficient to bore a hole in the top watertight strata, which formed later, to produce a gush of boiling hot water. Admittedly, this will not happen over a certain height above sea-level, but few places reach such a height. So Savornin's Sea can boast the most powerful artesian wells in the world.

'Allah, having created the desert, was struck with remorse so he gave man the palm and the camel.' For some years the people of the oases have been adding, without the authority of the Koran: 'And He imprisoned a sea under the desert. Praise be to Allah, Ruler of the World, the All-Compassionate.'

In an age when the Sahara is undergoing economic development the Alb, like oil, has become a word full of tremendous promise. For centuries, however, in fact if not in name, the Alb has been an important factor in the general water-tableau of the desert. In the south-west, along the fringe of the black Tademait plateau, the sandstone of the Alb has gnawed its way through to the surface, and there for centuries Savornin's Sea has been freely exploited through the foggaras that run from Timimoun through Adrar and Reggan to In Salah. Naturally the builders of these foggaras had no knowledge of geology. The owner of a palm-grove in Touat can hardly have suspected that he was drawing on the same water-supply as his mortal enemy in Gourara 120 miles away to the north and as his friend in Tidikelt 120 miles to the south-west. It was only when the French came to make the first artesian borings just before and just after the turn of the century at El Golea, Tidikelt and Fort Flatters—once again on the fringe of the Alb—that they began thinking about possible links.

On the last day of the year 1896 a boring was made at Ghardaïa, the capital of the Mozabite country. The engineers hoped to tap the same artesian basin under the barren rock-shelf of the Chobka that was already providing enough wells to give El Golea a new lease of life. With the boring equipment then available it took no less than twenty-seven months to reach a depth of a thousand feet.

This set-back put an end, for some time at least, to speculation about a possible extension of the water-table to the north.

It was Professor Justin Savornin who broke the deadlock. Since the spring of 1927 he had appointed himself the official spokesman of the Alb and its potentialities. Both in the spoken and the written word, in petitions, essays, articles and at congresses he kept pressing the view that the water-carrying strata of El Golea could be tapped not only in the Ghardaïa oasis to the north of it but even farther north and east. If the boring made at Ghardaïa had produced nothing, then not because there was no water but because the water lay deeper. Savornin supported his claims, which sounded very bold, with hydrological arguments. As a geologist with official standing it was possible for him to put his hypotheses to the test. Two experimental borings were made at Touggourt and Ouargla. For technical reasons the first had to be abandoned at around 3,000 feet, the second at just over that depth. But Savornin was not discouraged. In his view all that these ineffectual borings had proved was that the Alb which breaks through at Touat and is only 300 feet below the surface at El Golea must be overlaid in the north east by dense strata from earlier periods. Today we know that Savornin was right, that the rock strata, under which the Alb is buried, are more than a mile deep in places.

In 1938 at Ghardaïa Savornin had the satisfaction of seeing his most important hypotheses confirmed, but the Alb only came fully into its own after the war. In March 1946 twenty-eight men moved into a depression in the desert called Zelfana.

*   *   *

Water is road-builder Claude Razel's bitterest enemy. On the other hand it is Louis Tomasi's best friend. He is 'chef de chantier' at Zelfana, in charge of a construction project which is unique in the whole of the Sahara. Where ten years ago there was nothing but barren, murderous desert he is running up an artificial oasis, the first to be made to measure.

The buses stop at Zelfana on their way from Ouargla to Ghardaïa. One summer night in 1955 I made the trip for the first time.

On the roof of the bus sat a man playing a pipe; two goats occupied the rear seat. The rickety vehicle stopped for ten minutes at Zelfana, wheezing asthmatically, and the passengers, including the goats, took the opportunity to stretch their legs and make sure there were no bones broken.

When I visited Zelfana again from Ghardaïa in 1958 it was like travelling on a billiard table. The tarred road, which winds like a blue snake through the Chebka and had then almost reached Zelfana, seemed to me the finest in the world when I remembered the old track full of potholes. In the meantime the road has snaked its way forward to Ouargla, so it would have been more prudent on my part if I had written that the buses *stopped* at Zelfana. For why should anyone stop today at Zelfana, ninety miles from Ouargla and less than fifty from Ghardaïa?

Louis Tomasi quickly rejected any suggestion that Zelfana might be left out in the cold:

'Don't worry. We'll see to it that doesn't happen.'

With his basque beret and tweed jacket Tomasi is somewhat different from the common run of men who are changing the face of the Sahara. He is not the Boy Scout type with the smooth face of a child. The desert meant a new life for him. He owned a winter sports hotel at Grenoble. During the war he lost both his wife and child. He had no further ties in Europe and turned to the Sahara. It became a passion. He devoted himself particularly to Algeria's water supply. Up and down the country from the Mediterranean coast to the southern frontier of Algeria he is a familiar figure, his right leg hanging over the side of the Jeep because, he maintains, a draught of air is good for his rheumatic knee. Natives (and he is particularly proud of this) will travel several hundred miles merely to work for Tomasi.

I found him a generous, just and immensely hospitable man, with whom I disagreed on only one point. He loved hunting gazelle in his jeep, without, however, firing a shot but pursuing the animal till it collapsed and died from exhaustion.

'But surely that's forbidden,' I said.

'The army does it,' he replied.

When I pressed the point—'It's not hunting, it's cruelty to

animals'—he laughed somewhat pityingly at my pig-headedness. My reproaches left him completely cold. His birthplace might be considered an extenuating circumstance: Tomasi is a Corsican.

It was from him that I heard the first chapter of Zelfana's history. The word 'Alb' frequently cropped up. Tomasi turned it over almost tenderly on his tongue like a wine connoisseur tasting a favourite vintage.

According to Professor Savornin, a water-hole was bored at Ghardaïa in 1937/38, when the solid rock covering the Alb was pierced, but some five hundred feet of Alb had to be penetrated before a strike was made at a depth of twelve hundred feet. The water shot out in surprising volume. Yet it was by no means a complete success. The bore-hole was too high, so that the full pressure of the water was not released and over the last fifty yards to the surface the water has to be pumped.

Of the five towns in the heart of the Mozabite country Ghardaïa is the highest. So the second boring was made at El Ateuf, five miles down the valley. As expected a strike was made at twelve hundred feet but the water-geyser was ten yards short of the surface. Here too a pump had to be used. This not only makes the water considerably dearer, it also means that the pump is liable to break down just when it is most needed. In summer, for example. The people of Ghardaïa and the other Mozabite towns have quite a story to tell about this.

The borings made at Ghardaïa and El Ateuf before the war showed that the five towns in the heart of the Mzab would have to do without artesian wells. For the Mozabites it meant abandoning a long-cherished dream. The hydrologists, however, were not so unhappy, for they now knew the level of the Alb water in the Mzab. They also knew that the peak of a water-geyser from a bore-hole in the Mzab reaches a height of 1300 feet above sea-level. So if a boring were made at a point less than 1300 feet above sea-level, it was safe to assume that the water would break the surface under its own pressure.

After the war, such a point was found, forty-five miles south-east of Ghardaïa. Zelfana lies four hundred feet lower than Ghardaïa on the edge of a depression. When the twenty-eight engineers, technicians and labourers arrived there in March 1946, it was a mere name on the map: not a tree, not a blade of grass.

The drilling operation at Zelfana was a risky undertaking. The oilmen of today smile when they hear it mentioned, for they have inexhaustible resources at their disposal. 'Impossible' is a word that does not exist in their vocabulary. But the men who bored for water in 1946 worked on very limited credit and experience.

On March 4th 1947, a year after the preparations had started, the drilling bit began to pierce the rock. Water-supplies for the drilling-crews and for the machinery had been transported from Ghardaïa by tanker, but often less than half the water required was available. From June to October the work at Zelfana had to be stopped because of the intolerable heat. It was even suggested that the whole enterprise should be abandoned. But in October the work was resumed. At a depth of about 1800 feet the Alb sandstone was reached. By February 5, 1948 the boring was over 2,000 feet deep, but most of this was not piped in case the well caved in. Attempts to cement the walls of the bore-hole were fruitless. In March and April fresh difficulties cropped up but at the end of April boring was nevertheless resumed until 10th May, when the 'bit' jammed. It was still in the Alb at a depth of 3840 feet. When it was found impossible to set the bit going again, it was decided to release the well. On June 9th, 1948 two years of uncertainty and almost superhuman endeavour were forgotten when a stream of water shot out of the desert where no water had been heard of before. The fountain rose two hundred feet in the air, drenching the spectators in fine spray. The blazing sun conjured up something that had never been witnessed in Zelfana until then: a rainbow.

'It was not particularly refreshing,' Tomasi added soberly. 'On the contrary!' The water came out at a temperature of 102 degrees.

For three years, ever since my first visit to Zelfana, I had retained a mental image of what an oasis 'made to measure' must look like. How disillusioned I was when I finally saw Zelfana! Nothing is more depressing than an oasis in the making. The outstanding feature was rows of Egyptian sugar-cane about 10 feet high which acted as wind-breakers for young, unimpressive-looking date-palms. In some plots the shoots had not even taken root and were still standing in heaps of manure. Elsewhere the holes for the young trees had only just been dug. Zelfana seemed to have nothing to offer but hot water which was distributed through cement runnels parallel with the cane hedges. It was like blood circulating without bones, flesh and muscles. Not a trace of the moist shade of old palm-groves I had dreamed about.

The Moorish bath, a kind of Sauna, which was supplied with hot water from the artesian well, was a stinking hole, very different from the glowing description of it in the publicity pamphlets. The turbine, driven by the pressure of the gushing water, which was to keep a generator going and provide electricity—another major attraction according to the publicists—was not functioning. Nobody seemed in the least concerned and nobody seemed to miss the electricity. As for the population, I saw only a few grubby, ragged children, although I had been assured that a hundred and fifty families were living there, altogether about five hundred people. The only tangible reality was the basin in which the water from the well was caught for distribution.

I should perhaps explain at this point that there is no such place as Zelfana. There are Zelfana I and Zelfana II. Zelfana I is the small settlement clustered round the old fort and the well that was sunk in 1947/48. It comprises living-quarters for the agricultural advisers, a first aid station, a repair-shop, the power-station with the turbine, the Moorish bath, a general store selling groceries and a café with one rickety table. The streets are graced with a few tamarisk trees. Zelfana II is a more recent product and lies about fifteen hundred yards away on a small hill: a solitary house standing beside a second artesian well which dates back to 1955. When I was there about fifty workers were busy laying cement pipes. The noise of the spades and the singing that echoed across the dusty, sandy landscape seemed a slight improvement on the sense of desolation which Zelfana I had left in me. The fact remains, however, that ten yars after the first well was sunk Zelfana is still no more than a large building-site, the embryo of an oasis. Why?

Tomasi was in no mood to talk. He kept on quoting proverbs

like 'Rome was not built in a day.' Towards evening he became increasingly nervous and refused to answer any more questions. I would have liked to wait for the sunset at Zelfana. I wanted to take up a position near the grave of a Mohammedan saint or marabout, which gave a splendid view of the plantations in Zelfana I. But Tomasi insisted on leaving earlier.

'The Fellagha,' he said apologetically. 'Until recently we had a labour camp nearby for Moslems, those who refuse to fight against the rebels. As a result there were quite a number of soldiers in Zelfana. When the camp was broken up, the garrison was also withdrawn. Ever since then I haven't dared spend a night in Zelfana alone.'

I teased him about the gazelles which can hardly have felt much happier with Tomasi after them than Tomasi with the fellagha on his tail. The comparison put him completely out of temper and throughout the whole of the journey back he sat, one leg dangling over the side of the jeep, plunged in silence.

Back in Ghardaïa I found people equally evasive but gradually I got at the truth.

After the borings at Ghardaïa had met with only partial success, the experts turned their eyes north-eastwards to the Rhir area which with its Deglet-Nour dates has become one of the main economic centres of the Algerian Sahara. The Rhir area had always suffered from a shortage of water and some geologists began to toy with the idea of tapping the water-tank of the Alb there too. But as no one knew exactly how deep the boring would have to be— only that it would be very deep—and as some experts, including even that tireless champion of the Alb, Savornin, feared that in the Rhir district porous clays might predominate over the sandstone, it was decided to abandon the Rhir area in favour of Zelfana. But the boring at Zelfana I was a purely experimental one designed to give some clue as to the position and composition of the Alb in the general direction of the Rhir area.

The water-geyser that shot out of the ground on June 9th, 1948 took them completely by surprise. It confirmed their theory about the Rhir area to an extent they had never thought possible. It had simply not occurred to them to plan what should be done with the water, if a substantial supply were found. They were much too preoccupied with strata and rock-formations. So the sheer success of their experiment was a source of great embarrassment. They could not let 1700 gallons of water per minute simply pour into the sand, nor were they prepared merely to cork up the borehole. So the Administrator of Ghardaia, under whose jurisdiction Zelfana comes, decided to create an oasis, an imperishable and shining symbol of the blessings France had brought to the desert.

I was told that both the water and the agricultural authorities warned against the idea. The specialists washed their hands of it. And in the years that followed they have had ample opportunity of saying: 'I told you so!' For the oasis-creators had overlooked one or two important factors. The soil at Zelfana was good and it was flat but the young palms were planted in a depression, in the bed of the Oued Mzab, with the inevitable result that in 1953 the greater part of the young plants were swept away by the floods.

Another problem which had been overlooked was that of the waste water. What was to be done with the water after it had been used? The water-level near the surface rose rapidly and the roots of the young palms, which are very sensitive, were in danger of rotting. To build drainage canals would have been an expensive business, for apart from anything else they would have been very vulnerable to sandstorms or floods.

Fortunately when the original boring was made, the geologists had noticed a layer which was admirably suited for storing water but contained none. The engineers had unpleasant memories of this limestone, for they had found it impossible to seal up the cracks in it, with the result that so-called lubricating mud was constantly draining away. This limestone now proved to be the salvation of the artificial oasis. Two absorption-wells were sunk in them, and today the used water flows back below ground.

In other words, the experiment began not in 1948 but in 1958 and simultaneously Zelfana II succeeded Zelfana I as the centre of interest. Zelfana I is still threatened by floods. Its sole hope of survival is that the four thousand palms planted since the last flood have by now sunk sufficiently strong roots to stand up to the next.

If the future of Zelfana I has been jeopardised by natural

hazards, the dangers confronting Zelfana II are man-made. It is not so much an agricultural as a social experiment. The nomads of that area, the Chaamba, are tired of wandering, particularly in the last few years with their shortage of rain and therefore of grazing and water for themselves and their flocks. Zelfana was designed to accommodate them. The future oasis has been divided up into plots, which are given away. There are, of course, certain conditions attached. A Chaambi with four children who has served in the French camel corps is given priority over a fellow-tribesman with the same number of children who had had no military service. Social considerations are inextricably bound up with the old Roman custom of settling ex-soldiers on the land. Anyone receiving a plot of land must promise to cultivate it according to the instructions of the agricultural adviser. Only then does he receive his allocation of water. Rebellious elements are easily brought into line: the administration keeps a firm hand on the water-tap.

Land as such has no value in the desert and Arabic Common Law decrees very sensibly that land on which no palms grow belongs to no one. Whoever irrigates it, either by digging a well himself or channelling the water, thereby acquires a legal right of possession. In Zelfana both land and water are free. In fact the landowner is compensated, at least in the first few years, for cultivating the land. As soon as his small enterprise is self-supporting the subsidies stop. Later when the first profits begin to come in, the farmer repays the subsidies over a period of twenty years. Those responsible for this agricultural policy are under no illusions: at most their running-costs are being covered.

There is land, there is water, and the crops are growing, but this is not enough to hold a nomad who has become sedentary from resignation. As soon as conditions are favourable again he resumes his nomadic life. Early in 1958 a generous fall of rain covered the desert with a coat of fine, tender green. The nomads of Zelfana, who until then had been working in the cornfields, simply left their implements and disappeared one day. They had forgotten the bitter disappointment they had suffered in previous years. They were reluctant peasants for whom the desert still had a fatal fascination.

Will the day come when Louis Tomasi can wander through groves of forty thousand palms, which have brought shade and fertility to this god-forsaken spot? Will a few hundred Chaamba become deaf to the call of their blood and turn into settled date- and crop-farmers? That remains to be seen.

7. *Phoenix Dactylifera.*

THE time has come to present one of the heroes of this book: Phoenix dactylifera or the genuine date-palm.

The desert people have a saying that the date palm likes to have its head in fire and its feet in water. It is certainly an exacting tree, yet it also has great powers of endurance. It is not, for example, entirely wedded to fire. I have sat under palm-trees shivering with cold and trying in vain to warm my frozen fingers in my trousers pockets. Of all the palm family the Phoenix dactylifera is one of the least susceptible to climate. In the Rhir district, the main date-growing area of the French Sahara, night frosts are quite common. The palm-trees of Touggourt and Biskra have even experienced snow. But the date-palm does draw the line at certain climates. In Tamanrasset, the administrative capital of the Hoggar mountains, it will not grow. Tamanrasset lies well to the south but too high (4000 feet above sea level) and its winter temperatures are too low. One has to travel a good sixty miles from the Atlantic coast before one sees the first palm groves. The climate in this coastal belt is too misty and too humid. It is never too hot for the date palm but it dislikes wet feet, particularly if there is too much, or worse still stagnant, water. The palm tree's reaction to too little water is simply to stop bearing fruit; it shrinks and becomes small and ugly. But so long as its roots can draw on a mere handful of water it will remain alive. On the other hand it is not in its nature to bear a grudge. If from one day to the next it is given the water it needs, then it soon forgets that it was neglected and bears fruit again as if nothing had happened.

It is hardly surprising that when people talk of the date-palm they should use expressions which are normally reserved for the behaviour of human beings. For it is a blood relation of man.

Some say that Allah made the palm-tree from the clay that was left over after he had created Adam. Others have a different story.

When God had driven Adam out of Paradise, he told him through the Angel Gabriel to cleanse himself. Adam obeyed the command of the Almighty and, when he had washed, he buried the hair and the nails which he had cut. Then the Angel Gabriel said to him: 'Put thy trust in God, he will provide for thee.' As he spoke, a tree grew out of the earth with a slender stem, green leaves and juicy fruit. Lost in wonder at this sign of God's omnipotence, Adam threw himself on the ground and cried: 'Praise be to Thee, oh God! But whence comes this sign of Thine infinite goodness?' God answered him through the mouth of Gabriel and revealed to him his origin and that of the palm: 'I created thee from the substance from which the tree has grown before thine eyes, the tree that will nourish thee.'

Whether flesh of Adam's flesh or product of his hair and nails, the palm is man's nearest relation. For many inhabitants of the desert it ranks as an aunt, others treat it as a brother or an uncle on the mother's side. Like man whom the palm resembles, it has an upright stance, two sexes, and the gift of fertility.

This relationship has obvious advantages. There is, for example, the palm wine which is tapped from the stem and then fermented. The Koran forbids believers to take intoxicating drinks, but who could decline a drink which the maternal uncle brews, without committing the sin of ingratitude?

Palms that are grouped close together can become friends. If one dies, the others mourn for it; their leaves droop and they produce no more fruit. It is even alleged that a female tree will pine and die if its lover is felled. Whatever the real merits of artificial insemination, the natives are convinced that the nearer the male trees are to the females the better the harvest.

The palm is also capable of the most intimate relations with men. Es Sahraoui, who studied the palm legends in the oasis of Ouled Djellal and the customs connected with them, gives a particularly fine example of this.

One day a man entered a palm grove and heard the palms praying for their master. He immediately went to the owner of the palm grove and offered to buy it. At first the offer was rejected but finally such a good price was offered that the proprietor gave way. The new master returned to the palm grove to see the palms. Barely had he stepped inside than he heard the trees praying not for their new master but for the one who had planted them. He returned at once to the former owner, told him of the miracle he had twice witnessed and asked him to take back his palm-grove. The man gladly accepted the offer, exclaiming: 'If I had known that my palms loved me so much you would never have been able to purchase them, even if you had offered me the weight of each tree in gold.'

Because palms love their masters, they are very sensitive to re-proaches and warnings. In the palm grove of Ouled Djellal the date-farmers still occasionally enact the following comedy: If a palm is no longer bearing fruit, the owner arms himself with an axe and gets ready to fell the tree. Before he begins, however, he says out loud—so loud that he can be clearly heard in the neigh-bouring grove: 'Palm, you are barren and I am going to fell you.' Then he strikes the tree a light blow at the base of the trunk. In accordance with tradition the neighbour then interposes: 'Accursed fellow! What are you doing there? Leave this tree in peace. I guarantee that it will bear fruit next year. If I am proved wrong, then you can fell it.' This dialogue usually goes on for some time, the owner keeps striking (symbolic) blows at the tree, till he is finally won over by his neighbour's arguments and spares the tree. The natives are quite convinced that the tree will answer the charge of barrenness by producing a record harvest.

The fact is that, with all the reverence shown to the palm as brother, aunt or uncle, Caid Kaddour Koudia told me at Ouargla that there is a song of praise to the palm tree in which each verse describes a fresh use to which it can be put and which would take a full day and a night to recite!

The trunk provides timber, fuel, fibre for sacks and ropes; the stalks are used for fences and roofs; the central part of the leaf is woven by skilled hands into baskets, bags, brooms, mats and sandals; the juice of the young palm makes a very sweet drink or can be fermented into palm wine. The tip is edible as a sort of palm cabbage. And last but not least there is, of course, the fruit, the manna of the desert! Pressed in tanned goatskins, from which the hair has been removed and which are then sewn up, dates are the nomad's daily bread. Dried and ground, they provide date flour, which makes a welcome addition to pancakes and mash. The juice of the sugary, over-soft varieties make date-honey or syrup. The fresh, dried dates are the standard diet of the date-farmer.

The visitor who is still thinking of the tasty and hygienic box of dates under the Christmas Tree is in for a shock. Only the Deglet Nour, the high-quality dates reserved for export to Europe, are treated carefully and hygienically. In the date-market at Ghardaïa I found myself weaving my way between jute-bags full of dates which had been left open along the dusty road so that one could test their condition with one's fingers. In most of the sacks the dates had become a nauseating mess, like jam, full of fibres and flies. One merchant explained to me that, while there are countless varieties of dates, they all belong to one of three groups; soft, medium or dry. Grateful as I was for this piece of information I did not feel at all sure that my stomach was equal to the actual test. In fact the dry dates tasted like sawdust and reminded me of a dish of roasted locusts which I had had at In Salah, washed down by a glutinous syrupy concoction called mint-tea. And as that horrible memory flashed across my mind I saw to my dismay that a boy was making his way across the street balancing two glasses of steaming tea on a tray. I hope that Allah forgave my heathen stomach. Just as the merchant was plunging his right hand into a sack of soft dates, presumably to offer me a sample, I muttered an apology and took to my heels.

So far I have said nothing of the date stones. They too have to make themselves useful. Crushed to a powder, they are mixed with the fodder for the livestock. Or they can be roasted to produce a revolting brew called date coffee. But much more important than its material uses is the part the date-stone plays in religious proverbs: 'And no one shall suffer injustice, not even so much as a thread on a date stone . . . How can they hope to reach heaven who have not given their fellow men so much as the groove in a date-stone?' This is from the fourth sura of the Koran, which describes Jesus's birth under a palm-tree. And in the thirty-fifth Sura the faithful are warned: 'The idols which ye worship beside Him are not even masters over one small skin round a date-stone.' What the O-shaped indentation on the back of the date-stone means is, according to Es Sahraoui, a matter of dispute amongst the natives. Is it the mark of the seal that Solomon set on the stone of the first date, saying: 'Grow wherever my people are and be their heavenly nourishment'? Or does it represent the 'Oh!' of surprise and delight uttered by Jesus when he tasted the first date? There is a third explanation which is more prosaic and takes us from the world of legend straight to cold reality: the O is simply a stamp made by the Government to show that taxes must be paid on dates.

There are said to be two hundred different varieties of date palms and dates, depending on their size, shape, colour, complexion, durability, sugar-content, time of ripening, softness, taste and possible use. Many have names that speak for themselves: 'Temzezet' meaning 'bitter-sweet', 'bahdja' shining, 'el ketara' dripping, 'foulafoul' fibrous, 'deglet bou Sekhraja' the camel-driver's date, 'deglet el Hamar' the donkey's date, and so on. The natives can tell many stories to illustrate these names.

The Queen of the dates is the amber-coloured Deglet Nour. One of the Prophet's wives was called Noura. She always chose the same spot to do her washing, and on this spot a magnificent palm tree grew, which no one had planted and which produced finer fruit than any so far known. In memory of his wife the Prophet called it Noura, and the dates from this tree which until then had borne the common name 'degla' were known as 'deglet noura.'

As many varieties of palm tree are not progenitive, the peasant does not increase his stock by natural reproduction but by means of root-cuttings called Djebbars, which involve the farmer in no risk, for the new trees are like the parent stock. Moreover the farmer knows exactly how many male and how many female trees he plants. He needs only a very limited number of male trees, for pollination is artificial and, although it takes both time and care, it does enable the peasant to maintain between thirty and fifty female fruit-bearing trees with only one male.

According to one popular saying the palm begins bearing fruit as soon as a fully-laden donkey can pass under it without touching the leaves. This stage is reached when the djebbar is five or six years old. But if the peasant is wise he will wait till his tree is considerably older and stronger before he allows it to bear fruit. In any case the date-palm only produces a full crop when it is twenty years old and from then on it will continue to do so for fifty to sixty years, after which the fruit begins to deteriorate both in size and quality, but the tree can still go on producing after it has passed its century.

Like the camel the palm tree has become throughout the centuries an object of reverence and the subject of countless legends. But in more recent times both the camel and the palm have also aroused the interest of scientists.

*   *   *

It was a strange journey with pebbles rattling against the Land-Rover as it bumped over the 'tôle ondulée', ground that rippled like corrugated iron and set our teeth chattering. We were travelling through the Chebka country. Chebka means 'net' and is particularly appropriate to the Mzab area with its dry wadis and channels criss-crossing a plateau which is one of the most inhospitable and dangerous stretches of the desert.

The danger is, of course, small if it rains as it did in the beginning of 1958. In a landscape that usually seems devoid of life millions of seeds had been lying dormant, waiting for the magic touch of water. The Chebka, covered in a matter of days by a film of tender, lush green, suddenly looked like the Jura, and in the green background patterns were woven by countless pink and red flowers amongst which the violet camel-flower and the snow-white gorse stood out waist-high.

Michel Boulay, agricultural expert, on whose invitation I was making this journey to Guerrara, asked me for my impressions of Zelfana. I did not conceal my disappointment.

'A clammy twilight! Isn't that what you said?' laughed Boulay.

'Even in twenty years if all goes well and Zelfana is an established oasis you're not likely to find that. Your mental image of a palm-grove is hopelessly outdated.'

The point Boulay made is important. It is not enough to employ modern boring equipment and so provide the inhabitants of the desert with fresh supplies of water, they must also be taught to use the water more economically and more effectively. It is not economical to crowd 200 palms into two and a half acres. A hundred and twenty-one palm trees, if planted nine yards apart in the same area, will produce considerably more fruit.

'Our ultimate aim is to modernise the old-fashioned palm groves. With a steady water-supply the date-production of all the oases could be substantially increased. Quite apart from the fact that the more open system of planting means considerably less work, the agricultural research station at El Arfian in the Rhir district is making investigations into soil and cultivation which should improve date-production. A pollen-sprayer has been developed, for example, which cuts down not only the time spent on pollination but also the amount of pollen needed. The saving in male trees alone will more than cover the cost of a spray. But in the old-fashioned palm-grove there is simply not enough room to use a pollen-spray.'

For a two and a half acre palm-grove, using modern methods of cultivation, about 12 gallons of water a minute are needed. This works out at 6 gallons of water per hour for each tree. These figures, of course, vary according to local conditions. The palm is thirstier in summer than in winter. In laying out a palm grove it is pointless to try and work out the total annual water-consumption. The size of a grove depends on the peak water consumption in summer and the available supply. Surplus water in winter cannot be saved up for the summer. The normal practice is to use it for winter-cereals and vegetables, for even the most frugal inhabitants of the desert cannot live on dates alone.

'You mustn't assume that the twelve gallons of water per minute consumed in a modern palm-grove go into the roots of the trees. About two fifths of it drains away,' Boulay pointed out and added: 'There's nothing to be done about it. The gallons of water that are apparently lost are in fact essential. They keep the ground free of salt.'

Sand and salt are the palm-cultivator's chief enemies. Groves which are neglected are very soon swallowed up by sand-dunes or killed by salt. Yet one tends to forget that the salts dissolved in the water can also be very helpful to the gardener. Sterile sand is frequently regarded in the Sahara as good 'soil' not because it contains any nutritive substances or bacteria but simply because of its mechanical properties. Can it support palm trees? That is the most important question. All the more important when one considers the chronic lack of natural fertilisers in the desert. In some palm-groves there are huts for which the proprietor demands no higher rent than the excrement of his tenants. The nomads preserve the manure of their camels and sheep as if it was gold. The few francs they get for it in the next oasis make the mere act of bending well worth while. Artificial manure is far beyond the means of an ordinary date-farmer. In many districts the palms flourish with virtually no fertilisation at all. I had often wondered what took the place of the ingredients that were missing from the soil.

'Water,' said Boulay. 'In many parts of the Sahara cultivation of the date-palm is probably a kind of tank cultivation. There is no soil. Water provides the nourishment. I say "probably" because our investigations are still only beginning, but the research-workers at El Arfian received a shock when they tried to establish how much manure was needed to make a palm-tree produce the biggest and best fruit. The answer was: none. Both natural and artificial manures had the effect of reducing not increasing the crop, which suggested that the palm tree gets all the nourishment it needs from water.'

I watched my companion as he spoke, heard the note of warmth and enthusiasm in his voice as he gave me details of natural and artificial manures, and in my mind I placed him in that select group of men who, in their war against the desert, may lose the odd engagement or even, as at Zelfana, a major battle but will win out in the end. Mainly because they love the very desert against which they are fighting.

Guerrara! We stopped at the edge of the Oued Zegrir where we could survey the walls and watch-towers of the fort. The palm-groves formed a dusty, grey green mass in the midday sun that contrasted sharply with the dazzling light brown of the dry river-bed and swept away from the village like the tail of a comet. The village, clinging to a conical hilltop, culminated in the minaret of a mosque, a typical Mozabite minaret pointing its four fingers towards heaven.

The Mozabites are Berbers and a mass of contradictions. They live in the rocky Chebka country where the sun's heat is at its most merciless, yet they have the complexion of prisoners who have been rotting for twenty years in mouldy, dark, airless cells. Their black beards and the long white muslin scarves wound so grace-fully round their turbans only serve to underline their unhealthy complexion. Their home territory, the Mzab, is known, not with-out reason, as a desert in the desert. Nevertheless the Mozabites—again not without reason—are said to be very wealthy. They are known as cloth and spice merchants not only throughout North Africa, though more especially in the Algerian coastal towns, but also in France. They do not enjoy the best of reputations in the desert. The Chaamba, for instance, regard them as opportunists, toadies and cowards, but this severe judgment is partly based on the traditional contempt of the nomad for the sedentary population and on the envy of the rich by the poor. But this is not the whole explanation. Paradoxically, the history of the Mozabites is one of firmness, courage and an unshakeable devotion to their religious convictions. During the hundred years and more they have spent under French influence they have learned a great deal. Many Mozabites speak excellent French. At the moment a handful of young Mozabites are studying medicine and technical sciences at Geneva and other universities. The Mozabite leaders are Grand Officers of the Legion of Honour, their breasts covered with decorations. They also have the French to thank for the peace and order without which their business would not have prospered. And yet these same Mozabites have retained almost intact from any outside influence precisely those characteristics which in European eyes are most backward. When there was a serious threat of infiltration from Algeria the French placed little confidence in the Mozabites.

'They stick by us,' a French officer explained, 'because they haven't done badly by us, but they wouldn't be merchants if they hadn't also insured themselves with the fellagha. They pay taxes to us and at the same time contribute to the Algerian rebellion—and, who knows, perhaps even a few francs more than is required of them.'

The 30,000 Mozabites are Islamic Protestants, Puritans of the desert. They do not smoke; music is anathema to them; their mosques are bare, colourless places of prayer; they recognise no authority other than God's revelation in the Koran, all non-koranic traditions being false interpretations of the will of Allah; their aim is to apply the divine law strictly and without compromise in all walks of life: marabouts, religious fraternities and sainthood they reject; each Mozabite is his own marabout. They form a community of the elect. The orthodox Moslem looks upon his Mozabite brothers in Allah with deep suspicion; for him they belong to the heretical sect of the Ibadites.

When Ali, the cousin and son-in-law of Mohammed, was proclaimed the fourth Caliph at Medina, Moawija, the Governor of Syria, disputed his claim. The two sought to decide the issue in battle. At Siffin in 657 Ali was within sight of victory when suddenly his adversaries fixed copies of the Koran to the points of their lances and called upon Ali to submit his claim to arbitration. To avoid further bloodshed the rightful and wise Caliph agreed, whereupon twelve thousand men in his army deserted him. They reproached him angrily with having defied the Koran by agreeing to arbitration, to human bargaining, whereas God alone could judge who was their rightful ruler. The dissidents were called 'Kharedjie' which means 'Outgoing.' Ali fought the rebels but an assassin struck him down with a sword crying: 'Allah is our judge and not thou.' From then on a number of different sects arose, of which Ibadism is one of the mildest. It gained a particularly strong following in North Africa. The Berbers became Ibadites to protest against foreign Arab rule. In the ninth century Tiaret in the Atlas mountains was the flourishing capital of an

Ibadite kingdom till it was burnt down by the Fatemites in 909.
The Ibadites escaped the massacre by fleeing into the desert under
the leadership of their last Imam. Like the Israelites they found
their Canaan—at Sedrata, south of Ouargla. Before long they had
established a prosperous town in the heart of the desert, yet a
century later many Ibadites moved farther afield. Before Sedrata
was even threatened, they had built—in 1011—another town, El
Aleuf, in the barren Chebka country. When Sedrata was finally
sacked by an invading army, the majority of the Mozabites had
already moved to the country, Beni Mzab, after which they were
subsequently named.

Today there are five towns on the hilltops and rocky escarp-
ments in the dry bed of the Oued Mzab: El Ateuf, Bou Noura, Ben
Isguen, Melika and Ghardaïa. From El Ateuf, the earliest of these
settlements, to Ghardaïa, the most recent (1053), is a mere five
miles up the valley. The economic importance of Ghardaïa and its
16,000 inhabitants makes it the chief of these unique five towns, but
the real heart of the Pentapolis is Ben Isguen, where the population
is entirely Mozabite, where smoking is forbidden in the streets and
where the gates of the town are closed at nightfall. Ben Isguen is
not merely the Holy City of the Mozabites, it is also, so rumour has
it, the Mozabite treasury.

The Mozabite towns are like extravagant iced cakes with their
cube-shaped houses mounting in tiers to the mosque and minaret.
Streets and lanes wind and twist their way up the hillside; quite
often they are covered and become little more than burrows and
tunnels. The mosque is both the spiritual and the architectural
focal point. Seen from the roof of the mosque the town falls away
evenly on every side like the mantle of God. Whitewashed houses
intermingle with pale blue and green, and the red ochre of the
valley below and the surrounding slopes has a dazzling intensity
which not even the brightest yellow can achieve in Europe.

The Mozabites are born colonisers. Apathy, which is invariably
the undoing of white-skinned peoples in the desert, is not one of
their failings. It required an extraordinary amount of energy to
build and maintain in one of the most god-forsaken spots in the
world oasis towns which were and still are the envy of all other

desert peoples. They had to work their way down through some forty yards of solid limestone before they reached the water-table of the Oued Mzab. They then put down 3000 wells to irrigate 200,000 palms. Making a virtue of the necessity to feed themselves as oasis farmers, they developed into successful traders. It took remarkable courage and self-confidence to expose this self-contained community with its own peculiar customs, habits and beliefs to the hostile influence of the outside world without destroying it. The Mozabites succeeded, giving perhaps even more impressive proof of their iron discipline than the feat they achieved in building their five towns.

While the men emigrate, at least for a time, the women are forbidden to leave the Mzab territory or even the town in which they live. The language commonly used by the men is Arabic but most of the women only understand the Berber dialect, mother tongue of the Mozabites. In other respects too they are the repositories of Mozabite custom and culture, and as such they are kept locked up like hens that lay golden eggs. Only when the heat in the town becomes unbearable do they move with their children into summer houses in the gardens, but the strictest precautions are taken to prevent any contact with strangers. There is only one occasion on which this monastic seclusion is broken: when the Oued Mzab is in spate, which is once every seven years on an average, then women and children are allowed to watch the impressive spectacle as long and as often as they wish. For the rushing, muddy water is Allah's way of telling his favourite children that he has not forgotten their devotion to his laws.

A progressive party has recently put forward the idea, which is bitterly opposed by the conservatives, that in exceptional cases a man might be allowed to take his wife abroad. The more enlightened Mozabites have already come to realise that pregnancy lasts nine months and not two years or more. Up till now, when children were born only a few weeks after the husband's return from abroad, the women maintained that the foetus had simply slept during the father's years of absence—an ingenious explanation which Moslem husbands, not merely in the Mzab, have been swallowing since time immemorial. (At one stage, in order to pre-

vent irregularities, Cairo University announced that the maximum
duration of a pregnancy was two years!) For the moment the idea
that wives might accompany their husbands abroad has only
entered a few particularly bold heads and the news that three
emancipated Mozabites had smuggled their wives out must have
shocked both progressives and conservatives.

The position of these towns, their walls, loopholes and fortified
gateways and a mosque that can always be converted in an
emergency from a place of prayer to a bunker—all this tells its own
story. The Mozabite towns were built as places of refuge from the
marauding nomads, particularly the warlike Chaamba but also
from hostile tribes amongst their own people. Mozabite history is
full of schisms and secessions. Fratricidal strife became so widespread on some occasions that the Arabs were called in to help.
Usually with the result that they refused to leave. Berrian and
Guerrara, the only Mozabite towns that do not lie in the Oued
Mzab, were founded in the seventeenth century by inhabitants of
Ghardaïa, who had fallen out with their co-religionists.

In Guerrara, the second-largest Mozabite town, most of the
9,000 inhabitants are Mozabites with a substantial Arab minority.
The Jewish section of the population, however, has shrunk. In the
Mzab territory there are still a thousand Jews who for centuries
have been regarded as unclean and shunned. A Mozabite will even
refuse to employ manure from a Jewish house for his palm-trees,
a prejudice he can afford to indulge, for there is no shortage of
manure in the densely-populated Mzab country. During the last
few years all but one Jewish family have emigrated.

Lieutenant Ragozin, the S.A.S. Officer in Guerrara, was expect-
ing us. The sinewy face under the blue kepi was softened by a trace
of melancholy. We made immediate contact. We set out at once for
the artesian well on the other side of the valley. What a sight! It was
like a gigantic hot shower: 3,500 gallons of water pouring out each
minute at 100 degrees Fahrenheit. The catchment-basin is surrounded by a wire-fence to prevent animals from dirtying the
water.

On this side of the Oued Zegri the plateau drops away steeply.
The predominant feature is not limestone, as elsewhere in the

Mzab, but date-brown sandstone similar to the famous Nubian sandstone found in the Upper Nile Valley. The well seems to be under the protection of a marabout or local holy man, for just before the edge of the precipice stands his tent, a small circular edifice which tapers up like an English wedding-cake to a little pillar on top.

It was on the 8th of March 1949 that the borer first bit into the earth at the marabout's feet. At a depth of 2,100 feet the Alb was reached, then the boring continued to 3,800 feet, where there was still porous sandstone. The intention had been to bore through the Alb but lack of equipment made this impossible.

Why was Guerrara chosen for the second attempt to plumb Savornin's Sea? Mainly no doubt, because of its acute shortage of water. The inhabitants were entirely dependent on the surface stream in the Oued Zegrir. With the help of a dam they managed to spin out the supply, but there was no way of compensating for the irregularity of the flow. There was also the fact, however, that the Mozabites had been very much put out by the boring at Zelfana. They demanded a well of their own, but the administration placed Zelfana politically and socially under the jurisdiction of Metlili, the Ksar of the Chaamba. That their arch-enemies, the Chaamba, should have the first artesian well in the Mzab territory was a source of bitter resentment to the Mozabites. Guerrara was the only Mozabite town in which a second artesian well was a practical possibility.

The year 1950 is one the Guerrari will long remember. On October 17th the well began operating and a few weeks later the Oued Zegrir obliged with floods which turned Guerrara into a Venice of the desert. Lieutenant Ragozin showed me pictures taken at the end of 1950, when the palm-groves of Guerrara were five to six feet under water and the date-harvest had to be brought in on rafts made of palm-trunks.

The Mozabites took advantage of this unexpected surplus of water to practise a neat little piece of blackmail. They refused to take the water from the artesian well at the price fixed by the administration, arguing that the taxes imposed on their houses, their cattle and their female palm-trees already paid for the water.

The administration, on the other hand, wanted to cover the cost of boring. The Mozabites were in a strong bargaining position for they knew from experience that the flood water alone would guarantee good crops for the next two and possibly even three years.

The authorities, furious at the trick nature had played on them, stopped the water-supply. The war of nerves went on for four years, but by 1954 the Mozabites had weakened. Their palm-groves were again threatened by drought. The authorities made a certain reduction in the price and the dispute was settled to the satisfaction of both parties.

Guerrara's artesian well has not only made it independent from the dictates of the weather and replaced an ancient method of irrigation by a modern and less laborious one, it has also stimulated long-overdue reforms. Guerrara's palm-groves with their 40,000 trees, of which one in four bears no fruit, today wear a new look. Where there is overcrowding (and Guerrara has been particularly guilty of this) superfluous trees are being removed and the proportion of Deglet Nour, which are the finest export dates but have not so far been cultivated in any quantity at Guerrara, is now being increased. The water-consumers have banded together in two dozen cooperatives which are responsible for the fair distribution of the water in the various sections.

On our way through the palm-groves we kept stumbling over cement and plastic pipes. They made an ugy spectacle, which, however, filled Lieutenant Ragozin and Michel Boulay with obvious satisfaction. They were not in the least concerned that the romantic palm-grove of old had disappeared. On the contrary it thrilled them to know that the natives on their own initiative and at their own cost had tried out these new materials in an attempt to cut down losses through seepage and evaporation.

Even virgin land is to be irrigated and made cultivable. South of Guerrara an S.A.R. (Secteur d'amélioration rurale) is to be set up to experiment with new methods of palm-cultivation. So far Lieutenant Ragozin has not been very enthusiastic about this well-meaning plan, for it has revived the old feud between the Mozabites and the Chaamba. The S.A.R. is in a Daya or depression, and these Dayas, which are filled with pans of alluvial soil to collect water in the event of rain or flood, have always been the scene of a kind of agricultural game of chance. The nomads sow wheat and oats in them. Four or five months later they come back. If the water has achieved all that was expected of it, then there is a crop worth ten or twenty times the value of the seed. If the harvest is not forthcoming and the seed is lost, then they simply try their luck again next time. The Chaamba have cited this traditional method of cultivation in support of their claim to the S.A.R. But the Mozabites also have their claims. 'It's not uncommon,' Lieutenant Ragozin told me with a twinkle in his eye, 'for four or five Guerraris to turn up with proprietary claims to one and the same plot of land.'

Most of the old wells have run out, and the few still in use provide drinking water, for the people believe that it is healthier than the Alb water. Lieutenant Ragozin described this as an unwarranted prejudice but could not deny that, while the water from the Oued Zegrir is at most a few years old, the artesian water fell as rain centuries ago.

Water, pure water, sparked off an economic boom in Guerrara. It is available at three francs per thousand litres. Being good merchants, cunning traders and shrewd businessmen, the Mozabites sat down and did some rapid calculating. Only then did they commit themselves. Whereas before they had invested their money in the north they now put it into their own town and its gardens. New sandstone buildings are appearing on the outskirts of the town and there are even signs of a real estate market. A square metre of land which could be had for a few pence five years ago costs three or four pounds today. The Guerraris are trying to use the water which Allah and the French conjure from the earth as economically as possible. They are buying more expensive water-pipes. With their highly-developed business acumen they are fully alive to the industrial potentialities of the desert. I was struck, for example, by the large number of fruit-trees at Guerrara: apricots, mandarines, oranges, figs and olives. The quantity and variety of vegetables under cultivation also seemed to me remarkable.

When I said as much to Lieutenant Ragozin, he aired what in the Sahara is a more or less open secret:

'The people of Guerrara have got the idea into their heads that they can corner the whole fruit and vegetable trade of the desert. They're importing the best varieties from the North and trying them out under their own local conditions. Their aim, which is to gain a monopoly as fruit and vegetable growers, is particularly shrewd and far sighted, for an oil town like Hassi Messaoud could become an important market for our produce.'

There was a note of pride in his voice as he spoke of 'our' produce which was quite genuine. Lieutenant Ragozin, who has something of the mystical reforming zeal of his Russian fore-fathers, identifies himself completely with his protégés. They are no longer living on charity, they are developing an initiative of their own. It would be hard to imagine a finer by-product of Savornin's Sea and its miraculous springs.

I had intended on the return journey to question Michel Boulay further about palms, water and oases, but we had our hands full with other things. We kept stopping in the desert to pick flowers, huge bushes of white broom and bunches of small red snapdragon, and we vied with each other in gathering desert truffles as big as potatoes. This unexpected wealth of vegetation also had its culinary side. Each evening, as the market-place at Ghardaïa filled up, the cry 'Terfes! Terfes!' could be heard, as the nomads sold the delicious desert mushrooms. To begin with they had fetched about ten shillings a pound; when we asked the price it was less than sixpence. The nomads had met with competition; collecting truf-fles had become a major hobby of the Ghardaïa garrison.

* * *

Ouargla is an excellent beginner's course for anyone aspiring to become a Saharan. Some years ago in mid-summer I paid my first visit to it in circumstances which were not of my own choosing. Caught in a sandstorm, the plane I was travelling in had to make a forced landing. I shall never forget the intense heat; the strange caprioles of sand set up by the wind which filled the air with myriads of glistening crystals of quartz; a sunlight so sharp that it bruised one's eyes; roasted pigeons and tropical madness; the native town huddled round the market place, and the spacious European quarter that looked like the remains of a Colonial exhibition. I realised then that even life in an oasis, miserable as it is, acquires a splendour of its own when one sees it in its context of yellow, barren desert, standing stiff and solemn.

Ouargla lies in a trough of the fossil Wadi Mya. The deepest parts of this depression are filled with salt lakes, the largest of which was one and a half square miles of stagnant water when I saw it in the winter of 1958. The natives, half-blinded by the sun's glare, had picked off the thick salt crust.

In Ouargla and the few smaller oases nearby there are upwards of a million palm trees. Placed in a line ten yards apart they would stretch almost a quarter of the distance round the earth. But the crop they produce is unfortunately not so impressive. About half the trees rely entirely on the highest water-table which their roots can just reach. In a good year when the water-level is particularly high and the natives have taken the trouble at least to fertilise the trees, each of them will produce between five and ten pounds of dates. In a bad year they will produce nothing. In fact, only about a quarter of the total palm-population—around 250,000 trees—receive enough water to produce a regular, healthy crop of ten to twenty pounds of dates per tree.

At first glance the desert seems timeless, a frozen sea of sand-dunes with its palms, donkeys and camels as in biblical times, locked in an immemorial and merciless struggle for water. This is quite a false picture. Naturally there is little or no written evidence of the pre-French period, but against this the natives have long memories.

Ouargla, the largest oasis in the Sahara, suffers from a disease—insatiable thirst—which could only be cured after it had been properly diagnosed. J. Lablée after a careful investigation which involved long conversations with the peasants produced a paper entitled 'The wandering oasis.'

It began at Ain Sfa, a well which suddenly bubbled up in the desert and gave rise to a small river flowing northwards. Ancient Arabic chronicles tell wonderful stories of this well and to this day

Ain Sfa has remained a familiar name throughout the Sahara. No geologist has ever seen this well, which sprang up about eight miles south of Ouargla, but they know where its water came from. Ouargla's 'cellar', which belongs geologically to the Oued Rhir, has several storeys through which subsoil water flows. There are, for instance, the sands of the miocene period, a division of the tertiary, and somewhat lower down a stratum of chalk. Both water-tables are artesian and, according to the experts, are probably connected.

The first palm-groves were planted twenty miles north of the well by negroes from the Sudan. The first oasis at Ifran goes back at least to Roman times. In the seventh or eighth century a foreign ruler compelled the thirty or forty inhabitants of Ifran to move up-stream and where Ouargla is situated today, halfway between Ifran and Ain Sfa, they established a ksar or fortified settlement with extensive orchards: Ouargelan. In the tenth century the migration was completed when the Ibadites, later known as the Mozabites, who had been driven out of Tiaret into the desert, settled on the well itself at Sedrata.

At the end of the last century Sedrata was in the news. Harold Tarry wanted to restore it to its former size and glory under the Ibadites. He was a positive hive of energy who had a weakness for fantastic projects (he was also a member of the Commission for the Trans-Saharan Railway) and who dreamed of disinterring Sedrata's houses from the sand and making them habitable again.

The desert Pompeii was to reappear in new splendour. He even managed to get a government subsidy for his plan, but before long Tarry's dream had faded into obscurity.

In 1950 the Swiss archaeologist Marguerite van Berchem flew over Sedrata. The outlines of a town a mile long and half a mile wide were clearly discernible under the sand dunes: town-walls, fortified towers, houses, streets, low dykes surrounding extensive palm-groves and, above all, a close network of canals, which can be traced like a system of arteries as far as Ouargla and even beyond. As a result of this highly promising survey, Marguerite van Berchem made two excavations in 1951 and 1952 when she un-earthed a number of buildings, discovered frescoes of vital interest to the art-historian and found concrete evidence of Sedrata's water-distribution system. The canals, on the banks of which small sweet-water shells were still in evidence, were up to three yards wide, another indication of abundance of water.

The Ibadites in Sedrata could not possibly manage with water from the well alone; shortly after they arrived they appear to have sunk artificial shafts to tap the water in the miocene sand. The chronicler writes admiringly: 'And the water-geysers which shot with incredible force from the wells dug by the refugees soon made the desert bloom.'

Why at the beginning of the eleventh century the Ibadites emigrated from Sedrata to the Mzab is not known. It may be that the town was threatened by drifting sand or that too many of its inhabitants had died of malaria. Until only a few years ago Ouargla was a notorious fever-trap. But another possibility is that the water supply began to run out, thus forcing the swelling population to settle elsewhere and at the same time draining water away from Ifran and Ouargla. Eventually the Ksourians of Ouargelan, spurred on and supported by one of the Sultans, marched on Sedrata, drove out the last of the Ibadites and sacked the town.

When I visited Sedrata the sand had already reclaimed all that Marguerite van Berchem had wrested from it a few years before. But each year at the end of April many Mozabites still cross the high dunes by donkey or on foot to kneel at the spot where Sedrata's chief mosque is buried. And the pilgrimage ends with a prayer over the tomb of the Imam Moses who led them into the desert.

The story goes that the conqueror of Sedrata summoned the Rhtassin or well-keepers from Ouargla and ordered them to clean out the main shaft. The guild of Rhtassin is, of course, now dying out as the native-dug wells fall into disuse. The Rhtassin built the artesian wells at the Oued Rhir and Ouargla and cleaned them out every few years. I have already referred to the risks involved in sinking a well. Many were drowned in the sudden gush of water. But the cleaning of a well was every bit as dangerous. The shaft is between a hundred and a hundred and fifty feet deep and only ten or fifteen feet in diameter. The men could remain at the bottom of the shaft for no more than five minutes filling their baskets with sand, mud and rubble. Then they returned to the surface completely exhausted. This gamble with death was made six or eight times a day. The number of well-divers who died of suffocation, drowning or consumption was legion. The guild of Rhtassin was looked upon not only with admiration but respect and almost superstitious awe. In recognition of their dangerous occupation they were exempt from all taxes.

The divers tried in vain to carry out the Sultan's orders and climb down the shaft through which the water was pouring out of the chalk. Time and again they were forced back by the pressure of the water. But the Sultan was not so easily put off. He summoned the seven leading marabouts in the district to use their supernatural powers to reduce the force of the water long enough to enable the well divers to complete their work. The marabouts succeeded in reducing the force of the water but were unable to restore it afterwards. In a fury the Sultan had all seven holy men beheaded.

This story illustrates the most pressing problem of the time: dying wells. Shortly before the French came to Ouargla the migration in pursuit of water, first up, then downstream, reached its lowest point near the salt Shott. French technicians helped the natives to develop what still remained of this land.

I made a tour of the Shott with Francis Sagnes, chief engineer of the Algerian Water Board at Ouargla. The windscreen-wipers ticked; a thin drizzle of rain was falling. There was not a breath of air; on the edge of the salt marsh the blades of the high mechanical windmill stood motionless. The water of the Shott was leaden grey, not unlike the mood of my companion.

Sagnes explained how attempts had been made to avoid a too drastic approach to Ouargla's problem by systematically blocking the native or 'Arab' wells and replacing them, in part at least, by modern water-pipes. In Arab wells the lining of the shaft consists entirely of palm-trunks; before the water has even reached the surface, much of it has gone to waste. In the modern wells, on the other hand, where the water flows through pipes there is no wastage.

These steps are still being taken. Every month five or six of

Ouargla's Arab wells are shut down. But all the experts realise that
this is merely a palliative, not a permanent cure.

There were three possible ways of effecting such a cure. The first
was to drain the Shott, a ticklish and extremely costly operation
which would have prolonged the life of the patient but not saved
him. By draining the Shott fresh strata would, of course, have become accessible lower down but within a relatively short time they
would have gone dry.

The second possibility was to use pumps to draw up water from
the miocene sand which was no longer reaching the oldest and
highest palm-groves under its own pressure. But here too the cost
would have been prohibitive.

The third possibility was to look for artesian water at lower
levels which would have a high pressure of its own. The top layer
of subsoil water is of no use for irrigation. Near the Shott it is about
six inches, in other parts of the oasis two to three yards, below the
surface, and the water provided by evaporation of the Shott contains fifteen to twenty grammes of salt per litre (one and three-
quarter pints) a diet which even palm-trees not allergic to salt do
not find at all palatable. The miocene sands, which may be anything from a hundred to three hundred feet down, have served
until now as Ouargla's reservoir. A further four hundred and fifty
feet down is the Senon Lime, in which two absorption wells were
sunk at Zelfana to carry the used water back below ground.

The experts decided to adopt the third course but a hole bored
into the Senon lime produced disappointing results. A hundred
gallons per minute is not a great deal. It only remained, therefore,
to try still deeper in the Alb of Savornin's sea.

The boring began in April 1956 and on November 1st the topmost layer of Alb was reached. Its sandstone was pierced to a
depth of 6750 feet. On December 5th a wave of excitement swept
through Ouargla: the first well from the Alb went into operation.
It produced 3400 gallons per minute which was enough not only
to irrigate five hundred acres already under cultivation but also to
open up the same amount of fresh ground. The pressure of the
water is such that it can be used at any point in Ouargla, even on
the higher fringes of the depression.

'Now we have a surplus of water,' remarked Francis Sagnes wryly and, seeing my look of surprise, he added: 'In terms of demand, of course, we still haven't too much. On the contrary, a second boring should really be made. But for the time being we can't afford to do that. Ouargla at the moment is simply not in a position to consume that amount of water. You must remember that this first Alb well produces the equivalent of several hundred old wells. When the water has fulfilled its purpose, it flows into the Shott. As long as the supply of water was not excessive, evaporation alone was enough to empty the Shott. But the increased supply is raising its level to the point where between five and seven hundred acres nearby are threatened. A mechanical windmill was set up to pump the overflow into the depression north of Ouargla but not enough water has been diverted to remove the danger. Either we shall have to create an artificial outlet for the Shott, which would be technically possible but very expensive, or the palm-groves that are threatened must be abandoned.'

The second of these two alternatives will probably be adopted. This means that Ouargla, the wandering oasis, will again be on the move but this time upwards.

* * *

Whenever I saw one of these powerful artesian wells with the water gushing from thousands of feet below ground, I remembered what Professor Quézel had said about the green Sahara. Can the desert be made green again by tapping its subterranean water supplies in Savornin's Sea? I put this question to Tomasi, Boulay, Ragozin, Sages, and many others. All of them answered in the negative.

When I made my first tour of the Sahara people were talking with the greatest confidence about the Shott ech Chergui. It was one of the most ambitious projects ever worked out by the hydrologists. By 1958, however, any mention of it had become taboo.

The Chergui Shott, a salt marsh about a hundred miles long and between eight and twelve miles wide, lies some 3000 feet up on the Algerian plateau between the coastal and the Saharan Atlas. On the fringe of it are eighteen artesian wells, producing water which is either sweet or only slightly salty—an indication of substantial underground water supplies. Marcel Gautier, a leading engineer on the Algerian Water Board, developed the following theory: the Shott lies at the heart of a large basin or natural reservoir in which the water is under considerable pressure, as is demonstrated by the force with which it leaves the wells. But as the strata holding down the water are not completely watertight, it is seeping through to the surface and evaporating. In other words, the salt marsh acts as an artesian sponge. It was a tempting thought that this reservoir might be tapped and enough water drained off to reduce the pressure in the basin and cut out, or at least cut down, evaporation. A balance might conceivably be achieved whereby the same amount of water was drained off as was seeping into the basin.

This was the object of the Chergui project. The water was to be diverted through the coastal Atlas mountains to the plain, producing both electricity and irrigation. Some had visions of new industries and areas of cultivation arising merely by arresting the natural perspiration on the high plateau round the Chergui Shott. Fortunately Gautier and his colleagues were more realistic. They set up a research station at Ain Skhouna near the Shott, where the biggest of the artesian wells is situated. They measured evaporation and rainfall and made more than a hundred geological borings. But above all they pumped. They were assuming that if the amount of water pumped out was smaller than the inflow, the level of the subsoil water would drop, the pressure would fall and at some stage a new point of balance would be reached. For a whole year, from February 1956 to January 1957, five pumps were at work day and night removing 800 gallons of water per second, but there were no signs of outflow and inflow balancing up. It was gradually realised that a great deal too much was being taken out. The pumps continued working for another year but at a greatly reduced rate. The level of the subsoil water still dropped, however, slowly but steadily. In January 1958 the pumps stopped working. The plan to irrigate the coastal plain was quietly abandoned. The experiments showed that something like 450 gallons of water per second could be diverted from the basin. It is a great deal of water but not nearly enough to justify a project that would cost many millions of pounds.

The nomads and peasants on the Algerian plateau were greatly relieved by this setback. While the pumping was going on, all their wells had dried up, and if the water were to be diverted to the coast, the prospects for their flocks and their fields would be anything but rosy. The failure of the experiment left the scientists and technicians involved with something of a hangover. Apart from anything else, the Ain Skhouna experiment had cost between three and four thousand million francs.

The desert geologists and hydrologists are not visionaries. They regard plans to make the Sahara green again with the help of subterranean water supplies as a waste of time. They have other more pressing problems.

'We have no intention of drawing on our capital,' one of them remarked to me. 'We prefer to live on the interest.'

In other words, no more water will be taken from the Alb reservoir than flows into it from the Atlas mountains.

This reservoir is, in fact, an enormous size. Savornin estimated that the Alb contained about four hundred billion cubic feet of water. It would take the Rhine almost 190 years to fill a reservoir this size. If the experts are against drawing on this supply, it is not because they think it might run out in their lifetime but because they know that even a small reduction of water pressure in such a subterranean reservoir is enough to dry up all wells. How high the yearly interest on this capital is has not been established. The balance-sheet of Savornin's sea still has to be drawn up. It is not known, for example, whether rain also seeps through the sand-dunes of the Great Western Erg to the Alb sandstone. Or whether Savornin's sea loses water in the desert by sweating. It may be that it is connected—particularly in the east, in southern Tunisia and Libya—with other water-tables under less pressure. Yet another question that has not yet been answered is whether Alb water penetrates into the Shott of Southern Tunisia and evaporates there.

Savornin reckoned with a yearly supply of around 350 milliard cubic feet. The geologists who are 'in power' today are more conservative in their estimates; they have taken the last nought from Savornin's figure. They believe that the most they can safely extract from the Alb is 6,000 gallons per second, which may seem small by European standards—the Rhine at Emmerich has a flow of about half a million gallons a second—but it is a great deal in the Sahara. When the foggaras, wells and borings have taken their toll, there are between four and five thousand gallons a second left, enough to irrigate three to four million palms and increase the annual date production of the Algerian Sahara from a hundred thousand to nearly two hundred thousand tons.

When I mentioned Savornin's name in the air-conditioned restaurant of an oil camp, it brought a chorus of 'mountebank,' 'swindler' and 'good-for-nothing'—these were only a few of the pleasant names those pioneers of a modern, industrialised Sahara gave to Savornin. What they held against him was that as a brilliant product of the 'École Polytechnique' and the 'École des Mines', he had allowed himself to become involved in high finance and had saddled France with bad investments running into millions. Like Savornin the engineers of the Algerian Water Board also came in for some sharp criticism. A Ukrainian geologist dismissed them contemptuously as 'stupid' while a French colleague called them 'bunglers.' The attitude of the oil men is very patronising; they always know best. Quite often they do know best. They corrected many a misconception which, till they arrived, had gone un-challenged and they have filled quite a few blank spaces in the geological maps with accurate and reliable data. It was not that they were better geologists but simply because they had the wherewithal and the technical equipment.

'Short-sighted and wasteful!' said a hydrologist of the oil-men and he made it sound just as slanderous as the abuse I had heard from the other side. In fact, the industrial pioneers in the Sahara have an irresponsible way of using water that makes the water expert's hair stand on end. Between Ghardaïa and El Golea the road-builders tapped the Alb in five different places, and while they were repairing the track between Hassi Messaoud and Fort Flatters, they acquired from an oil company a test-drilling site that had yielded nothing but could be converted into an artesian well.

This is the Water Board's main problem: that in the search for oil the Alb is constantly being pierced. Each borehole which yields no oil is at least a possible source of water and the temptation to use these wells to supply camps or other installations in the desert is obviously very great. In Hassi Messaoud this has already happened: the oil town takes more than 2000 gallons a minute from the Alb. 'The "pétroliers" laugh at us for being so careful. They will not draw a distinction between oil and water. Oil-fields are exploited; when the last drop of oil has been extracted, the field is closed down. We, on the other hand, have to try not to live beyond our means but to manage with the income we've got.'

The hydrologist, however, hardly does the oil-man justice when he condemns him for wasting precious capital. Ouargla would not have had its Alb well as early as it did if it had not been for an oil-drilling in 1953 thirty miles south of Ouargla which enabled the water experts to ascertain the precise situation and character of the Alb stratum. The Rhir area would also probably have had to wait quite some time for its Alb water but for the intervention of the 'pétroliers.'

The Rhir area has had a spectacular series of rescue operations. I have already described how the French arrived waving a magic wand. In 1856, before the French made their first boring, there were 300 wells irrigating 360,000 date-palms. In 1924 there were 1033 wells and 1,610,000 palms. In the same year a new well at Mraier added its incredible quota of 8500 gallons per minute to the existing supply. By 1930 the total had reached 75,000 gallons per minute.

Ever since the early twenties the Rhir area had been regarded as an El Dorado. All that seemed necessary to become rich overnight was to sink a well and plant palms. Adventurers, fortune-hunters and capitalists arrived in shoals to cash in on the apparently inexhaustible water-resources of the Rhir district. But the result was bankruptcy. The drain on the water-supply was too heavy. Fresh borings no longer added to the total output but merely drew water away from other sources. A well sunk at Sidi Rachid ruined the Ghamra oasis, then the Sidi Rachid oasis lost its water to Tamerna, which in turn fell victim to new plantations 'downstream.' As was the case at Ouargla the palm-groves of the Oued Rhir began to migrate. They moved northwards. The authorities tried to stop the rot by forbidding any fresh wells but it was too late. Pumps were brought in and the water-distribution was tightened up, but demand and supply were completely out of touch.

For the Rhir district there was only one hope left: water from the Alb. Savornin thought it unlikely that there was sandstone of this particular formation under the Oued Rhir. Other geologists were more optimistic. But the Algerian Water Board with its limited resources could not risk a deep boring. Instead at Tamelhat, south of Toggourt, it acquired an oil-drilling which had been unproductive and turned it into an artesian well. At Tamelhat the Alb is as much as 6000 feet down and the water gushes out with tremendous force equivalent to a column 1000 feet high. Information gained from another oil-drilling enabled the Algerian Water Board to sink a well of their own at Sidi Khaled at the northern end of the Rhir district, and further borings have been made on the North–South axis between Sidi Khaled and Tamelhat. The work of rescuing the Rhir oasis is the latest but presumably not the last chapter in the success story of Savornin's Sea.

It is a commonplace that oil and politics are inextricably mixed. But in the Sahara water is also inseparable from politics. I looked through the earliest reports from the 1850s in which the hydrologists described their admirable work in the Rhir district. They distributed wells like prizes. The second French well in the Sahara, for example, was presented to Sidi Mohammed el Aid Ben el Hadj Ali, the head of a religious fraternity. This powerful marabout lived in the Temacine oasis in a monastery called Tamelhat. If the engineers chose to drill nearby, it was not from any geological considerations. 'Sidi Mohammed had given us clear evidence that his sympathies were with us. His influence extended even amongst the Tuareg and beyond as far as the Sudan. It was essential to our plans for the future that this marabout should be committed still more closely to the French cause. It is hard to imagine just how powerful he was; perhaps the nearest parallel is with the medieval bishops of the Holy Roman Empire.'

The French water policy paid dividends. The 'Bahar Taht el Erd' or 'The Sea under the Earth' never failed to produce the desired effect when the French engineers conjured it out of the ground. The natives gave the first wells names like 'well of Peace, of Friends, of Thankfulness, of Happiness, of Obedience, of Reasonable Men and of Heartfelt Warning'. Remembering the Arabic saying 'Kiss the hand you cannot cut off,' one is not inclined to take these epithets all too seriously, but the fact is that within a year of the first well having been drilled the officers of the Arab Bureau were able to move freely and unmolested in an area which had been notoriously unsafe. It is also a fact that at the beginning of the century General Laperrine had no difficulty in levying three Camel Corps amongst the Chaamba to restore order in the desert. The Chaamba nomads used Ouargla and the Rhir oases as bases. They were thus invested with some of the moral authority which the French had acquired from their artesian wells and they profited from the economic benefits which the natives associated with this authority.

Water and politics are still closely bound up today. The Algerian war has had considerable and direct repercussions on water projects. The unsettled situation on Algeria's borders with Tunisia and Libya has prevented a thorough investigation into the eastern part of Savornin's Sea. A well that had been drilled in the Souf had to be abandoned for security reasons. On January 25, 1957 the Moroccan 'army of liberation' raided the observation post at Djorf Torba, where the site of a dam was being surveyed. The observers were massacred and the post destroyed.

The conflict in Algeria has, of course, also had psychological repercussions in the Sahara. Although they would never admit it openly, the French do occasionally admit to themselves that they might lose the Sahara. Even more unsettling than the situation on the frontiers is the gnawing doubt whether the natives can still be won over by drilling fresh wells. For the time being at least water as an instrument of politics appears to have become blunted.

There are also economic arguments in favour of going slow. I said earlier that there is sufficient Alb water available and still untapped almost to double Algeria's date-production. This however is only true on paper. In practice water is not merely a geological and scientific problem but also a question of finance, a factor which is frequently overlooked. It is not a problem that worries the oil-prospector. He needs a great deal of water but, if it is not ready to hand, he has it fetched in road-tankers, pumped from enormous depths or brought in by pipeline. And the same is more or less true of any industrial project in the desert. This is something entirely new and unheard-of. Until recently men could only work or settle where there was water and this still applies to the date-grower. Water for agricultural purposes is only an economic proposition if deep-drilling is not necessary and if the water rises under its own pressure. Pumping makes the cost of water prohibitive. In Guerrara, where it is artesian, the cost of irrigation is less than a third of the cost at Ghardaia where it is pumped. The palm-groves in the Oued Mzab, which uses water from nine semi-artesian wells, are so to speak 'art for art's sake.' When I remarked as much to Michel Boulay, he replied: 'The Mozabites who take the water at ten francs per cubic metre maintain the palms for the shade and the coolness they provide in summer, not for the dates.'

In other oases, where the inhabitants live on their palm-groves, the depth at which pumps cease to be an economic proposition is determined by the cost of producing power and the market price of the dates. Twenty years ago in Touggourt this was a mere sixteen feet; today it must be even less, for both power and dates have grown dearer. This simply means that, where water has to be pumped out, date-growing is no longer profitable. Deep-drilling is ruinous. The deepest well bored in the Algerian Sahara at Sidi Khaled south-west of Biskra—it is, in fact, the deepest in the world—reached 8,500 feet. From between 6,300 and 6,900 feet it produces 1500 gallons a minute. This well cost more than can ever be earned from the palms and vegetables it irrigates. Understandably enough, France is reluctant to assume financial burdens of this kind unless she can be sure the natives are sufficiently appreciative to work on their land, to irrigate and fertilise their palms and to gather the ripe fruit. Meanwhile the higher wages which the natives can earn in the drilling camps and on road-building have created a serious crisis in palm- and date-cultivation. The situation in the Saharan labour market is tense; the companies working in the desert are in open competition for native labour. And why should a peasant slave in a palm-grove for a few francs a day when he can earn seven times as much—plus board and keep—with oil-prospectors? Many palm-groves are already overgrown and neglected, an easy prey to salt and sand.

At El Golea Captain Barba, who is in charge of the richly-scented and fruit-laden Jardin d'Annexe, said to me sadly: 'I can see the day coming when it will be too much for the young people to climb the palms and pick the dates. And the worst of it is—one can't really hold it against them. There's a great deal more to be got out of climbing an oil-derrick.'

The superflux of wealth that, heap on heap,
All o'er thy realm in earth lies buried deep,
Is practically lost. Thought cannot cast
A limit wide enough for wealth so vast,
And fancy in her wildest flight may strain
To picture it, yet find the effort vain;

GOETHE (*Faust*)

8. Tamanrasset

OVER the white arrow that points to the left is written: Arak 430 km., In Salah 710 km., El Golea 1110 km., Ouargla 1440 km., Ghardaïa 1430 km., Algiers 2060 km., Silet 150 km., Tessalit 660 km., Tin Zaouaten 530 km., Gao 1180 km. And nearby over the arrow that points to the right: In Guezzam 410 km., In Abangarit 690 km., Agadès 980 km., Zinder 1540 km., Kano 1800 km., Lake Chad 2120 km., Dosso 2300 km., Niamey 2500 km., Fort Lamy 2680 km.

The wall, on which the sky-blue boards are fixed, is rough cast in ochre-coloured clay, roughly patterned with perpendicular brush-strokes and crenelated in the Sudanese fashion. On the other side of the road stands a pale green tamarisk tree which casts a slender shadow in the late afternoon. A veteran camel rider trots sleepily past on a donkey. A goatherd with the dark skin of a Hartani but who may equally well be a freed slave or the half-breed offspring of a Targia and her Arab lover urges on his flock of long-haired, pitch-black goats. His Check or headcloth is white or black, his flowing gown white, yellow, green or wine-red. Sometimes it is even blue, which to the unitiated eye makes the freed slave almost indistinguishable from his former master, the Targi. Until the latter himself appears.

Tall and erect, the Targi strides along, scooping up the fine-

powdered sand with his broad sandals or Naïls. He has parked his
vehicle, the Mehari, outside the village. The wide baggy trousers
are hidden under the billowing drapery that clothes his dignity.
Over a white cotton Gandourah or robe he wears a second in indigo
blue, which is thrown back from the shoulders to reveal the dazzling white garment beneath as if it were the lining of a blue cloak.
The arms are bare; the sole decoration is a ring of cut stones which
serves, in case of need, as a knuckle-duster. Each of the two robes,
called by the Tuareg Eressoui, contains nine yards of cloth. The
Taguelmoust or veil covers neck, chin, mouth, nose and forehead.
Over the back of the head it is tied artistically in the shape of a
helmet. The eyes, in the shadow of the veil and blackened by khol,
seem to be looking through a narrow vizor. Legend has it that the
veil is designed to prevent the soul, the breath, from escaping
through the mouth and nose and the unclean spirits from entering
through the uncovered openings in the face. It is merely a happy
coincidence that the Taguelmoust protects the mouth and nose
against dust, the skin against the sun's reflection from the
ground, and the lips against chapping. The Targi even wears it in
his tent and in bed; he keeps it on while eating and drinking; if he
feels compelled to raise it he does so with a distinct feeling of
embarrassment.

There are various kinds of veil. The Targi who takes a pride in
his appearance employs a strip of blue material nine inches wide
and three and a half yards long which shines like the reverse side of
carbon paper—and loses colour. Once it is washed, it loses its
sheen. So the Targi, impoverished knight of the desert, is becoming more and more resigned to wearing the cheaper Check with its
fast colours. He drapes it round his head like the Taguelmoust but
only the tourists are taken in. Over his chest dangles a black satchel,
gaily decorated with fringes and coloured thread, which contains
his papers—even a nomad today needs his identity card—a small
amount of ready cash, chewing-tobacco, eye-black, natron for
sweetening the tobacco and the sort of odds and ends that can be
found in the trousers pockets of any eleven-year old boy. In the
strap of this satchel are small rectangular leather slots to carry the
scraps of paper on which the Taleb or religious scholar has written

texts from the Koran and exorcisms to keep off sickness, misfortune and malevolent spirits. In short, the Targi complete with leather satchel and decorations is like a walking totem pole.

Formerly any Targi warrior worthy of the name carried a white, rectangular shield made of a sable antelope's skin, a dagger fastened by a leather band to his left forearm, an elegant lance and a Takouba or longsword. Nothing is left of this today except the Takouba; every Sunday afternoon one can see them on the aerodrome at Tamanrasset, wrapped up in paper, carefully tied with string and jealously guarded by their new owners. In Algiers, where barely half a century ago the mere mention of the veiled blue men of the Hoggar Mountains was enough to cause a shudder of terror, no one shows the slightest surprise at the sight of geologists, non-commissioned officers, prospectors and tourists climbing with longswords into the Air France plane on a Sunday evening.

Tamanrasset in the heart of the Sahara is the main centre of the Hoggar country. The population of the 'Annexe du Hoggar' is roughly that of a medium-sized provincial town, although in area it is considerably larger than England. Only 10,000 people live in a space of 100,000 square miles.

Every Sunday a DC 4 lands on the airfield at Tamanrasset and Captain Bret, the administrator in charge of the Hoggar area, is always there to meet his 'customers': members of the 'Commissariat à l'énergie atomique' (C.E.A.), prospectors from the 'Bureau de Recherches Minières d'Algérie' (B.R.M.A.) and tourists belonging to the 'Touring Club de France' come to spend a week at Hoggar. On the face of the short, stout French officer as he studies the new arrivals one can see signs of very mixed feelings. The only place in the whole of the French Sahara where it was thought necessary to stamp my passport was Tamanrasset, the place where there is least call for it.

The new arrival in 'Tam' is not made to feel particularly welcome. To begin with, the accommodation offered is far from regal. The monastic austerity of the 'Hotel Amenokal' is clearly a concession to the termites which devour everything that is not made of iron. Even at that, however, I found it hard to understand why the proprietress should keep up a steady flow of complaints which even interfered with her guests' afternoon siesta. Yet I must in all fairness mention one picturesque detail: On Sunday evening, when the refectory of this monastic hotel is humming with the uninhibited voices of new arrivals and the subdued murmur of the residents, a prostitute appears, as solemnly as if she were the official delegate of her guild, and moves from table to table greeting the diners with a shake of the hand. Wives not excepted. . . .

Tourists, indeed, have little to complain of in the Hoggar. An extremely well-kept track leads through gorges, between towering crags and vast screes, past mountains which are so liberally sign-posted that the tourist does not have need of a map, right up to the foot of the Assekrem. From here half an hour's walk on a goat-track brings one to the belvedere of the Hoggar Mountains, the hermitage of Pater de Foucauld. And it provides even a topograph which is the particular delight of tourists who like to be able to identify every peak and pinnacle.

In the Hoggar the crystalline base, which elsewhere in the Sahara is thousands or even tens of thousands of feet down under superimposed strata of rock, comes to the surface. In simple terms the Hoggar massif is a shallow and almost circular vault of granite and gneiss. Although in parts it is extremely varied in formation, it is not to be compared with the Alps. It is only at the crown of the vault, which the Tuareg call Atakor and the Arabs Koudia, that the Hoggar looks like a mountain-range. Originally, as elsewhere in the Hoggar, this too was a high plateau, 6,500 feet above sea-level, then volcanic action turned it into a forest of stone. Enormous deposits of lava cover the granite, at some points from seven to ten different layers as much as six or seven hundred feet thick. Towering up from the lava to a height of 10,000 feet are great needles and turrets of rock and rock walls that have been worn and weather-beaten into fantastic shapes. In the Assekrem area alone, about twenty-five miles long and twelve miles across, there are at least three hundred of these weird formations, most of them of phonolite, a volcanic rock which has broken up into long prisms.

For a long time geologists were of the opinion that these strange needles were all that remained of volcanic craters after hundreds of thousands of years of erosion. The lava deposits were regarded as

the result of volcanic eruption. But on closer investigation this
theory was abandoned. The phonolite needles are more recent than
the lava, which moreover is not phonolite but basalt. So any direct
connection between them must be ruled out. Today volcanologists
believe that the needles pierced the basalt deposits after they had
become more or less solidified, like toothpaste that is squeezed out
of a tube or like mushrooms which find their way through a road-
surface and emerge with their shape unimpaired. What is still not
known is the origin of these basalt streams which formed such
gigantic deposits. Did they come from volcanoes like Vesuvius
which subsequently disappeared without trace? The geologist is
still baffled because in many places the flow of basalt reached the
highest points in the district. Some believe that the vault-formation
of crystalline rocks was originally due to volcanic action so far down
that there was no outlet for it.

There is another theory that must be revised. The Hoggar Massif
looks in many places like an enormous expanse of rubble. Deep
valleys have been gouged out of the lava and granite; at some
points the gneiss yields to a spade as easily as ordinary loam; rock-
faces in various stages of corrosion rise sheer out of huge piles of
rubble. All this suggests a tremendous amount of corrosion. There
is the flaking and general decomposition caused by the sharp
changes of temperature between day and night on desert rock
unprotected by any vegetation; there are the deep cracks produced
by gigantic blocks of granite when cold rain falls on the hot stone
and dislodges them; there is the sand-blast effect of the wind as it
plays on the rock walls and tunnels its way into every hole and
corner; and there is the process of chemical corrosion which no
teacher of geography fails to impress on his pupils when he is talking of the forces at work in the desert. Yet in recent years geologists
have proved that this textbook image of the desert is in fact a
mirage. Erosion virtually stopped in the Hoggar several thousand
years ago. The well-known geologist, Marc Côte, even denies that
there are any formative elements in the desert at all. The role of
the desert is rather to preserve the landscape in the form handed
down from previous ages. From a geological point of view, the
Hoggar relief is surprisingly young. But, as long as the desert

retains its present climate, it will not grow older. The Hoggar possesses the secret of eternal youth.

Seen from the summit of Assekrem (9000 feet high), the chaotic landscape of Koudia appears to bear out the theory of the geologists. This world of mountains seems to have been immobilised in one of the most exciting chapters of its history.

In the language of the Tuareg Assekrem means 'the end'. It is the end of the world. 'I am completely alone,' wrote Pater de Foucauld, 'on the summit of a mountain which towers above almost all others. . . The view is wonderful, comprising the whole Hoggar Massif which falls away from north to south to the endless expanse of the desert. In the foreground one has the strangest medley of mountain peaks, pinnacles and phantastically stratified rocks.'

Vicomte Charles de Foucauld de Pontbriand was born at Strasbourg in 1858 and at an early age showed signs of becoming an idle man-about-town. In terms of physical indulgence he lived up to the family motto, 'Never backward,' which in his later years he was to apply to the life of the spirit. His orgy of enjoyment and spending reached a point where the family had to place him in the care of a guardian. Yet even as a young man he could not be dismissed as a mere gourmand and Casanova. While the family were considering how they could induce him to give up his dissolute way of living, he set off in 1883 at the age of twenty-five on a visit to Morocco, a hazardous undertaking which he carried through with complete success. It was on this voyage of exploration, disguised as a Jewish rabbi, that the saintly hermit, Charles de Foucauld, was born. He became a Trappist, then left the Order to work as a domestic servant in a monastery at Nazareth, took his vows as a priest and built himself a cell at Beni Abbès partly in the hope that from there he would be able to enter Morocco. The plan fell through and, with the subjection of the Hoggar-Tuareg, Pater de Foucauld placed his services unreservedly at their disposal.

From 1905 onwards he lived at Tamanrasset. In July 1911 he moved to the hermitage on the Assekrem where he could worship God in solitude and work on his Tuareg dictionary. On this high tableland strewn with green stones he led a life of extreme privation.

His lodging was primitive, exposed to the harsh wind and the icy nights; supplies of water, wood and food could only be obtained with the greatest hardship. For months at a stretch he had no fresh food to eat, only coffee, sugar, flour and dates. Pater de Foucauld—although he had been on the verge of exhaustion since 1908 when he almost starved himself to death in order to help his friends, the Tuareg—was anxious to remain where he could find the peace and solitude so important to his work. But the Secretary of the Hoggar-Tuareg Amenokal or elected chief, who spent some time with him and helped him with his work, found the living conditions too much for him and urged Father de Foucauld to move. In mid-December 1911 he returned to the milder climate of Tamanrasset.

At the beginning of the century Tamanrasset consisted of a dozen wattle huts and a few bushes scattered over two miles along the dry bed of the Oued Tamanrasset. Today you can have a permanent wave 'Chez Mimi' and Captain Bret has imposed a local speed limit for motor vehicles. In thousands of ethel trees, a kind of tamarisk, are swarms of noisy Bengali birds, red-feathered immigrants from the Sudan, which are so happy in this climate 4500 feet up and are multiplying so fast that they are in danger of becoming a plague.

Tamanrasset is proud of its boulevard; of its small power-station which also provides the time-signal—punctually at ten-thirty every night the electric current is cut off; of its palatial post office flanked theatrically by pillars, on the steps of which natives and Europeans can be seen on Monday mornings devouring the letters which arrived the previous day; of the 'Jules-Carde' observatory which can detect H-bomb explosions at a greater distance than any other observer station, because there is so little ground movement under Tam itself; of the 'Jardin d'Annexe' with its fine selection of fruit and plants; of its administrative building, its spacious school and its hospital; of the loam-red villas in the Hoggar style which is a somewhat swashbuckling mixture of Acropolis and Sudan invented by the first administrative officers in Tam; of the new quarter of smart, white-washed stone houses fronted by flaming geraniums.

Nevertheless, the spiritual heart of Tamanrasset is still an unprepossessing, square fort of red mud bricks with a moat, a parapet walk and various loopholes: Pater de Foucauld's Bordj or fortress. Surmounting the wall over the entrance gate—it is more like a trapdoor than a gate—stands a simple wooden cross and near the entrance, in the wall of the corner tower, a wooden frame has been fixed round a bullet-hole.

When Pater de Foucauld set up his hermitage in 1905 on the left bank of the Oued Tamanrasset, his sole motive was to win the confidence of the Tuareg. He was not satisfied to gain a working knowledge of their language, he wanted to get the feel of it and learn to appreciate all its subtleties. 'I became like a Jew to the Jews in order to win over the Jews . . . I became like an outlaw to the outlaws in order to win over the outlaws. . . . I have become everything to everyone in order to save at least a few.' These words of the People's Apostle were also the motto of the hermit of the Hoggar. It was not long before the veiled men had lost their mistrust. Pater de Foucauld became their adviser; he was called in when disputes arose between the tribes and arbitrated between the sensitive Tuareg, who were still smarting from their defeat, and the administration whose methods were sometimes clumsy. He was a friend not only of Laperrine and other French officers but of Moussa ag Amastane, the paramount chief of the Hoggar-Tuareg, and he was a frequent guest of his cousin Dassine, a celebrated beauty and poetess. This clever, cultured woman opened up for Pater de Foucauld a veritable treasure-house of legends, myths, poems and stories. But the hermit was also constantly at the beck and call of the ordinary people, the toiling Hartani. A woman whose five children he had saved during the famine of 1907/8 said once to Laperrine how dreadful it was that such a good man must go to hell when he died, because he was not a Moslem. And she confessed that she and many of her friends had prayed to Allah daily that He might open the marabout's eyes so that he would become a Mohammedan.

In 1916 Tripolitania was in a state of ferment. Allied with the Central Powers the Senussi invaded French territory, seized Djanet and persuaded part of the Tuareg to revolt. Moussa, the leader of the Hoggar-Tuareg, assured the French of his continued loyalty.

Pater de Foucauld set up a bordj on the right bank of the Oued, not for himself but for the defenceless Haratin, not against Moussa's subjects but against a possible razzia by the rebels as far as Tamanrasset. On December 1st, 1916 he was alone in the Bordj. A Hartani, to whom he had been both nurse and helper on several occasions, enticed him out by calling: 'The mail has come.' He was seized by Tuareg rebels from the Djanet area and bound; thirty men plundered the bordj. Two meharists who arrived, unsuspecting, to collect the hermit's mail, were butchered; in the mêlée the fifteen-year old boy detailed to guard the prisoner was overcome by panic and shot the bound man through the head; the bullet lodged in the wall of the fort.

Moussa, the devout Mohammedan, who heard the news some weeks later, wrote sorrowfully to the hermit's sister: 'Give my greetings to your daughters, your husband and your friends and tell them: Charles, the marabout, died not only for you but for us all. May God be merciful to him and may we meet again in Paradise!'

Today 'Farfa', the helicopter, drops geologists on the top of the pinnacle; the gneiss rings under the axes of French mountain-climbers as they hoist the tricolore on the last few virgin peaks. The Power Dodges of the B.R.M.A. and the heavy lorries of the Atomic Energy Commission are churning up the sand on Tamanrasset's boulevard. Yet the mountain fastness of the Hoggar is still wrapped in that timeless mystery which Brother Charles made articulate.

The 'Little Brothers of Jesus' and the 'Little Sisters of Jesus' each have a small house near the hermitage of Tamanrasset where they keep Charles de Foucauld's ideals alive. Always cheerful, working not by precept but by example, the Little Sisters share the life of the nomads in the Koudia. In their indigo blue burnous and low, reddish-yellow tents they devote themselves to giving what help they can to the Tuareg, who are now reduced to beggary. The Little Brothers lead the same life of humility and poverty. A former lawyer from Milan and a French naval officer, Brother Carlo and Brother Jean-Marie, are typical of these men whose sole diet is sour milk, dates and millet. Their faces are veiled and their skins dyed by the indigo of the Eressoui. But even the Little Brothers and Sisters have not been entirely unaffected by the industrialisation of the desert.

Since March 1955 a weather station has been operating on the Assekrem beside the hermitage and in 1959 a radar station was also set up. A Little Brother or a Little Sister keeps constant watch on the instruments in the seclusion of the mountain-top. And the Society for the Study of Problems of Artificial Rain in the Sahara, which covered the Hoggar in 1957 with a network of rain gauges and unmanned observer posts for temperature, humidity, wind-direction and wind velocity, also enlisted the aid of the Little Brothers. Pater de Foucauld's successors turned themselves into nomadic meteorologists. Every month a number of them set off on the same fixed route to cover twelve hundred miles through track-less country or, at best, along difficult tracks to record and tabulate the data in the five observer-stations.

Tourists have complained that the instruments are desecrating the holy man's retreat, but the meteorologists have not found it difficult to meet this criticism. It was Pater de Foucauld himself who pressed for systematic observation and registration of the Hoggar climate and he himself carried it out while he was on the Assekrem. The earliest meteorological data from the Hoggar available to the rainmaker of today were assembled by a mystic who up to the last was also a scientist.

Elsewhere in the Sahara, however, the oil-rush leaves no room for mystics. In the North, under the shadow of the oil-derricks, they are dismissed as fools, whereas at Tamanrasset, where the crystalline rock makes drilling impossible, they are looked upon indulgently as being out of the ordinary or even, with faint disapproval, as eccentrics.

One of these is Fernand Claudin, a former Spanish artillery officer in his late seventies. Although a personal friend of France, he remained true to the oath he had taken to the Republic. He lost two sons in the civil war, one a captain in the air force, the other a naval officer. Later he went to France as a political refugee, but ever since he had read de Foucauld's accounts of his travels he had been drawn to Tamanrasset. He set off on the trail of the holy man.

Today he has only one wish: to spend the last years of his life at Tamanrasset. He gives Arabic lessons, works in the garden, helps the Little Sisters and Brothers and lends a hand wherever he can.

But the most colourful of all the personalities associated with Tam is the English doctor, Frances M. Wakefield, whom I have heard described as the 'Lawrence of the Sahara.' At our very first meeting it seemed to me that the comparison with Lawrence, although it was probably never intended to be taken too seriously, was singularly inappropriate for the small, carelessly dressed woman who received me in a miserable hut. There was nothing about this eighty-year-old woman with the straggling white hair to invite comparison with the 'uncrowned King of Arabia.'

Frances Wakefield comes of a highly-respected English county family. (Her nephew, Sir Wavell Wakefield, is a Conservative Member of Parliament.) But from her earliest youth she showed signs of rebelliousness and seemed to take a positive delight in shocking both her friends and her relations. She decided, for example, to study medicine and graduated at Edinburgh University, a bold course for a woman to take in her day. But she took the still bolder step of volunteering for medical service during the first world war. She managed—not without considerable wire-pulling—to get herself attached to a medical mission to Serbia. Later she went to Cairo, Omdurman, Basra and India and spent four years in Arabia. Then she travelled to Palestine where she improved her knowledge of Arabic, learned Hebrew, became conversant with a number of local dialects and explored the philosophy of Islam. She herself shows a certain reluctance to speak of that period. Even then she must have seen the future that lay before her, long years of sacrifice and renunciation.

In the course of various conversations with the old lady, I soon realised that my first impression had been deceptive. This unpretentious woman, who is a subscriber to *The Times* yet lives in a native hut, invites comparison with the 'Prince of Mecca' not only by virtue of her early life but also because, like Lawrence, she is a mystic of the desert, because the desert as the cradle of the world religions has cast its spell on her. She no longer has the strength to travel to the isolated Tuareg camps on the mountains but her eyes light up as she describes the long camel-rides on the white Mehari and her encounters with the veiled men of the Central Sahara. There is something very like affection in the way she brushes from books and manuscripts the sand which has drifted in from the desert through the cracks and joints of her primitive dwelling.

Frances Wakefield is not—and never has been—a prude. She is still proud of the fact that in 1905 she was English diving-champion. She comes of a sporting family. One of her brothers took part in the 1922 Everest expedition and her nephew was for many years captain of England's rugby team. She herself, until she was well over fifty, took a particular delight in jumping from the camel-saddle while the animal was still trotting.

It was as a doctor that she made her first contact with the Tuareg but her ultimate objective, to which she intended to devote the rest of her life, was to translate the Bible into the Hoggar-Tuareg language, Tamahaq, the only Berber dialect with its own script, Tifinagh. Several books of the Old Testament in her translation have since been published; a large part of the translation, however, is still in her own handwriting in the drawer of a rickety table in the cell which, remembering the magnificent book-lined walls in her childhood home, she jokingly calls the library. For twenty years she has worked with remarkable devotion at a task which to many must seem like tilting at windmills. For the number of people who speak or even understand Tamahaq is steadily falling. The Tuareg are under strong pressure from the Arabs. The number of those who can read Tifinagh is even smaller, for it is not taught in any school. Tuareg who are interested in a Tamahaq and Tifinagh version of the Bible could be counted on the fingers of two hands. But Frances Wakefield takes comfort in the knowledge that the merits or demerits of such an enterprise cannot be decided by statistics.

'This is a passing whim,' said her friends when she first travelled to Tam. 'She will soon be back.' But she never returned. For a quarter of a century she has worked in Tamanrasset without once taking a holiday like the other Europeans. In Tam also she is regarded as 'moody.' The servicemen and the officials look upon this 'crazy Englishwoman' with the most profound mistrust, not least because Miss Wakefield attaches no importance to associating with the notabilities in the French colony. The Tuareg and their black servants treat her with a mixture of timidity and admiration, and that is enough for her.

9. Rendezvous on the Tropic of Cancer

IT was the strangest appointment of my life, completely in keeping with the grotesque desert mountains of the Hoggar. 'We'll meet on Monday at midday on the Tropic of Cancer.' That was all Bernard Guérangé, a B.R.M.A. geologist, had said on the short-wave radio.

I was given a lift in a lorry driving north. About halfway light-green patches of sprouting corn appeared, carefully enclosed by small earthen walls and low thorn hedges to keep off the goats and camels. We knew we were approaching the village of Tit, an agglomeration of wattle huts and stone houses built into the ground so that they stand waist-high above the surface. Arrem is a typical, treeless Hoggar oasis.

On the Sahara rain-chart the Hoggar is marked as an area with a relatively high rainfall. In prehistoric times it was the watershed from which great wadis radiated to north and south. Today it is still the frontier zone between the northerly winter rains and summer monsoon rain. Sometimes the Hoggar benefits from both. And yet, apart from the fact that its ten-thousand foot peaks must, for purely physical reasons, get more rain than the open desert that surrounds the central massif of the Sahara, the supply of water in the Hoggar is highly precarious. There are no deep and ancient water-tables here like Savornin's Sea to draw upon but only rain-water which has seeped into the Oueds. At a depth of ten inches to fifty feet the water-courses trickle down the wadi; where a spur of rock crosses the dry river-bed, they become dammed up and there one finds small oases with very limited cultivation.

The main water supply comes either from wells or, above all, from foggaras, which, however, have little in common with the foggaras of Tidikelt, Gourara and Touat. The Hoggar foggaras are ordinary drains mostly open to the sky, although a few run underground with regular ventilation shafts. The Haratin build them in the sand and the sediment left by the floods, so that they are neither as long nor as deep as the classic foggaras. Moreover, a long drought will dry them up, while flood-water fills them with mud or demolishes them. On the other hand, anything more permanent is hardly possible, if only because cement in Tamanrasset costs roughly seven times as much as in Algiers.

The situation at Tamanrasset is particularly critical. The entire water-supply for agriculture, gardens and domestic use comes from four foggaras and two pump-wells. The water-shortage imposes a ceiling on the size of the population; the present two-thousand figure is very near the limit beyond which the ethels will be in danger. The tamarisk trees, which do not have to be irrigated but have deep roots that draw on the same subsoil water as the villagers, are an expensive luxury.

In the small oases on the edge of the oueds the natives sow wheat and some barley as winter fodder and in summer, on an area that is strictly limited by the water-shortage, they plant maize, millet and tomatoes. Few gardens in the Hoggar are permanent; the peasants are, for the most part, nomads. In all the oueds one finds abandoned houses and patches of fallow ground, where the peasants have moved on. They may have fallen out over the running of the irrigation system or someone may have died, for the superstitious Haratin regard death as the sign of a bad harvest. Another possibility is that the foggaras have simply dried up. But the most likely explanation is that after two harvests the soil is barren, for the fine, wind-blown sand on the edge of the oued where sowing is done contains no humus, no organic material whatsoever. It takes ten years for the soil to recover and acquire a fresh supply of the necessary minerals. Then the Haratin may come back. Migrations of this kind even take place inside an oasis where the peasants can move from five to twenty miles up or downstream. In this way on the fringes of the Koudia, which acts as a sort of water-tower for the oueds, there are twelve hundred acres of corn land with an annual yield of about two hundred tons.

I had no opportunity to observe at first hand this agricultural

lottery, in which to draw a blank may mean starvation: the driver
did not stop at Tit. He pushed his head through the broken window
of his cab and shouted back at me with a note of triumph in his
voice: 'The Gara Cottenest.'

Tit! Gara Cottenest! The mere sight of that small hill with its
scattered graves and the bones bleaching in the sun can still arouse
a fierce patriotic pride in most Frenchmen. And even today the
Targi will turn his head away as he rides past that hill of degrada-
tion and shame.

The Saharan explorer Henri Duveyrier had given the veiled
men of the Hoggar the romantic title 'noble cavaliers of the desert.'
When the Tuareg wiped out Colonel Flatters' expedition in 1881
the news came like a thunderbolt to the majority of Frenchmen.
They remembered then that in the fourteenth century, the golden
age of the caravan, the Hoggar-Tuareg had the reputation of being
crafty thieves. The cavaliers of the desert suddenly became in-
famous bandits. The French public, anxious to preserve its military
prestige, became highly critical of military adventures in the heart
of the great desert. The occupation of In Salah and Tidikelt in
1899/1900 was only accepted as a 'fait accompli' and even then
reluctantly. The Army, however, continued to act first and ask
afterwards. They had no alternative. It took a messenger at least a
month to ride from In Salah to Algiers and back.

In 1902 Baba ag Tamaklast, a Targi chief, led a Rezzou or
raiding-party into Tidikelt and had Fatima, the sister of a certain
Mohammed ben Mesiss, publicly flogged. Ben Mesiss, half-caste
son of an Arab father and a Targia, was an object of special contempt to the pure-blooded Tuareg; he in turn felt a burning hatred
for them and a new upsurge of loyalty and friendship towards the
French. Captain Cauvet, the commanding-officer at In Salah,
could not allow Ben Messis to suffer his shame in silence. France's
good name was at stake. But Captain Cauvet could not expect his
superiors in Algiers and Paris to approve if he staked his few
regular troops on a native family feud. So he adopted a course
which had already been successful in the conquest of In Salah.
That particular campaign had been conducted under the guise of
a geological expedition. On this occasion the pretext adopted was

also quite legal: a reprisal raid. Captain Cauvet's deputy, Lieutenant Cottenest, hastily recruited 130 natives, Arab and Berber. They
were not soldiers but men engaged on a family feud; their arms,
however, were French and they were commanded by a French
officer, who on the other hand, had no need to give orders in what
was ostensibly a civilian affair. With this motley collection of men
Cottenest set off after Baba. He covered 1000 miles in seven
weeks. . . . On 7th May 1902 the two forces met at Tit: 300
Tuareg with shields, lances, swords, daggers, and a few pistols and
flintlock guns against Cottenest's 70 Lebel rifles. The battle lasted
several hours and soon became a hand-to-hand fight with naked
weapons. But the outcome was decisive. Towards dusk the Tuareg
fled in confusion leaving almost a hundred dead. Cottenest's
casualties were three killed and ten wounded. And from that
moment on, without another shot being fired, the French remained
in control of the central Sahara. Cottenest fought not against men
but against hearsay. The victory he won was not so much over
three hundred desert warriors with medieval arms as over a legend.
The Tuareg, who had themselves obviously believed that they
were invincible, agreed to negotiate and to make a formal surrender.

Thirty miles north of Tit the Tropic of Cancer and the Hoggar
road intersect. A cruciform signpost—the Southern Cross—
erected by sappers marks the point north of which the sun never
reaches its zenith. I waited here, white as a flour-bag with dust
from the road. I waited an hour, two hours, three hours—the three
hottest hours of the day. With growing uneasiness I remembered
that some practical jokers were said to have moved the signpost
several miles from its original position. But why should that worry
me? Guérangé would be looking for the signpost, not the Tropic of
Cancer. When he finally arrived to the heavenly music of a coughing and spluttering motor car and with abject apologies for a
punctured tyre, I was so relieved that my three hours of gruelling
heat in that vast solitude seemed like a bad dream.

Bernard Guérangé is the head of a group of platinum-
prospectors, whose call-sign on the radio is R.V. II—Roches
Vertes II. He and his men comb the 'green rocks,' the serpentine
stone that runs through the black granite, for platinum. He casts,

as it were, an invisible net over the landscape. Here and there he piles up a Redjem, an ornamental heap of stones, on which he paints white numbers and letters. These stone cairns mark the perimeter of Guérangé's net, in each section of which a rock sample is taken. Carefully labelled cloth bags, each containing six-and-a-half pounds of stones, are flown to Algiers, where the samples are tested. If any are found to contain more than the average amount of platinum, a message goes back to the Hoggar and there the areas from which the most promising samples came are examined more closely. The net is then drawn tighter.

In this way, early in 1958 two areas were discovered near Tibeghin and only a few hundred yards apart, in which the platinum content of a ton of rock varies from 230 to 397 grains. At least, on the surface. In the first of these two areas a start has since been made on sounding out the depth of the vein. Shafts have been sunk in the rock and samples taken at intervals of three or four feet. But at a depth of twenty-five feet there was so much water in the rock that drilling-gear had to be used.

Guérangé was obviously excited about Tibeghin. He referred to the platinum deposits there as 'the only real finds we have so far made in the Hoggar.' Then he became more specific: 'Let's just consider Camp No. 1, where we are working at the moment: roughly 25 acres of rock-face, where the platinum content per ton is on an average about 280 grains. At a conservative estimate this proportion should continue to a depth of thirty feet. It might equally well run to three hundred feet. But let's say thirty. That should produce a minimum of two million tons. At the present market rate for platinum, this means at least thirty milliard francs from this mine alone.'

'And the fact that Tibeghin lies in the middle of the desert doesn't upset your calculations?' I asked.

'No. There's enough metal in this rock to cover the extra cost of running a mine in the heart of the Sahara.'

'What about the transport costs?'

'We can get round that by treating the platinum on the spot.'

'But for this process of pre-concentration won't you need water, a great deal of water?'

'We could also use compressed air. But it is better, I agree, to use water. To achieve a concentration of twenty to thirty pounds of platinum per ton we would need anything from two hundred to four hundred gallons of water. And,' he added with a look of boyish triumph, 'we have the water, possibly even in Tibeghin itself but certainly at Silet which is only two miles away. The real problem is the ore. The rock contains pure platinum, together with iridium and palladium, but it is so fine that it is difficult to extract. As the grains of platinum are no more than a tenth of a millimetre, the rock around them has to be ground to a powder— a process which is quite feasible in a laboratory but creates serious technical problems from an industrial point of view. . . .'

When we left Bernard Guérengé's mobile camp in the Oued Tihaliouine for Tibeghin, he remembered to take a bottle of anisette from his store of drink for Isidore Raspail, the head of the prospecting team.

It would be hard to imagine two men who are less alike than Guérangé and Raspail. The only thing they have in common is the conditions in which they live. Jackals howl round their bottle-green tents. Refrigerators and air-conditioning are the sort of creature comforts which they only hear about in letters from former colleagues who are now working for the oil-companies. In their remote camps the postman 'knocks' at most twice a month. Fresh meat depends on good hunting, which, good or bad, also supplies them with hunting stories. One is about the wild sheep which was so startled by the echo of the first shot in a narrow gully that it charged the marksman and sent him flying before he could fire again.

Guérangé and Raspail also have the same poor opinion of the 'Bureau Industriel Africain', which carries twenty-five percent of the financial responsibility for most of the B.R.M.A. enterprises. In their view the B.I.A. played 'a dirty trick' in depriving the B.R.M.A. geologists of the manganese deposits found at Guettara and the iron ore at Tindouf and 'flogging' them not merely to third parties but even abroad. The B.R.M.A.'s uneasy relations with its quarter-partner arise from a variety of very different sources: the latent frustration of the man who does the work towards the man who puts up the money; the deep-rooted mistrust felt by the French in Algeria towards the 'establishment' in Paris, which, in league with the international powers, they believe is out to betray them; the characteristic rebelliousness of young people (the brilliant Director General of the B.R.M.A., Georges Materon, is still in his early thirties), who sometimes have to accept fatherly advice from home; an understandable indignation at B.I.A. decisions which, though not without practical justification, are implemented with precious little tact so that they quite often seem inspired by jealousy. B.R.M.A. versus B.I.A.: this means in the last resort a healthy and honest enthusiasm, which believes that the desert can be made rich and fertile largely by individual initiative, as opposed to the sober calculation that only the big economic groups and a high degree of scientific specialisation really matter.

Apart, however, from their present mode of living and their feeling of bitterness towards the B.I.A., Guérangé and Raspail have hardly anything in common. For Guérangé, the hard life of deprivation he leads is, in fact, too comfortable. He is an idealist who at the same time has a faint streak of sentimentality. He envies the Army officer who spends his whole time in the desert, living with his camel corps as a nomad among nomads, sleeping in holes, eating nothing but dates, tea and an occasional handful of locusts. He finds it galling that the veiled men of the Hoggar do not—and cannot—take him and his kind seriously. The prospectors also sleep under canvas but at daybreak they go by Land-Rover to the mess tent for breakfast and then cable their wives in Paris the date of their approaching home leave. Guérangé knows that he is condemned to be an eternal stranger in the desert and this knowledge depresses him.

Raspail regards any such ideas as intellectual tomfoolery. Whether he is accepted by the Tuareg or not does not worry him at all. He took on this assignment in the Sahara—I quote his own words—'to get rich in order to guzzle and booze.' He prepares very tasty gazelle-meat sausages and peppers them as if the devil was at his elbow. He has little time for camel-milk; he prefers the milky anisette which he pours down his throat as an aperitif and also between meals.

Guérangé would like to accept the desert's challenge to man and is unhappy because he can't. If Raspail is ever unhappy it is only because the desert is a long way from his 'Café de Commerce' at home where he never fails to take his midday Pernod.

It is a strange world that brought these two men together to work on the re-creation of the Sahara, as strange as the mountains which the Tuareg see as creatures of both sexes with normal social habits. Legend has it that one mountain, Ilaman, once fell in love with Tararat, a female mountain of great charm. But she was already promised to her neighbour, Mount Amdjer, with whom she is in fact joined today by a high ridge. Ilaman and Amjder fought for the beautiful Tararat. Ilaman's lance pierced Amjder's side, inflicting a wound which has never healed and from which a stream has since flowed that never runs dry. Ilaman was also badly wounded and lost an arm. The Tuareg will still point out the one-armed Ilaman to the visitor. True, Ilaman moved away, but not from shame. The unhappy duel had not stilled his love-pangs. Before long he turned his attention to the graceful Tahat, but she too was already engaged to a neighbouring mountain. Wiser by experience, Ilaman did not venture to challenge his new rival. He simply moved again one starry night and settled down near the objects of his devotion, from which position he still gazes longingly at them. The legend adds that his original position can still be seen, a gigantic circular crater to the west of Oued Ilaman: a depression which, according to Claude Blanguernon, who makes a hobby of collecting Tuareg folklore, was until recently a mystery even to the geologists.

Tibeghin also has an air of mystery. At Tibeghin-Silet ten thousand palms have degenerated into an impenetrable jungle. The oasis is one of the few palm-groves in the Hoggar area, the origins of which the Tuareg cannot remember. The French authorities have tried to save it and to induce the natives to look after it. But in vain. The ground and all the trees belong to the Amenokal or elected chief. But the Amenokal is not interested in palm-trees, possibly because he regards them as a trap which would turn his followers into peasants. Scattered over the platinum mine are a large number of gravestones, curiously shaped, often no more than a hand's breadth above the ground: a circular disk about three yards in diameter; another shaped like a slice of orange; yet another which is not unlike a half-opened pair of compasses but with both legs a good twenty yards long; a thin slab of stone which runs for some thirty yards from north to south across the mountain face and which has a bulge in the centre like the eye of a needle. The Tuareg ascribe these and many similar graveyards in the central Sahara to legendary giants, who, they believe, inhabited the Sahara before them. In spite of excavations by Gautier and Monod, the experts are still completely baffled by these monuments. The graves are pre-Islamic and point to a highly-developed system of burial. More than that we do not know about these people. The graves have kept their secret.

On top of the hill stand three buildings like igloos. They are made of hewn stone roughly plastered with clay and on closer examination resemble bee-hives. One is empty, the other two are sealed. They appear to be millet-stores, which were presumably built by a caravan travelling between the Sudan and the north. No one knows when the rightful owners will return to collect the grain, but when they do they will find it untouched. The unwritten law of the desert keeps hungry plunderers at bay. Whether it will prove as effective against Isidore Raspail's platinum-hungry prospectors is not so certain. The echoes of their dynamite-charges roll menacingly over the serpentine rock, the abandoned oasis and the dry, sun-baked valley of Tibeghin, firing their salute to a new era.

* * *

In contrast to the sour soil of Mount Atakor the Jahalra massif is mainly basalt. It is also a perfect example of the mental image that the layman has when he hears the word vulcanism. In a mountain-range sixty miles long and between five and fifteen miles wide there are no less than six hundred of these recently, some very recently, formed volcanoes. Most of them have probably been active for only a few hours, at most a few days. And the Tahalra volcanoes all have the same unusual shape of antique theatres. The lava, in each case, had broken through part of the crater wall.

In the Tahalra massif I saw tiny tornadoes spinning and twisting like tops. The mountains were black; the jagged basalt rocks on the high plateau had an evil glitter; overhead the midday sky glowed white. The sand- and dust-laden spouts twisted and spun unceasingly on the plateau. Jean Thébault, at my request, manoeuvred the car till we came directly in the path of one of these 'pocket tornadoes.' The result was that sun glasses, hats, maps, notepaper and anything else that was not firmly battened down was whisked away. I am no longer surprised that the superstitious Tuareg, who, for example, honour the desert-lizard as a maternal uncle and therefore will never have it on their menu (whereas their black slaves, who are not bothered by any such family scruples, regard the large lizard as a great delicacy)—I am, as I say, no longer surprised that the Tuareg see spirits, Kel es Souf, in these whirling columns of dust. The Kel es Souf blaze in the fire, call in every echo, rage in the flood and bring stones raining down from the mountains. As for the whirling dust columns, the following story is told and retold in a whisper in the Hoggar tents: A Tuareg woman was gathering wood when a column of sand began to spin nearby. With ever greater speed dust and sand gyrated. When the column had reached a certain height, it began to move along the ground. The woman, delighted by the spectacle, uttered a happy and enchanted 'Yu-Yu'. Thereupon the column drew near and rewarded her richly, for it was on its way to a spirit's wedding. Later, at the same place and time, the woman met another wandering dust-column. Remembering her previous experience, she greeted it happily. At that the Kel es Souf were angry and punished her severely. She had chosen the wrong time to be happy. The sandspout was on its way to a spirits' funeral.

Jean Thébault, with whom I wandered through the Kel es Souf country, is the B.R.M.A.'s leading diamond-prospector.

'A djinn,' he explained, 'also played a nasty trick on us. Not here, however, but in Algeria. In the summer of 1954 when the samples collected the winter before were examined in our central laboratory, a point two carat diamond was found, a very pure stone. Unfortunately one of the staff had left the window open. A gust of wind blew all the labels off the table, where each sample had been sorted out and classified. It was impossible to say where this particular diamond had come from. It could have been any one of sixteen areas in which Jacques ('Coco') Ranoul had worked. One employee thought he remembered that the sample containing the diamond had come from In Zize, but when the area was prospected again the following winter nothing was found.'

It was not until 1957/58 that prospecting was resumed. The headquarters were set up in the cool fortress of Silet, an hour's walk from Tibeghin. Silet plays a part in the legend about the foundation of the Tuareg tribes, for it was there that Ti-n-Hinan and her servant Takama, two pious women from the Moroccan Berber tribe, stopped on their way south. According to the story told to Charles de Foucauld by his Tuareg sources, Ti-n-Hanan is the founder of the high-class Hoggar-Tuareg and Takama of their vassals. But in choosing Silet for their base the diamond-prospectors are not likely to have been influenced by the genus loci. There were much more compelling geological reasons, amongst them being the fact that one of the sixteen samples they had taken came from the Tibeghin area.

To date eight new diamonds have been found at Silet, seven of them small blue stones and one black Carbonado of 0.1 carat. Without overrating the importance of these finds, the B.R.M.A.'s geologists believe that the eight diamonds, small and insignificant as they are in themselves, provide sufficient confirmation of their general geological survey to warrant a systematic search. For the basic mineral in these diamonds is almost certainly to be found in the 'basalt organs' of Tahalra, volcanic chimneys which have become exposed by erosion.

Thébault's men work in the dry river-beds which radiate from Tahalra. At intervals of a mile they remove thirty-five cubic feet of gravel and alluvial sand. Pebbles more than half an inch in diameter are examined on the spot; the remainder is washed and put through a mechanical sieve until the hard core has been extracted, ready for despatch to the B.R.M.A. laboratory.

Thébault does not expect to stumble on a 'cache' of precious stones. An oued is not the kind of river-bed in which diamonds are formed by natural processes. All he expects to find is that, if there is a vein, the nearer they come to it the more diamonds will appear in the alluvial deposit. But even then it would remain to be seen whether the vein was worth exploiting.

Thébault is a remarkably practical man with little to say for himself. He has been less put out than his colleagues by the B.I.A.'s refusal to help finance the B.R.M.A.'s dream of a diamond-field in the Hoggar or by the jeering comment in Paris that two hundred million francs is a rather high price to pay for eight stones totalling less than half a carat—even if they are diamonds. He is not particularly optimistic about the prospects of success. He is simply anxious to follow this trail to the end, even at the risk of finding, after a search of several years, a mere handful of microscopic stones. That is why he deplores the tight-fisted attitude of the B.I.A. Thébault has a Russian story he likes telling. A Russian woman geologist ('maybe they should send us a woman from Paris sometime, whether she's qualified or not. . . .') discovered a vein in 1948 in the Siberian Taiga between the Lena and Jenissei rivers. The Soviet government, which had been compelled to buy many of the diamonds it needed for its wartime industry at black-market prices, immediately despatched hundreds of prospecting-crews. Almost every year since then fresh deposits of kimbalite have been discovered and quite a few veins worth exploiting.

10. Open Sesame!

THE Sahara's sand-box has come to be regarded as a gold-mine. Propaganda designed to attract France's small savings presents it as a national Open Sesame! Not without reason the satirical weekly 'Le Canard Enchaîné' remarked ironically at the end of 1958: 'In 1919 the magic formula was: "The Boche will pay!" Today it is: "The Sahara will pay!"' With a sense of reverent awe the man-in-the-street feels the wealth of the Sahara trickling through his fingers like an endless string of pearls: oil, natural gas, iron, copper, manganese, nickel, asbestos, coal, salt, wolfram, tin, zinc, columbite, tantalum, platinum, diamonds, zirlonium, titanium, thorium, and uranium. These words have a magical ring in his ears. He confuses geology with economics. He mistakes hopes for realities. He overlooks the fact that it is sometimes too costly even to stoop and pick up the treasures in or under the sand, that mineral ores cannot be sold merely because they were extracted from this incredibly exciting desert but only if they can compete on the world market. He underestimates the unlimited liability which the wealth of the Sahara carries with it: endless, empty and almost barren space.

The long distances which have to be covered to the nearest port or to an industrial area which can serve as a market, the necessary supply of water for mining and processing, the recruitment of acclimatised native labour and the importation of European personnel add so much to the cost of production that, in present-day market conditions, even many ore-deposits which are rich by European standards are not worth exploiting. And larger deposits which are worth exploiting require enormous capital investments which are not easy to organise. Hence the rule of thumb: What is rich in the desert is not rich enough. The natural wealth of the Sahara must be wealthier. . . .

Leaving oil and natural gas aside for the moment, there is a handful of words which are bound to crop up in the next few years in any discussion on the future of the Sahara. They represent an inventory of the Sahara's mineral resources which to date have either already been tapped or marked out for future exploitation.

Fort Gouraud in Mauretania: The Koudiat of Idjil, an impressive, triangular range of hills, fifteen miles long, which rises abruptly from the plain to a height of between nine hundred and twelve hundred feet, contains large deposits of iron ore. As long ago as 1067 the Arab geographer El Bekri referred to an 'iron mountain' in the Koudiat of Idjil. On the other hand General Gouraud, the first European to reach Idjil in 1909, made no such observation. Later, pilots flying mail between Morocco and Dakar reported that their magnetic needles reacted strongly over these mountains. The real discoverers of the 'iron stone' however, must have been the soldiers who in 1934 built a Bordj from blocks of iron quartz at Fort Gouraud to guard the frontier between Mauretania and the Spanish Sahara. The weight of the stone must have come as an unpleasant surprise to them. In 1934 it was brought to the notice of French geologists and mining-engineers but it was only after the war that systematic prospecting, both private and public, began. Five areas were marked out for exploitation with a total deposit of at least a hundred million tons and an average iron content of 63.8 per cent. Half of the ore from Fort Gouraud could be used for making steel. About forty million tons can be extracted by open-cast mining. On the other hand, the Fort Gouraud venture clearly labours under two major handicaps: the distance from the coast (the Atlantic is more than two hundred miles away as the crow flies) and the inadequate local water-supply. The first of these handicaps in particular could only be overcome by large-scale investment and by an annual production of between four and six million tons to cover it.

Gara Djebilet in the Algerian Sahara: the most important iron-ore deposit in the Sahara consists of a seam running through a steep wall. Structurally the ore at Gara Djebilet resembles the 'minette' ore in Luxembourg but with a much higher iron-content. Of more than four thousand million tons of known ore reserves four hundred million tons have an average iron content of 57.7 per cent. The biggest source of water in the area, the well at Aouinet Legra, produces too little for mining purposes but the geologists are reasonably confident that more artesian water can be drilled in industrial quantities. Here the greater handicap is transport. Gara Djebilet lies eighty-five miles to the south-south-east from the isolated oasis of Tindouf, which in turn is two hundred miles from Colomb Bechar and three hundred miles from the Atlantic. An iron-ore mine at Gara Djebilet would need a railway-track at least three hundred miles long with several series of tunnels and port facilities on the Moroccan coast.

Unlike the ore at Fort Gouraud, the deposits at Gara Djebilet contain phosphorus and can therefore in present-day conditions only be treated by the so-called Thomas process, a fact which considerably reduces the number of potential markets. Experts in the iron and steel industry say that at present the world market simply could not absorb another ten million tons of Bessemer-ore.

In Algiers I called on the man who discovered Gara Djebilet and who today works for the Algerian Water Board. Pierre Gevin was one of a group of geologists—Meyendorff was another—who in 1941 were commissioned by the 'Mediterranée-Niger' Society to make a geological map of the Sahara. The Germans, then occupying France, were attracted by the old, still unfulfilled plan for a Trans-Saharan Railway, and five young French geologists were only too happy to be able to disappear into the desert—particularly if it was with the enemy's approval. At that time a geological map also had to be topographical. The ground was virtually un-explored.

The five men travelled on foot and by camel, a watch in one hand, a compass in the other. Gevin, who had chosen the Western Sahara as his beat, noticed that in the area round Gara Djebilet the compass became completely unreliable. Gevin did not give it much thought. Who was likely to be interested in iron in the desert! In the winter of 1946/7 he returned to the same area and again decided that the iron contained in the rocks was not an economic proposition. Not until 1952, when he paid a visit to the Sahara under the auspices of the International Geological Congress, did it dawn on him that the deposits at Fort Gouraud might be worth closer inspection. In November and December 1952 he was also able to take another look at Gara Djebilet. In a letter dated 9th January, 1953, he told the Director-General of the B.R.M.A. about his discovery. The B.R.M.A. immediately started a systematic investigation, only to be "cheated" later of Gara Djebilet by its partner, the B.I.A., which decided that this project was too big for Algeria's limited resources and must be planned from the beginning on a European basis. Even as an international venture Gara Djebilet has not run very smoothly: Morocco's appetite for the Western Sahara has grown by leaps and bounds since she realised what a juicy morsel was lying at her very door. Gevin, ill and overworked, refers to these by-products of his discovery with mingled resignation and scorn. Although the deposit is one of the five or six richest in the world, the discovery has so far earned him nothing but fame and honour. 'An iron feather in my scientific cap and one day perhaps even a medal, that's all,' he jokes wearily.

Akjoujt in Mauretania: two hills west of the outpost at Akjoujt contain the only copper deposits so far found in the Sahara. Discovered in 1946 by the geologist A. Blanchot, they were subsequently examined at government cost and it was estimated that there were eighteen million tons of ore with a copper content of one and a half per cent and nine million tons with two to two and a half per cent. In 1953 the 'Société des Mines de Cuivre de Mauritanie' (MICUMA) was founded which has since been operating two experimental plants. These produce concentrates of both ores which are transported by truck to Nouakchott, Mauretania's new capital, and Port Etienne. Eventually, all supplies will undoubtedly go to Port Etienne. The necessary water-supply (over a million gallons a day) has already been guaranteed, partly from fossil water-tables. Each ton of virgin ore also contains one to three grammes of gold as well as between thirty and fifty-five percent iron. Akjoujt could produce, in concentrated form, 25,000 tons of copper, 3,300 lb. of gold, 300,000 tons of magnetite, and, from a deposit in the south, a million tons of iron ore. But the magnetite and iron ore could only be exploited if there were a rail connection between Akjoujt and the sea. At present an extension of the projected Fort Gouraud–Port Etienne railway is under consideration. Estimated capital expenditure: twenty million pounds.

Guettara in the Algerian Sahara: in 1935 a B.R.M.A. geologist, surveying the country by helicopter, discovered important deposits at Djebel Guettara a hundred miles south of Colomb Bechar. The prospect showed resources of 900,000 tons of ore with a manganese content of forty-four per cent. There are a further 450,000 tons with forty-five per cent manganese, an ore that unfortunately contains a fair amount (five per cent) of arsenic which is difficult to separate. The B.R.M.A. is unhappy about the 'Guettara case' because the B.I.A. had played into the hands of a special research organisation, in which the B.I.A. but not the B.R.M.A. was actively interested. So far, however, the quarrel is an academic one, for the present military and political situation in the Djebel Guettara has forced the 'Société des Mines de Guettara' to suspend operations.

Aïr in the Nigerian Sahara: in May 1945 Maurice Roulais discovered tinstone in the Aïr mountains about forty miles north-east of Agades. A year later the same geologist found tinstone and wolfram together sixty miles north-east of Agades. The Société Minière du Dahomey-Niger (SOMIDANI) acquired the prospecting rights and the concession. Later the Société Minière de l'Air (SOMINAIR) also acquired an interest. There is enough metal in the ore to make the laborious and costly exploitation of it worth while. The raw material is concentrated on the spot, then transported by lorry by way of Agades to Kano (Nigeria), by rail from Kano to Lagos and from there by boat to Liverpool where it is treated. It leaves the French Sahara by a back door. Patriotic Frenchmen have reckoned that even air-transport from Agades to Tamanrasset and Algiers would be feasible. Sufficient brackish water has been found in the area, while drinking-water is transported in road tankers for the hundred and fifty natives and three Europeans. The production of pre-concentrated tinstone runs at present to a hundred tons a year which is to be doubled; in 1951 the wolfram production was one ton.

Kenadsa in the Algerian Sahara: as early as 1907 veins of coal were discovered near Colomb Bechar by Flamand, the man who found the rock-carvings and unwillingly conquered In Salah. But no one believed or was even interested in his reports. Then in the first world war a German Foreign Legionary from the Ruhr and a Vietnamese Captain Cao Van made the second discovery, this time at Kenadsa. In 1917 the Algerian Railways began extracting the coal. Since 1947 geologists have found two new fields (at Ksi Ksou and Mezarif), which brought the known resources in the Colomb Bechar area up to nearly a hundred million tons. The annual production of the State-run 'Houillères du Sud-Oranais' is barely 350,000 tons, a figure that has special significance for the tax-payer, because on the northern coast of Algeria the price of Kenadsa coal with its meagre deposits, its low rate of output and its high freight costs is fifty per cent more than that of coal imported from the Ruhr! The coal mines in the Sahara receive an annual State subsidy of a thousand million francs, in view of the fact that they employ 2,500 former nomads. But in the long run the discovery of natural gas in the northern Sahara will almost certainly mean the closing-down of the Saharan coal-mines.

Salt: Salt is the only mineral which the natives themselves have been mining for thousands of years. The total value of the yearly salt production is low by comparison with the important part played by the salt caravans and the salt-trade even today in the lives of many nomadic tribes. Of all the deposits in the desert only those at Colomb Bechar are an economic proposition.

This inventory may appear impressive or unimpressive, depending on one's expectations. But it is not yet complete.

The main ore-prospecting organisations are state-financed: the B.I.A., which, with the collapse of the Fourth Republic, ceased to be the 'Bureau des Ensembles Industriels Africains' and adopted the more modest title of 'Bureau d'Investissement en Afrique,' the BRGM or 'Bureau de Recherches Geologiques et Minières', and the CEA. The BRGM emerged at the end of 1959 as the result of a merger between the 'Bureau Minier de la France d'Outre-Mer' (BUMIFOM), the BRMA and corresponding bodies in French Guiana and in Metropolitan France. The B.I.A. was founded in 1952 to encourage industrial planning on a big scale in

Africa, above all in the Sahara. Since then it has played the part of a rich uncle from abroad, coordinating and stimulating, mainly by taking an interest in new projects or in existing schemes which are in keeping with its declared aims. As large-scale planning is only possible if the end and the means are both clearly established, the B.I.A. has become actively involved in general prospecting and the early stages of mining.

The B.R.M.A. was founded in 1948 to carry on France's work in the desert. The penetration and organisation of the Sahara were to be followed by a detailed stock-taking. But the geologists of the B.R.M.A. were probably less inspired by these somewhat theoretical considerations than by the recent wartime shortages. Algeria was to become self-sufficient in precious metals. Prospecting for minerals is a matter of luck, but the B.R.M.A. had armed itself with some reassuring statistics according to which every million square kilometres (380,000 square miles), regardless of any geological or technical considerations, must contain between five and twenty-five ore-fields worth anything from six to two hundred million pounds a year. The B.R.M.A. had ear-marked 350,000 square miles of virgin territory which, on the geological evidence, seemed suitable ground to prospect for rare metals. More than half this area lies in the crystalline Hoggar and the sandstone layer of the Tassilis that overlaps it. So the Hoggar and the Tassilis became the main stamping-ground of the B.R.M.A.

As there are certain geological similarities between the Hoggar on the one hand and Nigeria and the Aïr mountains on the other, the B.R.M.A. hoped in its first campaign (1948–49) to discover tin and wolfram ores. There were certainly traces of both but no worth while deposits. But the prospectors had learned a valuable lesson: no successful venture can be launched in the heart of the Sahara without, firstly, aerial photography, secondly, a two-way radio link, and thirdly, helicopters.

In 1953/54 a systematic onslaught was made on the Hoggar and Tassilis. In the meantime the prospectors had equipped themselves with radios and become familiar with the geologist's taxi, the helicopter. But, most important of all, their field of operations was now laid out in black and white, thanks to aerial photographs, which served not merely as maps but also as photo-geological charts. By the beginning of 1960 more than nine-tenths of the Hoggar and the Tassilis had been explored. Prospecting has naturally not been confined to these parts of the desert. In 1957/58 the BUMIFOM, CEA and BIA formed a syndicate which investigated the Tibesti and Ennedi mountains. Encouraged by previous indications of copper and zinc deposits the BIA and BUMIFOM began to prospect in the Adrar des Iforas early in 1958. At the end of 1958 the BIA decided to investigate the Yetti Plain south of Gara Djebilet and the Eglab mountains east of Yetti.

And the results? An American mining-engineer in the course of conversation enlarged on a plan to build a pipeline twelve hundred miles long linking the desert mountains of the Central Sahara with the Mediterranean coast—a pipeline through which the ore, broken down and washed by sea-water, would be pumped to the quayside in the North.

This has not yet been achieved, and it probably never will be. In the mountains of Tibesti and Ennedi lead, wolfram and tin ore as well as radioactive materials have been found, in the Adrar des Iforas copper, zinc, lead, nickel and chromium, in the Yetti and Eglab gold, silver, mdybdenum, copper, lead and radioactive elements, in the Hoggar and Tassili nickel, tin, cobalt, copper, uranium, thorium, zinc, lead, gold, platinum metals, wolfram, diamonds and asbestos. None of these, however, exists in commercial quantities. Early in 1960 the BRGM was highly optimistic about a deposit of uranium which was discovered in 1958/59 a hundred miles south of Silet and two promising deposits of wolfram which were found in November 1959 a hundred and fifty miles south of Tamanrasset. But how many optimistic visions have already come to nothing in the Sahara! The Tassili-Ennedi syndicate was dissolved only a year after it came into being, because of high prospecting-costs and lack of results. The BRMA abandoned its search for diamonds in 1959.

It was not always the desert that was at fault. In January 1959 the engineer in charge of the spectrographic department in the BRMA's central laboratory was arrested for systematically overstating the platinum content in the samples of rock from the Hoggar. There is platinum at Tibeghin but in much too limited quantities to be worth extracting. I often think of Bernard Guérangé and the note of credulous enthusiasm in his voice when he described the platinum deposits at Tibeghin as 'the only tangible discoveries we have so far made in the Hoggar area.'

*Very well, we shall scratch in this sand.
We shall lay railways, we shall put up telephone poles, we shall make the artesian
water bubble up and in the oasis
we shall hear the Gallic cock crowing his
loudest and happiest fanfare from the
height of the Kasbah.*
JULES CAMBOU, *Governor General of Algeria*, 1890

11. Black Gold

THE barrel of the submachine gun chafed my knees till they were
sore. Every time we hit a pothole it bounced up between my legs
and clattered back on the floor of the car. The sun had gone down
behind the dunes like an enormous fried egg. From time to time a
jerboa was caught in the glare of the headlamps and eyed us,
motionless. We had lost our way several times. Mustafa was on
edge. Whenever lights appeared at the edge of the track, he slowed
down nervously, glancing at me to make sure I had the gun at the
ready and my finger on the safety-catch. This time it was a truck
with all six wheels clear of the ground. Beside it two men sat round
a camp-fire happily eating sardines out of a tin. With a sigh of
relief Mustafa realised that they were friends and that this was not
a trap. They waved and shouted us on. They expected help to
arrive from Fort Flatters within the next twenty-four hours. I
knew, as we drove on, that Mustafa was silently cursing the track,
cursing me for bringing him out at night into the sandy ocean of
the Great Eastern Erg, and cursing the rebels. He knew quite a
number of good stories about the fellagha, which he told with grim
humour and considerable relish. They all ended very unhappily
with burning lorries and slit throats.

This uncomfortable journey had come at the end of a fascinating
day in the dunes of the Erg, or to be strictly accurate, between the

dunes. The popular image of a rolling sea of sand with one line of dunes succeeding another is only partly true. Occasionally several chains of dunes build up to form a range of sandhills which is never more than a thousand feet high and almost inaccessible to motor vehicles. At midday it loses its shape but when the sun is low these sandhills stand out in all their classical beauty like the blades of scimitars. I know no other landscape which so perfectly combines freedom and order. Countless billions of grains of sand, swept together in great depressions by capricious winds, have fallen into layers with mathematical accuracy. The natives, whose vocabulary contains two thousand words for a camel and two hundred for a date, have twenty different ways of describing the shape of the dunes. Between the sandhills, however, there are, strangely enough, lanes free of sand, so-called 'gassi'. A gassi may be as narrow as an average road or ten, fifteen, even twenty-five miles wide. Two jeeps can pass in a gassi without seeing one another. How the gassi arose is something that has so far baffled the geologists, who are glad to use them, however, as express routes on which a detour of sixty miles and more is preferable to crossing the sandhills. Many of the gassi are as smooth as a parquet floor. G. A. Fifis, for example, drove me along one at top speed without taking his foot off the accelerator.

Fifis is a Dutch electro-engineer, who is in charge of a seismic party. When we reached the site where he was working, I realised why Fifis is using a new instrument, which Shell had produced in the United States and which is now being tried out in the Sahara.

One need not be an expert to know that artificial earth-tremors are now used all over the world in the search for oil. The sound-waves penetrate below ground, but the speed at which the sound travels varies with different kinds of rock. The waves are either broken or reflected by the geological strata. The most common seismic prospecting process used today, the refractory method, is to register on seismographs the echo sent back by two strata. The result is a seismogram which provides the experts with important data on the position and depth of each layer. And the course of these strata is traced on a continuous graph or profile.

Until recently dynamite was the means usually adopted to

create the necessary earth tremor. Fifis, on the other hand, instead of using explosive has a truck with a kind of guillotine mounted on it. He presses a button and a ton-weight drops ten feet to the ground. This is repeated every ten yards or so, often as much as sixty-four times. Naturally the noise underground is not very loud compared with a charge of dynamite, but this weight-dropping method is used where the more professional method has not produced any appreciable results.

With a dynamite explosion the echo is heard by seismometers, converted into an electric current, passed on to the laboratory, filtered, mixed, amplified and put on film. With weight-dropping it is possible to 'play' with the incoming signals, modulate their frequency, store them up and even 'add them up' so cunningly that after the weight has been dropped sixty-four times the final graph is entirely free of distortions or unwanted noises.

As the dunes on both sides of the gassi turned red in the late afternoon, Fifis told his men to down tools. The truck with the drop weight and the mobile laboratory were left unguarded in the desert. The two German ex-legionaries who had been sent along as guards were shocked at such irresponsibility. The crew returned to the camp and Fifis took me off to try the oilman's favourite sport, dune-hopping. After gathering enough speed in a Land-Rover or a jeep, one climbs the windward side of a sand dune at full throttle and hops over the crest into the unknown. This is not the safest of sports for a beginner. He may get away with broken bones, to say nothing of a broken car, but one of the more serious hazards he has to reckon with is drowning. On the leeward side of the dunes, at the foot of the steep sandhills, he is quite likely to find a treacherous trough of sand. Camels and their riders, motor-vehicles and their drivers have disappeared in these troughs without a trace.

Fifis contented himself with a short slalom and a few moderate hops, but more from lack of time than of enthusiasm. He insisted on my taking a bite of food at the camp. When I suggested that it might be wiser to make a start with Mustafa as soon as possible, he replied with an invitation which I found it impossible to refuse. Would lobster not appeal to me? We returned to the camp and

until shortly before sunset I sat with my feet in the warm sand
eating a Grand Hotel meal. Very much to Mustafa's annoyance,
for the prospect of a night journey did not attract him.

On the route-map, which the 'Compagnie des Pétroles d'Algérie'
(C.P.A.) had prepared for my tour of the Saharan oil, Fifis' crew
were marked 'Sismique 3.' The point that Mustafa made for that
dark night was Sismique 2, a hundred and twenty miles away on
the fringe of the dunes.

We reached the camp about eleven. It had a ghostly appearance.
Between the tents electric bulbs swayed in the cool night wind.
From the surrounding darkness came the hum of a diesel engine.
We arrived quite unnoticed. A council of war was being held in the
main tent, where the atmosphere was tense though with no sug-
gestion of panic. A time-fuse was missing.

'We have eight tons of dynamite in the camp. The disappear-
ance of a time-fuse might have unpleasant implications.'

The geologist in the party, Dr. Pierre Crettaz, a Swiss, criticised
the general lack of security arrangements, particularly in connection with the explosives. The head of the Security branch spoke
up in his own defence. One thing led to another and finally Crettaz
wagered two cases of champagne that he could remove a time-fuse
from the stores without being caught. I could not believe my ears.
Two cases of champagne! Yet not one of the men present seemed
in the least surprised. The bet was taken without the flicker of an
eyelid and it looked as if the champagne might, after all, be drunk
here on the spot six hundred miles from civilisation.

I remember the following night with painful clarity. Twice I
rolled off my camp-bed on to the saffron-yellow sand and was
assailed by the most vivid dream. I saw champagne-bubbles
sparkling as the rebels toasted Mustafa who was busy under the
camp-bed exploding eight tons of dynamite. I was trembling in
every limb—then woke up to realise that Crettaz was shaking me.

The man in charge of the explosives, a Dutchman, took me with
him to the 'shooting-range.' The air was still chilly as we started
off shortly before sunrise. We had a journey of seventy-five miles
in front of us. The previous day my athletic young companion had
been forced to come back to camp for a few minutes. This meant

that in one day he had travelled three hundred miles empty-handed, three hundred miles along the express roads between the sand hills of the Erg. This journey was due to be shortened, however, when the camp was moved the following week. The move would have taken place earlier but for the water problem. Even now it had to be brought 120 miles from Fort Flatters by road-tanker—between seven hundred and twelve hundred gallons a day for the hundred natives and forty Europeans. When the camp moved, it would be even farther from Fort Flatters; the cost of the water, which was supplied free at Fort Flatters, had gone up nearly to champagne level by the time it reached the camp.

I told my companion about the lobster I had eaten with his compatriot Fifis. He whistled through his teeth.

Fifi's team is given special treatment, a fact which arouses the envy of the other two seismic groups in the C.P.A. And yet the dynamiters admit that they would not like to change places. 'These princes with their electronic toy,' said one defiantly, 'never get off the mark. Half a mile to a mile a day is about as much as they can do. And they're proud of it! We cover a hundred and fifty miles and more every month!'

The company has no reason to worry about this rivalry: competition is healthy. The dynamiters in the C.P.A. are constantly trying to improve on their methods if only to outdo the weight-droppers. They have tried small and cheaper charges of dynamite and, to reduce vibration, have replaced one charge by a number of simultaneous lesser ones. My companion assured me proudly that he would challenge Fifis any time with forty charges totalling fifty pounds of dynamite.

The 'pétroliers' of the Sahara have a special word for the geological formations which are of particular interest to the oil-driller. They call them 'potatoes.'

'Finding oil is still something of a miracle,' said my companion, 'only today it happens a little more often. That's all.'

Prospectors in the Sahara have always been provided—and rightly so—with the very latest equipment, for the chances of finding oil, which are small anywhere, are a great deal smaller in the Sahara.

It was here that the oil-prospectors first ventured into the heart of the desert. The Saudi-Arabian oilfields are a mere thirty miles from the coast; in the Sahara prospectors are working as much as six hundred miles from the coast. This sounds very adventurous, but in fact oil-prospecting in the Sahara is anything but an adventure. It calls, above all, for organisation, superb organisation. The desert dictates very stiff terms. Even the most elementary transport system is lacking. In order to develop its concessions, the C.P.A. was forced to put down twelve hundred miles of new roads and repair a further fifteen hundred miles. The newcomer is particularly impressed by the company's thirty-six airstrips but the cost of them was, in fact, mere chicken-feed compared with laying roads over difficult country. Airstrips in the desert are, on an average, cheaper than the most modest aircraft. Today they are much more numerous than oases.

Transport costs in the Sahara are enormous. Foodstuffs are tremendously expensive but they are not the oil-prospector's main problem. A few pounds here or there make no odds. The derrick, mud-pump, miles of steel rods and pipes, settling-troughs and power-units are much more important. The deep-drilling operation on the Djebel Berga southwest of In Salah swallowed up 131 million francs for transport alone. Lack of water also sends costs up. Every hole drilled develops a considerable thirst. To quench it at Berga, the 'Compagnie de Recherches et d'Exploitation de Pétrole au Sahara' (CREPS) had to spend another fourteen and a half millions. Another factor is labour costs, which are shockingly high. The CREPS in Edjeleh have to pay as much for a casual labourer as a trained engineer earns in Western Europe.

Small wonder that 'potatoes' are at such a premium in the Sahara. Not, of course, that a 'potato' is any guarantee. Only the drilling-bit can tell if oil is there. But the more costly the drilling, the more important it is to employ every available means of gaining information about the subterranean architecture and so about the most promising location for drilling.

The geophysicist acts as a scout to the drilling-engineer. There is theoretically a kind of hierarchy of geophysical methods of prospecting. The seismic method, which is the most expensive, usually comes last. It completes the picture which has already emerged from measuring the field of gravity, by adding a number of refinements. But in practice the choice of one process or another depends on the nature of the ground. In the north, where the belt of land between the parallels of Laghouat and Hassai Messaoud is of particular interest to the oil-prospector, gravity measurements have produced no appreciable results. The refractory method of seismic explosions also failed. On the other hand, the refraction method, which is not widely used as a rule, was responsible for detecting the deposits at Hassi R'mel and Hassi Messaoud, two names on which today the industrial future of Algeria and France's hope of becoming self-sufficient in oil both depend. Geo-magnetic measurements from the air, similar to those developed by the Americans at the end of the war to detect enemy U-boats, were taken long after the discovery of natural gas at Hassi R'mel and oil at Hassi Messaoud. It was not until 1958 that planes carrying torpedo-like magnetometers droned over the northern coast to add still more details to the subterranean map.

The position in the southern areas of the potential oil-bearing basin between Atlas and Hoggar is quite different. The structure containing the oil of Edjeleh can be seen by the geologist without the help of geophysical spectacles. In the Edjeleh oil-field the Schlumberger process was employed, which derives its data from the different reactions of various kinds of rock to an electric current.

On the shooting range in the Great Eastern Erg they were waiting impatiently for my companion. The broad gassi between the dunes was sprinkled with vehicles and with men stamping their feet against the morning chill. The main feature of that scene was oil-stained overalls. It was hard to believe that until very recently only the occasional camel-nomad had passed that way, with no more than the sun and stars to guide him. Someone stood on the bonnet of the laboratory-truck and waved a red flag. In the middle distance, under the crest of the sand-dunes, forty fountains of dust shot up into the pale blue sky. Fifteen hundred and thirty-six seismometers registered the echo of the tremors and transmitted it to the laboratory. A cloud of whitish dust was still hovering in the air as the lorries, power trucks and Land-Rovers started off. The native workmen had exactly twenty minutes to collect half the seismometers and set them up again a mile further on. The dynamiters distributed the explosive. They did not bother to bore holes but simply laid the packets of dynamite on the ground. Then the thunder of another explosion rolled across the sand-dunes, and the caravan moved on.

In the newly-rich Sahara, time is money, a great deal of money. The Company which acquires the prospecting rights for hydrocarbons must commit itself to a minimum expenditure which runs not into millions but into billions. The concession is for five years, after which only half of it can be renewed, and so on till after fifteen years it expires altogether. When part of a concession expires, the area concerned must be handed back with all the geological, topographical and partly even the geophysical data that have been collected. That is why the oil-prospectors in the desert are always working against time. That is why, as the expiry date approaches, the atmosphere at any oil company's headquarters becomes more and more tense. Before the pétrolier's colourful map of the Sahara, on which the various concessionaries are jostling one another for black gold, the man in charge of the prospecting operations stands cudgelling his brains in an attempt to decide which half he should keep and which return.

The search for oil in the Sahara began shortly after the second World War. In 1946 the 'Société Nationale de Recherche et d'Exploitation des Pétroles en Algérie' (S.N. REPAL) was founded. The geologists of S.N. REPAL, who were soon joined by colleagues from the 'Bureau de Recherches de Pétrole' (BRP) and later from the 'Compagnie Française des Pétroles' (CFP), had certain preliminary questions to clear up. Was there any point in looking for hydrocarbons in the Sahara? Where were the zones most likely to yield oil? The desert, like the sleeping princess, was waiting to be roused from its long slumber, but the geologist who returned with sackfuls of stones was not the long-awaited prince. In 1948 geophysical teams took the first gravity measurements but prospecting continued to be on a very modest scale.

In 1951 came the turning-point with the first artificial earthquake. In 1952 the S.N. REPAL and the CFP together with their

Algerian branch, the CFPA, acquired the concession on the north coast. Here the strata which presumably contain the oil are overlaid by more recent formations. But the companies which chose the north were obviously reckoning that the additional cost of the geophysical investigations and the drilling would be offset by proximity to the coast. On 30th October, fourteen days after taking over the Concession, the S.N. REPAL started the first deep oil-drilling operation in the Sahara. In 1953 two new companies came in: the C.P.A. (with Royal Dutch Shell as major shareholder) and the CREPS (in which the same concern was also represented) acquired prospecting rights in the centre and the south respectively of the great depression, which stretches from the southern foot of the Atlas to the Hoggar and from Tanezrouft to Tripolitania. The CREPS was the first to make a strike. In March 1954 the deposit of natural gas at Berga was discovered so unexpectedly that the drilling crew were almost overcome by the escaping gas. In 1956 there followed the discovery of the oilfields at Edjeleh, Tiguentourine and Hassi Messaoud and the gas deposit at Hassi R'mel.

The desert was seized by an oil-fever. In 1957, the Big Four of Saharan oil were joined by the 'Compagnie d'Exploration Pétrolière' (C.E.P.), and the turn of the year brought a new situation in so far as the companies which had first entered the Saharan oil business now had to surrender half their concessions. The finds made in 1956 had great publicity value; there was a queue of applicants. Besides purely French firms there were five American concerns (Cities Service, Phillips, Franco-Wyoming, Sinclair, Pan American), a Canadian-American firm (Canadian Delhi), a Japanese-American concern (Newmont Mining), an Italian firm (Ausonia Mineraria), and British Petroleum, associated with French capital or French undertakings. There was widespread interest abroad despite the Algerian war. But two years after Edjeleh and Hassi Messaoud had been discovered it was still not known on what terms France would grant ore concessions. What taxes would she impose? The 'Code pétrolier du Sahara' which was passed in November 1958, brought the long-awaited clarification and paved the way for increased foreign participation by clearly defining the rights and obligations of the oil companies in the Sahara. Mining concessions are granted for fifteen years. The concessionaires are allowed to extract the oil themselves and to market it but they are encouraged by special tax concessions to make long term investments. They must share their profits from the sale of the crude oil with the State on a 50-50 basis. France has thus adopted the system prevalent in the Middle East. As a proposition it is made more attractive by the fact that, following the inroads made by the Italians, the Japanese and the Russians and even by an American concern in Morocco, Persia, Saudi Arabia, Kuwait, Egypt, Libya, Sudan and Irak, the traditional percentage-system in the Middle East has become associated with the 'colonial-imperialist era' and has been undermined. Even Venezuela has had second thoughts about the share she has been receiving of her own oil. On the other hand, France will not revise agreements which have already been concluded, till they have run for 25 years. In December 1958 the Standard Oil of New Jersey was allowed to join in. Eight years after the first seismic explosion in the Sahara the most powerful oil concern in the world gave the desert its blessing. If anything, however, the French were still more delighted when a German concern, 'Wintershall', decided to begin prospecting for oil in the Sahara in 1960. Western Europe, whose future expansion (and markets) had already been very much in France's mind, seemed at last to be sitting up and taking notice!

* * *

'Attention, please! Attention, please! Will passengers travelling by Air France flight No. 180 to OM1 and MD1 please go to exit number 2 . . . This is the final call to passengers by Aerotec to K15. Please board the aircraft at once. I repeat: final call . . . Passengers travelling by Air Algérie to HR1 are requested to submit their luggage for examination. . . .'

To the new arrival at Maison Blanche, the Algiers airport, the strange letters and numbers sound like charades: HR1, TR1, OM3, K15, MD1, OM1 . . . The indestructible DC3 and the double decker Bréguet-Deux-Ponts, 'the flying kangaroo,' take off for nameless destinations which are no more than a symbol on the map of the desert. Water points, which until recently were known only to caravans and camel-nomads, are broadcast in the same breath as Paris, London or Rome. And amongst the ordinary passengers there is always a smattering of pétroliers, the men who are changing the face of the desert. Many of them are in working-clothes, without ties, carrying bulging suitcases. They look almost aggressively young as they lounge in armchairs or sit perched on the bar-stools. They are the pioneers of the newly-rich desert.

After two, three, four hours flying the plane prepares to land. Dominating the skyline is the oil-derrick. The landing strip is marked out with white stones. The windsock hangs limply in the hot, stagnant air. Wheeltracks radiate out into the endless wilderness. Three trucks and a jeep are parked near the landing-strip at odd angles as if they had suddenly broken down. A late arrival who did not want to miss his black coffee is racing over from the derrick in a cloud of dust as the pilot circles for the last time.

When Vuillemin, the Lindbergh of the Sahara, made his first landing at Menaka, the natives, who had never seen an aeroplane, were overcome by amazement at this 'wonderful thing which flies, which lands and from which two Frenchmen appear.' Today this 'wonderful thing' not only carries dozens of men away on leave, it brings in refrigerators as big as a garage, power-trucks, pre-fabricated houses, steel tubes and even helicopters. And from the belly of the DC3, which calls once a week at these remote camps, much stranger things than Frenchmen emerge: carbonic acid snow, a cask of whisky, cases of artichokes, mandarines, apples, oranges and grapefruit, the weekly meat ration, fresh cabbage and out-of-date films. And, of course, the mail.

'Two letters at once? She must have a bad conscience . . . just look at that: the first asparagus! . . . That's what they call service! This is the second time we've had "The Pirate of Capri" . . . Always complaining! Can't you read? "The Pirate of Capri, Part II".'

Even in the desert Father Christmas has his work cut out.

＊　　＊　　＊

MK1, one of the CPA's prospecting sites, lies seventy-five miles

by air to the north-west of Port Flatters in the Great Eastern Erg.
From a distance only the drilling-tower was visible. The camp was
tucked away on the open ground about two hundred yards off.
Robert Pieuchot, the man in charge of the camp, explained that
this was in order to deaden the infernal noise of the drilling-
machine. Even so the camp's inhabitants fall asleep with that noise
in their ears and wake up to it in the morning. If the diesel engine
that drives the drill suddenly stops, the camp is plunged in the
deafening stillness of the desert and to the drilling-engineer the
silence is ominous. Has the drill jammed? Or is this the driller's
nightmare? Has the mud drained away?

Although the derrick stands by itself, like a church steeple at the
end of the world, the rotary table that keeps the drill revolving
underground is the real focal point of this small community. Day
and night, weekdays and Sundays, summer and winter one of three
shifts is on duty. The engineer in charge of the drill keeps a watch-
ful eye on the mud; the shift-leader is constantly checking the
flickering needles on the instrument panel. There is not a man
round that derrick who does not listen constantly to the throb of
the machine, to the gasping noise it makes as it forces its way
through the rock.

Every now and then there comes a moment when the drill,
reinforced with special steel, blunts itself on the hard rock. Then a
fantastic operation starts: dismantling. The string of pipes, to
which the worn drill is fitted, has to be extracted. The block-and-
tackle, which hangs in the tower, pulls it out. If the high derrick
were not there over the drill hole, a whole series of steel pipes
would have to be unscrewed one by one, but the derrick
makes it possible to detach several of these pipes together and
stack them in sections. This is a magnificent operation to watch, in
which both rhythm and strength are needed. It is carried out to the
roar of the diesel engines and the clatter of a huge mechanical
swivel on which the pipes rotate. And one of the men is perched at
a dizzy height near the top of the derrick like a circus acrobat.
Balancing on a narrow platform, he fishes out the various sections
of the piping and bundles them, like gigantic knitting-needles, in
the corner of the tower.

After I had paid my respects to M'Kratta's camp mascot, a little desert fox which, for all its seeming innocence and charm, had a vicious bite, Pieuchot took me to the scene of operations in the derrick. The dismantling had just been completed and the blunted drill emerged. It was a so-called roller bit with three mobile, sharp-toothed rollers. The camp geologist examined the fragments of rock which were still clinging to the teeth of the drill. He looked anything but happy. He ordered a core-drilling. Unlike the ordinary drill, which crushes the rock, the core-barrel cuts out a cylinder of rock, breaks it off and pulls it out. The geologist then has a piece of rock intact. As soon as the core barrel with its glittering diamond crown had been assembled, the operation began. The drill pipe with the core bit was driven down, as it had been pulled out, piece by piece. The drilling was 4,000 feet deep. Within three months it should reach 7,000 feet, beyond which point the geologists hoped to strike oil. Until then nothing was likely to happen to disturb the day-to-day routine.

Part of this routine is the sandstorm that batters its way through goggles and tortures the eyes, that penetrates into mouth, nose, ears and sandwiches, and covers the camp for hours at a time with an impenetrable brown cloak. Then there are the strange magnetic and electric storms that fray the nerves and produce tropical madness. There is the dry air that sucks moisture from the body like a vampire. And, above all, there is the daily striptease. The men on the early shift look like mummies. They cannot have too many scarves, pullovers and underclothes to pad out their muddy khaki suits. For they know from experience that, especially in winter, the desert is cold—'a cold country,' say the Arabs, 'in which the sun shines hot.' Then, as the morning advances, layer after layer is discarded until young men emerge with muscular, sunburnt bodies dressed in shorts, Wellingtons and rubber gloves. There is every reason to wear gloves, for the metal becomes so hot from the sun that it will raise blisters.

Can anything be done to make life in the desert tolerable, to cope with the sun, the dry air and the sandstorms? The answer of the oil companies is a simple one: comfort. Healthy young men, who can have a shower when they feel like it, who are treated like princes, who live in air-conditioned, well-furnished huts and can fly home on leave every few weeks, are quite prepared to work an eight-hour shift in the desert.

I learned quite by chance that in the early stages the oil companies had not much confidence that comfort would prove an effective secret weapon against the desert. The C.P.A., for example, were quite resigned to the fact that they might have to close down certain prospecting stations for several of the summer months when the heat was particularly fierce. Against all expectations, however, this did not prove necessary, mainly because, when the company spoke of comfort, they meant comfort.

Incidentally, it is provided almost free of charge. A small deduction is made from the salaries of the drilling-crews which is little more than a symbolic gesture. The geologists, topographers and geophysicists, who are subjected to extremes of heat and cold in their tropical tents, are exempt from any such deduction.

The meals served in drilling-camps would do credit to a two-star restaurant. When General de Gaulle, while he was still a private citizen, paid his first visit to the drilling-stations in southern Algeria, he was regaled with blue trout, fresh oysters, lobster which had been caught the day before, and pheasant which had been shot the day before. The daily menu of the drilling-crews is almost as choice.

A telephone conversation, which I overheard in the office of a Director of the 'Société Générale de Ravitaillement' in Algiers and which I noted down, speaks for itself:

'Thirty Europeans? That's a bit of luck. We already have a client with the same number of staff . . . We make a weekly delivery by air: 6½ lb. of raw ham, 90 lb. of beef, 52 lb. of veal, 25 lb. of pork chops, 6 lb. of calf's liver, 25 lb. of fish, 25 lb. of chicken. All best quality, of course. Bresse chickens. Then 25 lb. of rabbits and 6lb. of sausage. That means nearly 101 lb. of the best meat per head per week. . . .'

The list seemed endless: several hundred eggs, eight varieties of cheese, thirteen different vegetables, seven kinds of fruit, butter and spices. Then come the monthly consignments of non-perishable foodstuffs, mainly in tins, which are delivered by the lorry-load. I felt as if I had been invited to the annual stock-taking at a chain of grocery-stores! Nothing had been overlooked that could tickle the human palate. And lest I should give a false impression let me add that the list of foodstuffs for the native workers is only somewhat shorter because they prefer their traditional dishes. Mutton is the main feature of the weekly deliveries, while millet, couscous and green tea are the chief monthly supplies.

The 'Société Générale de Ravitaillement', which has discovered a gold mine of its own in the desert, sent two million francs worth of pâté de foie gras to the Sahara for Christmas. By contrast, the Tibbus in the Tibesti mountains are said to be able to live for three days on one date, the first day on the skin, the second on the meat, the third on the stone. This is, of course, primarily a tribute to the date, but not entirely. An English traveller in the nineteenth century reported: 'When a Tibbu makes a journey, he takes with him a goatskin bag full of water and a few handfuls of dried dates. When he has eaten every morsel and has fasted three days thereafter, he tightens his belt and continues on his way. The following day he takes in another reef. If he then finds nothing to eat, he is seriously concerned.'

Against a background of such proverbial frugality the oil prospector seems like a combination of Gargantua and Gargamelle. The plain fact is, of course, that the chronically undernourished Tibbu would never dream of dismantling a 9,000 foot drill and reassembling it. For the industrial worker in the desert the maximum comfort is an essential minimum.

Amongst the abbreviations that have showered down on the industrial Sahara PROHUZA is one of the more recent. It stands for 'Centre d'Etudes et d'Informations des Problèmes Humains dans les Zones Arides,' a research group set up in 1956 by the B.I.A. to investigate human problems, and especially labour problems, in arid zones. PROHUZA's experts call themselves eremologists, their branch of science eremology (from the Greek word 'eremos' meaning 'desert'). They work closely with the Laboratory for applied physiology in Strasbourg and to a large extent they draw on experience gained during the last war and since then in the semi-deserts of the United States. In the Sahara, where they

maintain a permanent research station at Gara Djebilet, they are
making ambitious investigations of their own. Their aim is to persuade the responsible authorities that the human element must be
given priority over the technical, not vice versa. If they had a
motto it would be the words which the ancestors of the Tuareg
inscribed on the wall of a prehistoric wadi. 'The man who sticks
his head in a bran-tub is eaten by donkeys.'

Dr. Claude Vigan is PROHUZA's 'travelling delegate for the
Sahara.' He has had wide experience of the tropics and the desert.
He spent eight years in the Congo, Chad and Nigeria, eventually
as an itinerant doctor and as the leader of an anti-tuberculosis
campaign. In the drilling stations he is known simply as the 'Sahara
doctor'. The oil companies have placed him in charge of their
entire health services in the desert. He is always on call. If an
accident or a serious illness occurs at any of the drilling stations,
he is immediately consulted by radio. There is a listening-post at
Algiers, which functions day and night, taking incoming messages
on a special frequency for the 'Secours Radio Médical Saharien.'
Once a month he makes a tour of the desert, hopping by plane from
oasis to oasis, from camp to camp. Once a year the 'young lions'
go to him for a thorough medical check-up.

Dr. Vigan has established that after two, at most three, years
Saharan fatigue sets in, even a kind of desert allergy. For a man to
undertake heavy work in the heart of the desert is contrary to all
the laws of Nature. His body temperature is 98.4 degrees, his
skin-temperature only a few degrees lower. Whether he is capable
of working in the desert in summer depends on his capacity to
keep the temperature of his body at normal height. Body-heat is
caused in the first instance by the digestive processes. Even in
sleep the human body generates seventy-five calories an hour.
Heavy manual work brings this up to four hundred calories. In
addition, the human body also absorbs warmth from outside, from
the direct and indirect heat of the sun (quite independently of the
temperature of the air) and, in certain circumstances, also from the
air. In a temperate climate excess warmth is easily disposed of. It
is absorbed by the ground and the air. If the body becomes heated
to the point where enough warmth is not escaping, then the human

organism has its own air-conditioning system that comes into operation. Two million glands draw off water which cools the skin as it evaporates. The blood, which conveyed the surplus warmth to the skin, flows back into the body at a reduced temperature.

In the desert during the summer months, when the temperature rises to more than 120 degrees in the shade, the body's air-conditioning system is constantly working at full pressure. Evaporation at the rate of nearly two pints of perspiration an hour is not uncommon. One windless day in August Dr. Vigan measured the loss of weight through perspiration of a drilling operative. The shift began at seven o'clock in the morning when the air-temperature was 93.2 with about the same percentage of humidity. It ended at three in the afternoon when the temperature was 125.6 in the shade with 31 per cent humidity. The worker in question returned to camp 18 lb. lighter. Naturally this was an experiment and one not without risks. No one in the desert can afford to lose through sweating more than twelve per cent of his weight. Beyond that there is a danger of explosive overheating in certain important tissues, which means a heat-stroke. In normal circumstances a drilling operative will not lose so much. Thirst functions like the red light which warns a motorist his petrol is running low. The cabin in the drilling tower is like a soft drinks bar in summer with a plentiful supply of mineral water and fruit juice. But it is not enough to satisfy one's thirst, for research has shown that Nature's safety mechanism does not function smoothly in the desert. Quenching one's thirst merely replaces half the water which the body has lost. This is particularly dangerous during very dry periods when no beads of perspiration appear on the skin. The air sucks the water from the pores so quickly that it has no time to evaporate. Only when the body is resting, or still more during meals, does Nature's warning system start functioning again.

It is true that a camel-rider can manage for several days on five or six gallons of water, but this does not mean that he has discovered a more effective way of shedding the excess than by perspiring. It simply means that he takes great care to keep the excess heat as low as possible. He spends the hottest hours of the day in the shade, he avoids any unnecessary exercise, and he keeps almost his entire body covered. To work in the sun, as many drilling crews do, naked to the waist is unwise because it places a considerable strain on the body. As many as a thousand calories can be generated in an hour, whereas the evaporation of two pints of perspiration will only release six hundred.

'When the Congo-Ocean line was laid, every rail cost one human life,' Dr. Vigan told me at the M'kratta camp. 'Fortunately disasters of that kind are a thing of the past. There are even technicians who believe that any problem of environment can be solved in terms of expenditure of energy. I don't share that view. After a certain time the Saharan fatigue my patients suffer from shows physical as well as mental symptoms, which suggests that air-conditioning and luxurious meals don't in themselves compensate the human body for being transplanted to such an aggressive environment as the desert. You can't fool the desert as easily as that. If we are going to achieve anything really great in the Sahara, we'll have to learn much more about man and his behaviour in relation to his environment. At present we're much better informed about the petrography of the Alb than about the physical, mental and spiritual factors that determine the well-being of human labour in the desert.'

Dr. Vigan and his colleagues in the Prohuza have now turned their attention to a number of individual problems. What is the ideal type of house for the Sahara? What are the most suitable varieties of air-conditioning plant? What basic diets should a camp cook adhere to? Are highly-seasoned, thirst-making dishes out of place? Should vitamins be added? Is it advisable to take salt pills to replace the salt lost through perspiring? What are the ideal clothes and headgear for the Sahara? Is the eight-hour shift, imported from more temperate zones, suited to the special conditions in the desert? Dr. Vigan, for one, doubts if it is. The body is capable of exuding nearly two pints of perspiration an hour for eight hours, then the sweat glands grow tired. They can achieve an even higher figure for short periods but then they will not last out a whole shift. An eight-hour stretch is, therefore, too long, for it inevitably includes brief spurts of intense effort.

Are short and frequent leave-periods essential, either in Algiers or in France, to rest the body? Fifis and Crettaz, for example, whose work in the desert is suspended from mid-June until September, fly to Algiers for eight days every six weeks, Pieuchot once a month, and they have a long leave once every year or two years. Usually the arguments quoted in support of this system are psychological. Eighty per cent of the pétroliers are married and have families in Algiers or in France. Dr. Vigan believes, however, that it would be better to take a longer leave at longer intervals, for the body needs a week to readjust itself to the cool, humid northern climate. From a physiological standpoint eight days' leave is usually more of a strain than a recreation.

Then there is the question: what factors should be taken into account when selecting personnel? Work in a drilling-crew is extremely dangerous. Only mining and quarrying have a higher accident-rate. In a hostile climate it is particularly important to choose the right man for the right job. Perfect fitness is essential. The personnel manager much prefers a man who is attracted by the fat wage packet to the romantic type who either has visions of grandeur or has been crossed in love. Yet not all the tough, materialistic young men can stand up to the heat. The small, slightly-built man is better able to cope with it than one who is big and heavily-built. But other factors must also contribute: the type of constitution, race, age, family background and so on. PROHUZA is trying to explore this almost virgin territory in the hope that the selection of personnel can be made more scientific.

Dr. Vigan has even found himself compelled to extend his enquiries to more intimate questions. It seems that the behaviour of the 'monks of the desert' on home leave sometimes gives rise to a 'Saharan complex' in their wives with the result that the husband turns his back on the fool's paradise in the desert and even on the fat wage packet and hands in his notice.

A typical evening at M'Kratta. In the mess the cinema operator was blowing the sand out of his projector and winding the film. In the bar the men from the early shift were trying to calm down one of their colleagues who had more than quenched his thirst with beer. Another group had just returned from a game of volley-ball. The cook was swearing at the kitchen-boy as he humped a case of

Evian mineral-water into the caboose. Water for drilling was being transported by road-tanker from a nomads' well but it was too salty for cooking, drinking or shaving. For these purposes, mineral water, imported from France, was used.

The lights went on in the derrick, turning it into a desert beacon, a function which it not infrequently performs. The story is often told of the worker at another drilling-station who got caught in a sand-storm between the camp and the derrick, which was poorly lit. Hours later they found the unfortunate man dead, five miles from the camp.

As a tourist I was anxious to have a look at the camp when it was lit up. On the way out a guard stopped me. I had to wait till someone could be found to go with me. A fellow-Swiss finally appeared wearing slippers and clothes which were nothing if not colourful. An ex-legionary, he had volunteered for the small private army which the CPA, like the other oil companies, have maintained for the protection of their staff ever since the incident at Timimoun.

In November 1957 there was a mutiny in the camel corps and the mutineers, who deserted to the fellagha, served as a tragic reminder of the FLN's threat to carry the war into the Sahara. They attacked a survey party at Timimoun and killed eight CPA employees. News of the incident came like a bombshell. The CPA decided for the time being to suspend all their operations in the west. Colonel Bigeard's parachutists combed the oases as well as every possible hiding-place in the desert, while the oil companies organised their own security forces. Company personnel remained unarmed in order not to provoke attacks by the fellagha. At M'kratta the camp was moved a bit nearer to the derrick, a barbed-wire fence and a mud-brick wall were put up to enclose both, and a ten man security squad guarded the entrance. When I visited M'Kratta these precautions had already become routine. No one worried. To begin with, several months had passed since the Timimoun incident. Moreover, the absence of water-points in this part of the desert virtually ruled out military operations. Not even a ghostly caravan could arouse any anxiety. The fresh tracks of a camel caravan, which had apparently passed unnoticed during the night, had given rise to a certain amount of speculation but even

that had long since died. No one took the security force seriously.
One of the drilling-workers said to me with a shrug of his shoulders
and a contemptuous glance at the barbed-wire and the tents of the
praetorian guard: 'The big cold-storage room by the kitchen and
the two-way radio are more important for our survival than a
dozen bodyguards.'

I came back from my walk to find Rober Pieuchot in the radio
room. The walls were covered with 'cheesecake.' It seemed
strange that in the middle of the Sahara one should be surrounded
by nudes. 'Passion,' Pieuchot said impatiently into the telephone.
He spelt it out. 'P-a-s-s-i-o-n.' He was ordering a new film.

*   *   *

It was like travelling through an artillery barrage, as locusts flew
blindly against the station-wagon and burst on the windscreen.
The screen-wiper became clogged up with corpses. Every now and
then the driver stopped to remove the nasty mess that obscured his
vision. The hailstorm of insects thickened each time we passed a
Daya, a green depression with winter fodder, lucerne and an Atlas
pistachio tree. We tried reducing speed to walking pace but it
made very little difference. The air seemed to be full of suicide-
flyers.

We finally reached TR1, the first German drilling station in the
Sahara.

The French began to take an interest in oil prospecting at home
and in their oversea territories in 1945, but interest alone was not
enough. New industries had to be created and an ambitious training programme drawn up for the technicians and skilled workers.
Foreign experts were greatly impressed by the speed with which
the French mastered the highly specialised technical problems of
prospecting. But France had underestimated the height of the
stakes that would be needed. Shortages soon became apparent,
mainly of prospecting gear, for example drilling equipment and
the skilled personnel to handle it. The French army decided that
geologists on national service should be made available as civilians
to the oil companies in the Sahara and that drilling apprentices
who were prepared to work later on in Algeria or in the Sahara

should have their national service reduced by four-fifths. The main effect of this shortage, however, was that companies holding prospecting rights and concessions began to engage other firms under contract. Early in 1960 four concerns specialising in geophysics were employed in this way, three of them with mostly American capital. Of the forty-six drilling plants which were operating simultaneously in the French Sahara only eleven were company-owned. The remainder belonged to eleven contracting firms, some representing chiefly German and Italian interests.

In November 1956 the S.N. REPAL struck a deposit of natural gas 7,200 feet down at Hassi R'mel. Each of the first two producing wells—HR1 and HR2—which are ten miles apart, produced in tests 35 million cubic feet of gas. They are therefore amongst the richest natural gas deposits in the world. The methane produced is moist, and it contains a hundred and fifty grammes of gasoline and eighty grammes of butane and propane per cubic metre. After eight successful drillings experts at the beginning of 1960 estimated the proved reserves at 800 milliard cubic metres. That is equivalent in heating capacity to a little over a billion tons of coal. (The estimated coal reserves in the Ruhr district are sixty-five billion tons.)

The natural gas at Hassi R'mel will undoubtedly play an important part in the industrial development of Algeria. And yet the REPAL would prefer a bird in the hand to two in the bush; it would rather have a modest oilfield than a gigantic deposit of methane. In the hope that they had tapped the gas cap of a particularly long, oil-bearing layer, they began fresh drillings. One of these was TR1.

The most sensational feature of TR1 is the derrick. It was the first of its kind in Africa. Instead of the traditional Eiffel Tower model on four legs, it is a so-called Gulliver mast on two legs. It can drill to a depth of 12,000 feet. Although it weighs 270 tons, this German giant is incredibly easy to erect.

I arrived at TR1 to find everyone in a great state of excitement. The mud was leaking. The REPAL drillers had warned their German colleagues that this was liable to occur beyond a certain depth and the worst had in fact happened. To the layman the most

interesting objects are the derrick and the bit and he may well go
away without asking a single question about the most scientific of
all drilling-operations: lubrication.

The lubricating fluid, which the Anglo-Saxons and the French
call 'mud', is prepared in a trough next to the tower. The black,
snake-like hose through which the mud is pumped into the hollow
pipe quivers over the heads of the drilling-crew. At the end of the
drill pipe the mud is squeezed through holes in the bit and rises
between the wall of the drill-hole and the pipe to the surface, where
it is cleaned out and returned to the mixing-basin.

Mud is the life-blood of the drill. It performs many functions.
In the first place it swills the rock fragments out of the drill-hole
and by examining them the geologist can gain valuable information
about the rock-strata which are being drilled. It smears the mobile
parts of the drill and keeps them cool. It forms a protective crust on
the walls of the drill-hole. But above all it is sufficiently heavy to
prevent an unexpected gush of oil, gas or water.

No cocktail is mixed with greater care than the driller's mud.
Into it goes a combination of scientific expertise and intuition based
on long experience. The basic element is water. A deep drilling
will consume 10,000 gallons a day, enough to irrigate two and a
half acres of palm-grove for the same period. But water itself is too
light to prevent subsidence or to keep down high-pressure oil, gas
or water. By mixing it with clay the necessary weight is achieved.
By adding other substances such as heavy spar, twice the weight
of water can be produced. Together with the clay another substance is included in the mixture, which determines the rate of
flow. The driller expects mud to become thinner with changes of
pressure and to thicken to a kind of jelly when the pumps stop. In
this way, if the flow of mud is interrupted, the fragments of rock
it contains are prevented from sinking back and blocking up the
drill bit.

I have given, of course, no more than an outline of the recipe
employed. The choice of ingredients used in the mixture depends
on the particular geological conditions in which the drill-bit is
operating. And, apart from that, each mud-specialist has his own
recipe by which he swears.

The latest development in drilling technique envisages an entirely new function for mud. It will actually drive the drill bit. A hole can be drilled simply by suspending a heavy steel bit from a cable and lifting it up and down rhythmically. This type of drilling was apparently practised by the Chinese two thousand years ago, and the first systematic oil-drilling operation a hundred years ago was of this kind. Even today this method is still occasionally used. In hard, solid rock which is not too deep it has considerable advantages. On the other hand, since the turn of the century the so-called rotary technique has been universally accepted for deep-drilling. All the deep-lying oilfields in the world were drilled with a rotating bit. It is only quite recently, since oil deposits near the surface became exhausted and deeper and more expensive drilling was called for, that the drawbacks of the rotary method, which have always been apparent, became a practical problem.

From a technical point of view the rotary process is a mixture of the miraculous and the unimaginative. Enlarging the drill-bit to monumental proportions is not particularly imaginative, but, miraculously enough, it works. The deepest hole ever drilled, in Texas, reached a depth of nearly five miles. This is roughly equivalent to using a fifteen-yard long telephone wire to drive a dentist's drill. The drill pipes would collapse under their own weight if they were not a hundred times stronger than ordinary steel.

The defects of the rotary process are obvious. A blunt drill cannot simply be withdrawn and changed. The whole string of pipes has to be extracted and dismantled which is not only a time-wasting and therefore costly business but also imposes a tremendous strain on the crew. It is not unusual for a hundred drill bits to need replacing on one deep-drilling operation.

But the rotary method has a second and even more serious handicap. More than ninety per cent of the power is used in sinking the drill. The flexible pipes rub against the side of the hole and to overcome the effect of this friction a great deal of power is needed. The solution is clear: the driving-power must be transferred to the bottom of the drill-hole. The first to experiment along these lines were the Russians. The mud, which is pumped down, drives the turbine-drill. In the Soviet Union four out of five drillings are already being made in this way. American drillers call this innovation 'the Russian revolution.' Soviet technicians are planning to drill a hole ten miles deep, and the Americans are thinking of a drilling-operation from a floating-raft which will pierce the earth's crust at certain points under the sea where it is no more than three miles thick. This would enable them to probe the secrets of the earth-cap. Experts differ as to whether experiments of this kind are only financially feasible with a turbine-drill.

But, to return to the mud, if the drill bit pierces rock-layers with clefts, seams and pockets, the mud may seep away. This can be both costly and dangerous. There is one simple method of stopping the leakage, to remove a section of the drill-pipe at the appropriate depth. But this a driller will only do as a last resort, particularly where, as in the case of TR1, the hole is not very deep. For as the drill-pipe grows longer, the hole, which at the top is a bare eighteen inches in diameter, grows smaller and it is always desirable to have as much leeway as possible, when entering the oil-bearing layer. So an attempt is made to seal up the cracks.

In addition to the clay and spar used for drilling-mud, large quantities of cement are imported into the desert. It is not for building but is employed to make the mud more cohesive and less likely to seep away. Cement by itself is, however, seldom enough. Cellophane strips, husks of cotton seeds and nut-shells, sponges, sugar-cane fibres, sawdust, feathers, straw and even hay, together with various minerals and chemicals are pumped by the ton into the crevices; even food-packages, sandwich-wrappings and cement-bags are used in an emergency.

The whole of that night the atmosphere at TR1 was tense. Searchlights lit up the camp and the desert around. At the entrance gate, which had been barricaded since sunset, the guard was changed. But the thoughts of the nightshift workers were not with the fellagha. The drillers were thinking of the radio report that would have to go to Algiers, unless something happened soon. They redoubled their efforts. Ghostly figures, covered in white cement-powder, rushed about in the icy Sahara night under the towering Gulliver mast. Then, as the sky began to lighten, the drillers heaved a sigh of relief. They had done it; the leak had been plugged. Before long the drill bit was once more eating into the rock and chocolate-coloured mud, carrying chips and splinters, was surging out of the hole.

* * *

It is all too easy to conjure up an image of the past, of a Wild West atmosphere with the saloon and the Sheriff's office. Yet the decor is essentially futuristic. The gleaming, silvery storage tanks, the red, green and yellow pipes, the flicker and glow of the gas-flames which cast their eerie light over the camp at night, the fire-extinguishers, the No-Smoking signs, the security zones, and coloured warning-lights, the masts, rigs, pumps and machines, men wearing goggles, helmets, asbestos gloves and divers' boots—all this suggests stations in outer space and settlements on Mars. Migrating storks, which are sometimes driven down by a sand-storm on their flight northwards and come to rest on the oilfield at Hassai Messaoud, seem to belong to another planet.

This particular science-fiction film is, however, no soap-opera. The actors represent neither past nor future but a very real present. The man who sat in the sheriff's office had no frills on his trousers. His suit had been made by the best tailor in Paris; instead of a Colt, his pockets bulged with papers: statistics, balance-sheets, estimates . . . And the man whom I had met at the gas-trap, where the oil and gas are separated, told me in the bar that he was putting aside ten pounds a month to buy a vineyard in Burgundy which his grandfather had always coveted.

There is something of a Fata Morgana about Hassi Messaoud. The word 'Messaoud' means both 'good fortune' and 'blessing.' Ten years ago no one would have dared suggest that either of these might one day emerge from that desolate landscape with its well of brackish water; five years ago no one would have believed that a small town could spring up like a mushroom in the dry bed of the prehistoric Igharghar river. Today the three hundred visitors who make an oil-pilgrimage to Hassi Messaoud every month are given two almost legendary accounts of how the town was born:

The headquarters of the S.N. Repal decided to abandon the

drilling which had been in operation for six months near the desert track from Ouargla to Fort Lallemand and exactly half-way between the two oases. The drill-bit had reached a depth of 10,000 feet without finding the slightest trace of oil or gas. The chief drilling engineer happened to have a single ten yard long steel pipe. Contrary to his instructions from Algiers he lengthened the drill by these last ten yards. The extension was decisive; the bit pierced a layer of sandstone containing large deposits of oil.

The second version: The decision had been reached to abandon the drilling but an unaccountable delay arose with the vehicles. The Chief Engineer was tearing his hair over this twenty-four hour hold-up which would cost a fortune. But the camp geologist, taking advantage of this unexpected reprieve, told the chief driller to use the hollow drilling bit and take a sample from the bottom of the hole. On June 4th, 1956 the section of rock was brought up. Against all expectations it showed distinct traces of oil. The work was immediately resumed and on June 15th oil gushed for the first time at Hassi Messaoud.

I was unable to get any official confirmation of either of these stories. The engineers who told them to me begged me not to mention their names. For higher authority is anxious that the discovery of oil at Hassi Messaoud should be attributed to deliberate calculation, not to chance.

The strike at Hassi Messaoud produced the finest quality sweet or sulphur-free petroleum together with 7,000 cubic feet of gas per ton. Once the sand has been removed, it can be used, without any refining, to drive the drilling-engines and produce electric power for the camps. The oil-bearing layer proved to be extraordinarily dense (450 feet) and the oil is under very heavy pressure, so that no pumping is necessary. The first well at Hassi Messaoud is called MD1 in the matter-of-fact atmosphere of the conference room, but to the drilling-crews it is the Jean-Riemer well, in honour of one of their colleagues who died following an explosion of odourless gas.

MD1 lies on the fringe of the S.N. Repal's concession. Adjoining it is the CFPA, which struck oil at OM1. The two companies, which had already been collaborating fairly closely, agreed that the oil-field which straddled their two concessions should be jointly developed and exploited. By January 1960 forty-eight wells were working and the proved reserves were put at 500 million tons of crude oil. Hassi Messaoud therefore ranks amongst the ten largest fields in the world. Up to the beginning of 1960, however, the precise extent of this long, oil-bearing stratum, a classical hump or anticline, was not known so that an exact estimate of the oil reserves was not possible. The drilling at OMG57, which the CFPA made a good fifteen miles to the north of the original well to locate the limits of the field, at the end of 1958 had again struck oil-bearing sandstone, which even at that distance still had a density of thirty yards. OMG57 greatly improved Hassi Messaoud's prospects of remaining high up on the world's list and possibly even moving into one of the top places.

For years the French had been putting up a tremendous barrage of propaganda about the Sahara. Hassi Messaoud at last supplied it with live ammunition. The fabulous riches of the Sahara, about which the French taxpayer read every time he opened his morning paper, had been, until then, not merely a mirage but an expensive one. Development of the Sahara was a gamble that ran not into millions but billions. So the authorities and the various companies involved lost no time and spared no effort in giving people at home a sniff of Saharan oil. 'Monsieur Lacoste (who was then Minister for Algeria) is determined,' wrote an English observer, 'to fill a tanker with Saharan oil, even if he has to carry it to the sea in tea-cups.' But Robert Lacoste could dispense with the tea-cups; a baby pipeline from Hassi Messaoud to Touggourt and an extension of the railway-track between Biskra and Touggourt did the trick. As national prestige was at stake, expense was no object. The important thing was that, as from January 1958, first 600, then 1200 and finally 1800 tons of oil reached the port of Philippe-ville by road-tanker every day. Every barrel of Saharan oil that arrived in France to be refined cost ten times as much as the same amount imported from Texas. But it was still considered cheap at the price, so long as it gave a new lease of life to the rather threadbare magic of the Sahara. Even without it, however, the CPA and S.N. Repal would have found no difficulty in issuing enough new

shares to meet development costs. There were plenty of buyers
who thought themselves fortunate to be able to invest in REPAL
at a murderous price, namely 650 per cent of the nominal share
value.

Looking for oil is expensive but it is probably more expensive
still to have found oil. Developing the field, extracting the oil and
laying pipelines require vast sums of money. The oil at Hassi
Messaoud lies deep down, between 10,000 and 11,500 feet. (The
average depth of Middle East oil is 1,600 feet at Kirkuk, 4,000 feet
in Kuwait and 7,000 feet in Saudi Arabia. Libyan oil is also about
7,000 feet down.) Moreover, drilling at Hassi Messaoud is comparatively difficult. Each operation costs eventually about five
hundred million francs. A yearly production of fourteen million
tons requires more than a hundred wells.

At the end of 1959 the 22-inch pipeline, which, with financial
help from the International Bank, had been laid across the Atlas
Mountains to Bougie, was opened with great ceremony. Further
pumping-stations are planned which will increase the yearly flow
of oil from the present 4.6 million tons to 14 million tons in 1961.
This will mean an additional million tons of liquid gas at Hassi
Messaoud.

France hopes by 1963 to produce 31 million tons of crude oil
from Hassi Messaoud and Edjeleh (this corresponds to France's
present internal consumption) and thereby to save 350 million
dollars in foreign exchange. If it is left to France's technicians, this
hope will certainly be fulfilled. The oil of the Sahara, however, is
a political not a technical problem. It has forced both parties in the
Algerian war to raise their stakes. France is no longer fighting
merely for an overseas province in which she could create decent
living-conditions and so fulfil a mission belatedly but with some
prospect of success, which would require all her spiritual, moral
and material resources; she is also fighting to salvage from the
desert the treasure of the Niebelungen which will gain her re-
admittance to the exclusive circle of world powers. André Malraux
said not long ago: 'Thanks to the Sahara France will . . .
become the leading Mediterranean power. Thanks to the Sahara
the economic conditions in southern Italy and in Spain will under-

go a radical change. Thanks to the Sahara France will be able to negotiate at a summit conference on an equal footing with the Soviet Union.' The wealth of the Sahara still represents for the Fifth Republic what it was to the Fourth: a miraculous cure that will restore France to her former 'grandeur' and 'gloire.' The Algerian rebel government, on the other hand, has deposited the black gold of the Sahara with the Arab League as security, against which its cheese-paring Arab brothers have advanced a war loan. The wealth of the desert is a gift from Allah, which might convert Algeria's freedom into independence. The frequent threat of the rebels to open a Saharan front has never progressed beyond the occasional raid. The reason may quite simply be the constant watch kept by air reconnaissance planes, the probing searchlights, the barbed-wire fences and sandbags, the parachutists and the small army of oil-mercenaries. But it is also possible that the fellagha realise they have no interest in seriously disturbing the French development programmes, by which they hope to benefit.

1956 was the Sahara's jubilee year. It was also the year in which the Suez Canal, a vital artery of Western Europe's oil supplies, slipped out of Western hands. So to many Frenchmen the oil of the Sahara is still 'manna from heaven,' a miracle worked by the Almighty and French geologists before the very gates of Europe, in order to teach the strong man on the Nile a lesson. The irony of it is that the manna from heaven increased the audience to which Cairo was calling: Arabs of all lands, unite! As the living-standard of the natives improves so the number of radio receivers grows. Until recently the peasants in the El Golea oasis did not possess a single radio set. Since the CPA set up their forward base-camp there and offered a large section of the population good wages, the number of radios has increased to over three hundred. Captain Barba knows exactly what this means: three hundred listeners who tune in to Cairo.

It is also ironical that the enemy should again be sitting almost on top of the Saharan oil. Air-reconnaissance, jeep-patrols, special security forces, armoured vehicles, military police-stations—but for these elaborate military precautions the oil of Hassi Messaoud would never have reached the coast. The French are under no illusions that the flow of oil from the Sahara will only become safe and economic when the Algerian conflict has been settled.

Pierre Desforges is twenty-six years old, a former Lieutenant in the Foreign Legion, and now a general commanding the security force which would have to defend the CFPA camp at Hassi Messaoud in the event of an attack. The force also carries out police duties. For there is no lack of formality and bureaucracy at OM1. No one takes a stroll through France's newest town without papers and permits. Desforges keeps a close watch on visitors and sees to it that they go home with the most favourable impression. His leather jacket and his metallic voice are never far out of sight and hearing.

In the newly-rich Sahara there are two classes: bourgeois or middle-class and proletariat. Crettaz belongs to the proletariat, Desforges to the middle-class. Both are equally well paid. Both expect, when they sit down to a meal, to be served with three courses followed by cheese, fruit and coffee. Both go regularly on leave by air. And both would agree that their survival depends much more on the refrigerator than on barbed wire fences and submachine guns. But the proletariat live in tropical tents: sticky heat during the day, freezing cold at night. There is a constant battle against the desert, which begins anew every day. So the proletariat feel that they are following in the footsteps of the Saharan explorers, who suffered untold privations in order to bring the outside world the first news from the land of thirst and terror. They look down on the bourgeois with that soupçon of envy which lends flavour to contempt.

The middle-class, on the other hand, live in luxury. Air-conditioned cabins are taken for granted. So too are bars, restaurants, casinos, non-stop cinema-shows, an eight-hour day, lemonade factories, multiple bakeries, rush-matting to shade camp-streets from the sun, a telephone and telegraph service, tobacco shops, and so on. Desforges proudly showed me the swimming-bath and spoke enthusiastically of a football pitch and tennis-courts. The previous day a load of humus had arrived from Algiers—after a journey of six hundred miles! Where, only a year before, bulldozers were churning up the desert, Desforges was sowing rye, planting eucalyptus and palm trees, thinning out vegetables, putting in bulbs and setting 500 birds free. The town was already living up to the name earmarked for it: Maison Verte.

Hassi Messaoud is a well-organised community with a distinct flavour of the arts and crafts. Social rank is represented by the colour of one's shirt. Barmen are red shirts, blue shirts are chamber-maids, yellow shirts serve the food, white shirts cook it, green shirts help in the kitchen, grey shirts bake the crisp Paris bread, purple shirts look after the stores, violet shirts sweep the streets. Only brown and black shirts are missing. The drilling crew's favourite is tartan. The visitor, however, is allowed to wear his own shirt. When he arrives, the receptionist presses into his hand, together with the key of his cabin—the acme of hospitality!—a card which gives the opening-times of the Cha-cha-cha, Bikini and Rhelli Bars, the hours at which meals are served in the four eating-places (breakfast from 3 to 8 a.m.), and an address at which complaints can be registered.

Hassi Messaoud is a town under notice. Its reply to the un-flattering story that it owes its existence solely to a twenty-four hour delay by a few articulated lorries has been to grow with almost feverish zest. Not that this helps. No sooner is the complete expanse of the oilfield known than a new town will be founded in the centre of the CFPA drillings, and the present booming capital will be reduced from one day to the next to a mere provincial backwater. 'Fortunately,' say the town-planners and architects. There is something overdressed, overdainty and essentially bour-geois about Hassi Messaoud (and other mushroom-towns in the Sahara) that gets on their nerves. In the oilmen they find an unpleasant mixture of technical know-how and hair-raising dilettantism. The most trifling problem that arises in the course of drilling immediately brings a swarm of specialists. Yet a minor employee is left to decide the layout of a camp, a base or a small town.

The experts want to have a say in the planning of future oil-towns. To them the ideal Saharan town is not, as one might expect, a futuristic dream in plastic and concrete. The air-conditioning plant seems to them a mere short-term solution, for with it the desert-dweller can never feel at home. But the desert town of the future is not to be inhabited entirely by exiles. The Sahara must be conquered, not cheated. So the oil-town of the planners is a small oasis in which only building-materials are used which are available on the spot: gypsum or sun-baked mud bricks. There will be none of the pompous colonial architecture with its wide squares and broad avenues which are open invitations to sunstroke and heat-stroke. The native models will be followed on lines suggested by Le Corbusier who called the Kasbah 'a masterpiece of architecture and town-planning.' The desert town of the future might even be completely underground like the south Tunisian troglodyte town Matmata. Daniel Fouqué submitted to the School of Architecture in Lausanne the plan of a 'sand city,' in which semi-spherical steel building-components with shaft-ventilation are embedded in the sand: igloos in the desert.

Every evening in the tents of the proletariat conversation turns inevitably to the desert; to the Bahr el Sheitan, the 'Devil's Sea' with its treacherous mirages; to the venomous Ghibli, the sand-laden south wind; to the white dunes on which the hoar-frost, the cold breath of the night, melts faster than a dream in the warmth of the rising sun; to petrified forests and the carvings on the rocks. The events of the outside world make little impact, least of all the sputniks and explorers, Lunik and Pioneer: to live in the desert is like hovering on the edge of outer space.

The air-conditioned middle-class have more tangible things to discuss: the next leave, the terms of one's contract, the drinks-bill, and women. Chiefly women. The average age of these men is twenty-five. There are innumerable pin-ups in Hassi Messaoud but not a single woman amongst them. And the same is true of every other oil-camp in the Sahara. An attempt was once made to introduce a young telephonist. The experiment is still talked about in the desert, where gossip is as rife as in a country village. The crude details are hardly suitable for print. The telephonist had to be hurriedly transferred to the north. Since then women have not been allowed into Hassi Messaoud, even on a visit.

What Pierre Desforges had to say about the oil of the Sahara I had heard time and again from many active, self-assured French-

men of his age, who are convinced that every nation has its own
destiny and that France's destiny is the Sahara. The conversation
on this topic in the desert today begins with Lord Salisbury,
Queen Victoria's Prime Minister.

On August 5, 1890 the French Ambassador in London signed
an agreement which placed the areas south of an imaginary line
from Say on the Niger to Barroua on Lake Chad in the British
sphere of influence. The French were given, in compensation, the
stretches of desert between the Atlas Mountains and Sudan, to
which France's claim was in any case uncontested and which had
purely theoretical value as a link between the French colonies in
West and Central Africa and her Atlas possessions, for at that time
to cross the Sahara was still a gamble with death. Not unnaturally
the British Prime Minister regarded this agreement as a first-class
business deal. His compatriots, however, considered it much too
generous. Salisbury made several speeches in his own defence.

He and the French Ambassador, he said on one occasion, had
exchanged gifts of mountains, rivers and lakes, and the only disturbing though relatively unimportant fact was that neither of
them knew where exactly these mountains, rivers and lakes were.
In a speech in the House of Lords he remarked that it was important to judge a country not merely by its size but also by its value.
The area in question, he continued, was what a peasant would call
very 'light soil'. In other words, it was the Sahara that was under
discussion, so that, to assess the real value of the country over
which France had claimed sovereignty, the vast expanse of desert
must be discounted. On another occasion, Salisbury, who had a
weakness for making sarcastic and none too diplomatic comments,
remarked scathingly that he had given the Gallic cock sand without
driving any hard bargain. In could now be left to scratch to its
heart's content.

Not all Frenchmen were satisfied with Salisbury's conditions.
The biting, acid comments he made on the agreement were doubly
hurtful to French pride, and Salisbury's remarks in the House of
Lords even offended France's official negotiator, although what he
heard from the diplomat's gallery was no secret to him. Not even
The Times, whose leading article on the 'brilliant potentialities'

of the Sahara he read at breakfast the following day, brought him
any consolation. 'Doubtless the Sahara is no garden,' he wrote
angrily to Salisbury, 'and contains, as you say, much light soil.
Yet it was hardly necessary to give a reminder of this in public.
You might very well have left it to us to find it out for ourselves.'

The Governor General of Algeria, Jules Cambon, immediately
took up Salisbury's challenge. In a speech at Ain Sefra he painted
an imaginative picture of the unexplored possibilities of the
British gift: 'Very well, we will scratch in this sand. We will lay
railway-lines, we will put up telegraph-poles, we will make the
artesian water-tables gush to the surface, and in the oases we will
hear the Gallic cock crowing his most melodious and happiest fanfare from the rooftops of the Kasbah.' Today, when the Sahara is
ceasing to be an economic burden, when oil is welling out of the
'light soil,' the Gallic cock is crowing Salisbury's unhappy pro-
nouncement across the desert. With a note of malicious triumph,
mocking, ironical, mistrustful, it rings in the ears of every non-
French traveller as if he were a grandson of the noble Lord. Before
he is aware of it he finds himself standing like a prisoner at the bar
while a charge is brought against him of conspiring against the
genius of France. The most the accused can do is to plead extenuating circumstances, such as that he does not carry a Swiss passport
('because Switzerland is neutral in the Algerian conflict') or that
he is not an American ('because America is not neutral in the
Algerian conflict').

What Pierre Desforges had to say about the internationalisation
of the search for oil in the Sahara can be summed up in two
sentences: France is surrounded by enemies. The Americans, in
particular, are not to be trusted.

France's relations with the United States are based on a confused
mixture of hopes and fears. Conjuring up the bogey of Wall Street
is a favourite pastime: American oil-companies are financing the
Algerian rebellion in order to cash in on the prospecting and
mining concessions in the Sahara, after the French have withdrawn, as a reward for good conduct; the Americans are merely
waiting 'to buy up the Sahara as they bought up Indo-China.'
On the other hand, the same Frenchmen who ascribe the most

dastardly motives and deeds to these American concerns, would like nothing better than to draw them in. For years a particularly succulent slice of the concessions cake has been kept on one side as bait for the Americans. If only one major American were to bite, it would be regarded as a sure guarantee that Washington was on France's side.

The hot-headed nationalists would have preferred to keep the riches of the desert to themselves. But the exploitation of these riches, which the Gallic cock has scratched out of the sand, is beyond France's means. The oil of the Sahara alone swallowed up 300 thousand million francs in investments from 1952 to 1960. According to conservative estimates a further 500 thousand million will be needed up to the end of 1962. The State, which promoted oil-prospecting, can no longer muster funds of this magnitude. Nor can France's private investment capital, which has been supporting the State's initiative since 1956. Two loans have already been obtained from the World Bank. There are also other factors which argue in favour of foreign investment: France's shortage of equipment and personnel, which is threatening to slow down the development plans considerably; the valuable experience which foreign companies have gained on other oilfields, particularly in methods of exploitation; and, last but not least in view of an impending oil-glut on the world-market, the need to open up new markets outside the franc-area.

It was a bitter discovery for France that it is easier to find, extract and transport oil than to sell it. The French refineries and marketing-organisations for mineral products are in the hands of the large oil-companies, a cartel to which, for example, two concerns in the Sahara, the S.N. Repal and the CREPS, do not belong. Understandably enough the cartel shows little enthusiasm for Saharan oil, which threatens the market for its own crude oil from the Middle East. Furthermore Saharan oil suffers from one drawback which can only be overcome with the help of the cartel: it is too good for the French market. It contains a high proportion of benzine and comparatively little fuel oil. But French manufacture is geared to the rich, heavy type of crude oil. Until such time as Saharan gas can take the place of fuel oil, the French have therefore

no choice but to exchange some of their Saharan oil for the heavier
Middle East oil, as the Danes exchange their butter for margarine
—a transaction which again involves the great international oil-
concerns. Not without reason, the American journal 'Petroleum
Week' warned the French that petrol would soon be running out
of their ears.

Up to the middle of 1959 France could at least contemplate
risking, if necessary, a price-war with the companies in the cartel.
Transport-costs are lower for Saharan oil than for Middle East oil.
Moreover the profit-margins are wider and more flexible. But the
picture changed in the second half of the year, when the importance of the oil deposits in Libya became apparent. Libyan oil is
nearer the surface and nearer the coast than Saharan oil. And it is
in the hands of the cartel.

France exerted pressure on her refineries and marketing-
organisations to guarantee a certain consumption over the next few
years. At the same time efforts are being made to set up a special
joint concern which will combine refining and selling.

The marketing as such should not be an insuperable problem,
between now and the time when France's own needs are completely met by the Saharan production. But from 1964 onwards it
will be difficult to get rid of the surplus. The fact that the Sahara's
oil-production is guaranteed by the French Army and is not
dependent on the whim of an Arab Minister or ruler may—or may
not—be a trump card in Paris, but in Bonn this is far from true.
As long as the Algerian war lasts, no European State can trade
openly in Saharan oil without offending the Arabs. And, quite
apart from that, others are also interested in Europe's oil-market;
the pipeline from Marseilles to Strasbourg and Karlsruhe will not
be the only one. Enrico Mattei is planning a pipeline from Genoa
to Munich, while other pipelines are creeping forward from
Eastern Europe bringing Russian oil to the very doorstep of the
free world.

France has appealed to her partners in the OEEC for support
and has suggested that Saharan Oil might be given preferential
treatment by the Common Market countries. But she seems likely
to receive a dusty answer. The main objection is that any guaran-

teed market for Saharan oil in Europe would inevitably mean imposing restrictions on imports of heavy petroleum from the Middle East with political consequences that are not hard to foresee.

The only solution for France lies in a free market based on supply and demand and in a liberal policy of internationalisation. The Oil Code, which at the last moment almost came to grief on blind nationalism and short-sighted monopolistic ambitions, has now paved the way. Foreign companies and financial groups are allowed to take up to a fifty per cent share. Not surprisingly, France, after making such great sacrifices to open up the desert, is not prepared to sell out. The Oil Law, while it makes the riches of the desert available to foreigners, also establishes France's controlling interest: strict precautions have been taken to prevent the desert from becoming a battleground for international oil-interests. Even the Standard Oil of New Jersey, which is in the habit of laying down its own terms, finally agreed, after years of hard bargaining, to accept fifty per cent instead of the fifty-one it was demanding.

The French are inclined to overestimate the political value of foreign participation. It may well have the psychological effect on many Frenchmen of a tacit guarantee of the status quo. The Russian Sobolev who, during the Algerian debate in the United Nations at the end of 1958, condemned 'the secret understanding between the great American oil-concerns and the French colonialists,' can only have confirmed this impression. In fact, however, it is rather naive to assume that the State Department would allow its future Algerian policy to be conditioned by the relatively small American oil-concerns in the Sahara. And the competition amongst other foreign concerns for the black gold of the Sahara also reflects their confidence not so much in the political stability of North Africa as in their own ability, should the need arise, to negotiate reasonable terms with France's successors.

What of the future of Saharan oil? M. Desforges's reply made it clear that for him (as for many other Frenchmen) Hassi Messaoud is the hub of the universe. Comparisons come thick and fast. Some regard the Sahara as another Venezuela or Texas, others see in it a new Saudi Arabia or even a new Middle East—depending on the context and on the individual's degree of optimism. And not a shadow of doubt is felt that the Sahara is richer.

The sober truth is that Hassi Messaoud is an important and probably even sensational oil-field. Those who estimate its reserves at 1,000 million tons (one fortieth of the known world reserves) are, however, indulging in wild speculation. Hassi Messaoud must be seen in the setting of the northern Sahara as a whole. The field at Bordj Nili, half-way between Ghardaïa and Laghouat, which was drilled in 1958/59 by a German company under contract to the S.N. Repal, and the field at Al Gassi, fifty miles south of Hassi Messaoud, where a strike was made in the summer of 1959 by the 'Société Nationale des Pétroles d'Aquitaine' (SNPA), have not yet been sufficiently exploited for their importance to be assessed. But the prospects of the Northern Sahara developing into an oil-zone of major importance to Western Europe have vastly improved. On the other hand there is a great deal of wishful thinking in the claim that the Sahara is another Texas, that, like Kuwait and Saudi Arabia, it is swimming in oil, and that its available supplies even overshadow the reserves in the Persian Gulf area (more than sixty per cent of the proved world supplies).

The total number of drillings made up to the beginning of 1960 (including so-called core-drillings) was about 400, with another 29 in preparation. In the United States 58,160 drillings were made in 1956 alone. Of the four great depressions with potential oil deposits—the Taoudenni basin, the Tindouf basin, the Sudan Niger basin south of the Adrar des Iforas and Aïr mountains, and the Northern Sahara basin between Hoggar and Atlas on the one hand and Tanezrouft and Tripolitania on the other—only the Northern one has so far been explored. Out of altogether half a million square miles of stratified rock which are of interest to the geologist, rather more than half has been lumped together in concessions (permis de recherche). Only one company with a concession in the Tindouf depression possesses drilling-rights outside the northern Sahara, although it has not yet started drilling.

Another point is worth bearing in mind if one is to have a fairly

accurate picture. It is conceivable that the oil-reserves at Hassi
Messaoud may turn out to be of the same order as those in the
Middle East. But there is one important difference which affects
the production costs: the oil-bearing rock at Hassi Messaoud (and
still more at Edjeleh) is much less porous. For every single well in
Saudi Arabia there are ten in the Sahara. There is, it is true, one
'miraculous well' at Hassi Messaoud which produces 1500 tons
of crude oil a day, but the average yield of the drillings is much
nearer to that of the weakest well which produces 50 tons a day.
The Saudi Arabians can be sure of obtaining 1,000 tons and often
more than 2,000 tons a day.

I asked Pierre Desforges if, in his view, this search for unlikely
comparisons might not arise from a—quite unjustified—inferiority
complex on the part of the French? Would he not at least admit
that it had added a few tragic pages to the blood-stained chronicle
of the Sahara?

On November 16, 1880, Colonel Flatters started off from Laghouat on his second expedition to the south. His orders were to
push forward to the Hoggar-Tuareg and reconnoitre a possible
route for the Trans-Saharan railway. One of the main arguments
in support of the railway was that the Americans eleven years
before had built a railway across their continent. France did not
want to lag behind the Yankees. And after what the explorer Henri
Duveyrier had said about the chivalrous behaviour of the veiled
men in the Hoggar massif, they could hardly be compared with the
scalp-hunters of North America.

Colonel Flatters' first expedition to the south had been short and
fruitless. He insisted on leading the second in order to make good
his previous setback. He was no lover of the Sahara. At fifty he had,
in fact, no real motive for embarking on such a dangerous venture.
He was a spiritless, pedantic man with many enemies, who openly
referred to him as a psychopath without any of the qualities necessary for such an enterprise. He was only able to muster half as
many men as he had taken on his first expedition, and they were
plagued by dark forebodings, 'as gloomy as the soldiers of the
Grand Army who took up their positions to die.' Under Flatters'
command were ten Frenchmen, engineers and officers, and eighty-

six natives amongst them Chaambas, sworn enemies of the Tuareg. This military expedition, which had a scientific objective, started off as a peaceful caravan. The Algerian riflemen left their uniforms at home and acted as drivers for the 280 camels. They were no more heavily armed than any normal Saharan caravan. Everything possible was to be done to avoid provoking the Tuareg, whose warlike deeds of valour had become legendary in the desert.

Blissfully confident, Flatters ignored reports that reached him of the hostile attitude of the Hoggar-Tuareg chief. In January 1881 the ominous, black mountains of the Hoggar loomed up ahead. At the end of January Flatters reported triumphantly back to Paris that the Tuareg appeared to be favourably disposed to the expedition (although, if it succeeded, it would ruin their caravan trade!). He also recorded that they had offered to supply him with guides and he was considering whether to return by way of the Niger or through the Ajjer-Tuareg territory. That was Flatters' last letter.

On March 28 a small group of men staggered into Ouargla, half mad with hunger and thirst, more dead than alive. These living skeletons were among the few survivors of the Flatters expedition. Flatters himself and some of his men had been drawn into an ambush and massacred. All the camels were seized.

Five Frenchmen and forty-eight natives escaped the slaughter, but only to become prisoners of the desert. For forty days they marched under appalling hardship. Their supplies ran out. The Tuareg gave the starving men poisoned dates which sent them mad, then they pretended that they were ready to sell a few sheep, but when emissaries were sent they were butchered. Eventually the exhausted band of men decided to fight. The Tuareg lost thirty dead and disappeared from the scene. Such of the expedition as had survived the skirmish continued their retreat. By now they were little more than beasts. The last Frenchman was cut to pieces by his subordinates, before he had succumbed to his wounds, and eaten. He himself had been living on human flesh for several days. And it was only cannibalism that enabled the last handful of natives to survive and return with the gruesome news. Not until much later was it realised that they were not the only survivors. A

Tuareg woman took pity on some of the wounded and instead of killing them as custom demanded, she sheltered them in her tent. There she nursed them back to health, despite the fury of the Targi who had led the attack on Flatters and had himself been severely wounded. These men were able to return home later by way of Tripoli. The admirable conduct of this Tuareg woman was to influence Charles de Foucauld later in his decision to settle as a hermit at Tamanrasset, but the immediate effect of the destruction of Flatters' expedition was to plunge the desert in a wave of horror that did not recede for ten years.

Such were the consequences of one unhappy comparison: between the Trans-Saharan Railway and the American Trans-continental.

One last question, Monsieur Desforges: 'Why did the search for oil in the Sahara only begin after the war?'

The answer I received did not entirely satisfy me, but it was as good as any I had received before: France had its own oil-processing industry, the biggest in Europe, but the chief source of power was coal. It was only after the war that oil acquired such tremendous importance both as a source of power and as a raw material that oil-consumption became a barometer of a country's economic development. But more than the demand was lacking; the technical resources available were inadequate for an assault on the Sahara: geophysical methods of prospecting were not yet sufficiently advanced, motor transport had not yet been designed for desert conditions, the Dakota, the air freighter and the helicopter still had to be adapted, and research into the climate was in its infancy. Most important of all, however, the desert had not yet revealed its hidden treasure. None of the nomads had ever reported the discovery of an asphalt deposit, no Meharist had drawn his corps commander's attention to a pool of tar, no explorer had noticed a mud volcano, an escape of gas or any other sign of oil. (It was only after oil had been drilled at Edjeleh that CREPS geologists discovered a few small oil-pools—so far the only ones in the Sahara.) Information about the geology of the Sahara was scant and sometimes even false. Most of the geologists believed that the Hoggar and the Eglab massif continued far to the north and concluded from this that the existence of oil-bearing rocks on a scale worth exploiting was highly unlikely. As late as 1949, when drilling had already started in the Sahara, Hallis D. Heldberg, chief geologist of Gulf Oil and a leading authority in his profession, described the rock-strata in the Sahara as 'of little interest.' Again in 1952 he dismissed the Sahara as 'of no real interest for future prospecting.' When the gas field of Berga was discovered in March 1954 he had to admit his miscalculation. Not unnaturally the misguided American prophet enjoys the same kind of dubious popularity amongst the oil-men today as Lord Salisbury.

In conversation with a geologist at Edjeleh I reproduced all the arguments I had heard to explain why the search for Sahara oil had begun so late.

'I can understand,' he replied, 'why you don't find these arguments altogether satisfactory. In almost every case you could produce a counter-argument. But whereas one reason alone would not be convincing, several taken together surely are. It was only after the war that the word "Sahara" came to mean something to a great many people. And incidentally you must rid yourself of any idea that for the oilman the desert as such has no kind of attraction. Here in Edjeleh it just hasn't been possible to underestimate the difficulties. When we first started working here—1,200 miles from Algiers by road and desert-track—we found ourselves in virgin territory, with no radio communications, irregular supplies, a hellish climate, and not another human being or a water-point within two hundred miles. And yet the desert isn't entirely the oil-prospector's enemy. It's also his friend. One of the main reasons why the Sahara had to produce its underground treasures as quickly as it did was air-photography. Wherever the rocks that particularly interest us are not overlaid by later strata, as, for example, here on the northern fringe of the Hoggar, a complete survey of the area by aerial photography is worth more than an army of geologists. The photographs are specially processed till the ground relief stands out crystal-clear. In 1952 50,000 square miles were photographed for CREPS within a week. Four months later the company had a complete set of photographic maps for the whole area. More than a third of it was immediately ruled out; in what was left geologists began to make detailed investigations. But the aerial photographs had already given indications that there might be oil at Edjeleh. Now vegetation would have made this photographic sorcery impossible. And there are other ways in which the desert helps the oil-man. Ask any geophysicist who has worked in the tropical jungle or in the swamps of Louisiana. There he would "shoot" at most a cross-section six to ten miles in length, but in the Sahara he can do ten, twenty times as much. In developing a field, too, the desert's more of a help than a hindrance. But it's always the same: everyone believes that his particular location is the toughest . . . How did we get started on this?'

'I asked why oil-prospecting had begun so late in the Sahara.'

'It's a fact one simply has to accept. Before the war the time wasn't yet ripe for Saharan oil. And if you want to prove it, you've only got to remember the men who said it was there. Nobody would listen to them.'

It was in Edjeleh that I first became aware of the voices in the wilderness, the forerunners of Saharan oil. And of one in particular: Conrad Kilian. It was no mere accident that the man who told me about Kilian looked not unlike a Russian emigré Count and bears in fact a Russian name. It seemed most appropriate that an exile who had put down fresh roots in the desert should know so much about a man who was born in the wrong part of the century and was regarded as a nuisance by his contemporaries.

A Chaambi was responsible for starting the rumour that Flatters, shortly before his death, had found the legendary treasure of the Garamanti. Forty years later an Algerian capitalist felt the urge to acquire the emeralds, which were reputed to be the size of pigeons' eggs, and he commissioned a former N.C.O. of the Saharan Troops to find them. For safety's sake he decided also to have a scientist and he asked Wilfrid Kilian, a well-known French geologist, to suggest someone. Kilian proposed his son. Conrad was twenty-three when he entered the Sahara. Within a matter of days he had fallen out with the leader of the expedition, who, he discovered, was less interested in finding the emeralds of the Garamanti than in fleecing his rich and credulous employer. They quarrelled and finally came to blows, and Kilian eventually parted

from his companion in the middle of the desert. For four months
he wandered about the Hoggar area on a camel. This handsome,
elegant young man was given a warm reception in the Tuareg
camps. A Tuareg woman saved his life with native medicine when
he went down with appendicitis. He was able to return the compli-
ment by performing a successful Caesarean operation with the
dissecting-tools which he carried with him for zoological investigations. From this romantic tour young Kilian returned with
enough data to revolutionise the accepted teaching on the geological formations of the Central Sahara (and so of a quarter of the
African Continent). On each specific point Kilian maintained precisely the opposite of what was generally accepted. Wilfrid Kilian,
who mistrusted his son's generalisations, arranged for one of his
colleagues to go to the Sahara and make a check. Kilian's findings
were completely vindicated. Today the geological terms he used
have become universal. To take only one example, he was the first
to see and name the 'Continental Intercalaire'.

It was also no accident that I first heard Kilian's name at Edjeleh.
In 1926 Kilian went to the eastern Sahara. His expedition lasted
three years and had already become something of a legend before
Kilian returned with a rich store of information on geology, botany,
zoology, palaeontology, geography and folklore. The powerful
Senussi sect had put a price on the head of the impudent Frenchman, but he calmly rode on his white camel, accompanied only by
a standard-bearer carrying the tricolore and the Kilian family
banner, into the forbidden city Ghat. The population treated him
like a Sultan. A delegation offered to make him ruler of the Fezzan
and promised him 8,000 soldiers if he would drive out the Italians.
Kilian resisted the temptation. He contented himself with a chain
of mountains, 250 miles long, between Ghat and Toummo, which
had been a no-man's-land since the Franco-Italian Treaty of
Fezzan in 1919 and of which he now took possession on behalf of
France. He called the mountains Monts Doumergue after the
President of the Republic. The French government, however,
never recognised the annexation and did not even reply to Kilian's
memoranda and white papers. The Quai d'Orsay was not risking
any unpleasant incidents on account of a very romantic geologist

who might be a genius but was undoubtedly a little mad. Undismayed, Kilian invested himself with the title of 'Sovereign Explorer' on the basis of one of the laws of the Ancien Régime which had never been repealed and which not only bestows this title on any Frenchman who explores unclaimed territory at his own cost and occupies it symbolically on behalf of the 'patrie,' but also elevates him to the rank of Ambassador.

During this three-year crusade in the desert, which consumed every centime his father had left him, Kilian is said to have realised the importance of the Fezzan and of the Edjeleh area as possible oil-fields.

The first strike at Edjeleh—and in the Sahara—on 6th January, 1956 was broadcast by radio and two days later the champagne arrived at drilling-station LD101. In June 1956 a second strike was made forty-five miles west of Edjeleh at Tiguentourine. In January 1958 came the discovery of the field at Zarzaïtine, twenty-five miles to the north; in May the field at El Adeb Larache, seventy-five miles south-west of Edjeleh; in November at Ouan Taredert, fifty miles south-west of Edjeleh; in December at Dôme à Collenias, sixty miles south of Edjeleh; and in August 1959 at Ouan Taredjeli, just north of Zarzaïtine. The last of these came just in time to give a boost to the large 'Edjeleh 1959' loan which the CREPS negotiated for the construction of the pipeline to the Mediterranean.

This brief survey includes only the more important discoveries. In fact, it is estimated today that in the Edjeleh oil-field—or, as the 'pétroliers' prefer to call it now, the Fort Polignac basin—there are more than a dozen separate oil-bearing strata. In the three best-known fields the productive layers lie between 1300 and 2600 feet (Edjeleh), between 1600 and 6000 feet (Tiguentourine), and between 1600 and 4500 feet (Zarzaïtine). At the beginning of 1960 the total reserves of these three fields were estimated at 125 million tons.

When a hairdresser in Algiers finds red dust in his client's hair, he draws the obvious conclusion:

'How are things at Maison Rouge?'

Maison Rouge is the provisional 'capital' of the Edjeleh oil-province, a somewhat unimaginative settlement of bungalows and huts in the most colourful surroundings. The wide valley, broken only by small, weirdly-shaped hills which look as if they might come alive, is a mixture of purple, violet and burgundy. On one side rises the sheer, grey, corroded sandstone of Zarzaïtine, while the other side is flanked by dunes which are combed afresh each day by the wind and are red in front, sunflower yellow behind. Beyond the dunes lies the Djebel Edjeleh, a black, deep-creviced sandstone massif which takes its name from the black beetle, the fearless denizen of the shifting sands. The only relieving feature of this melancholy mountain landscape is the occasional outcrop of yellow, green and blue soil.

The choice of Maison Rouge as a base was dictated not by the picturesque environment but by the hard, red soil on which the double-decker Bréguets can land at night as safely as on a concrete runway. And the thousand men who work today in the Edjeleh oil-province seldom even glance at their natural surroundings. For there is no more inhospitable place in the whole of the desert than Edjeleh. On an early winter morning the thermometer drops to fourteen below freezing, in summer it rises well over a hundred and twenty, with a ground temperature between a hundred and sixty and a hundred and seventy-five. The sand becomes so hot that the gazelles do not know where to put their tortured hooves and the camp-leader's alsatian has to wear sandals. The workers at Edjeleh drink twenty to twenty-five pints of liquid a day, the maximum the human body can absorb in twenty-four hours, and after six weeks in this inferno, their lips cracked, their mucous membranes dried up, their muscles aching and their eyes red and inflamed, they fly home to France to recover.

France can consider herself lucky that the Edjeleh oilfield actually lies in French territory. The 1919 Treaty with Italy had deliberately left the boundary undefined. France was anxious to give the Italians the impression that they were acquiring areas which she, in fact, was determined not to relinquish. At the time of the first oil-strike, Edjeleh, strictly according to this Macchiavellian treaty, belonged to Libya, but the Franco-Libyan frontier commission chose generously to interpret the spirit rather than the letter of the treaty. In 1956 the French, in accordance with the Treaty of Friendship of the previous year, had evacuated the Fezzan, so Tripoli responded by showing indulgence over the question of the frontier. The Commission designated as permanent frontier a camel-track which appeared on an old map but which had been completely obliterated by tyre-tracks. A third of the aerodrome at Maison Rouge was declared to be Libyan territory and the CREPS pays King Idriss a yearly rent of one Libyan pound. But, although the oil-derricks at Edjeleh and Zarzaïtine almost throw their shadows across the Libyan border, both oil-fields lie on the French side. Whether similar oil-deposits exist on the Libyan side still remains to be seen. The Esso-Standard Company which had already acquired a concession in Libya before the CREPS struck oil and which originally included Edjeleh in its prospecting-area, has been drilling sixty miles from Maison Rouge with, according to recent reports, considerable success. So far the oil deposits found in the Fezzan lag far behind those in the Libyan desert south of Sirte.

The oil at Edjeleh, which is a sulphur-free light petroleum of the highest quality, is still—four years after it was discovered—a blocked credit available only to the diesel engines used for drilling and to the CREPS trucks which use the crude oil as it comes out of the ground. But one Christmas tree after the other was set up. The Christmas tree is the contraption erected over a new well. When the tap is opened there is, first of all, a rush of gas then, after a dramatic pause, the gurgle of oil. The daily output of each drilling at Edjeleh is small, about thirty tons, so the Christmas trees stand very close together. On the other hand, the oil is fairly near the surface, which means that a well can be sunk in a matter of weeks at Edjeleh as against months at Hassi Messaoud.

By the beginning of 1960 nearly 200 Christmas trees had been erected in the Edjeleh oil-province, half a dozen of them producing only gas. They will increase in number rapidly in the next few years, for the 24-inch pipeline between Edjeleh and La Skhirra on the Gulf of Gabes, which comes into operation in 1960 and, with one pumping-station, carries 8 million tons, is intended to take 17 million tons by 1963. This will mean not only more pumping-stations but also the gradual linking-up of other oilfields with the pipeline. At In Amenas, where the pipeline ends, a new town is being built at break-neck speed. Three hundred miles of it run through Tunisia, a fact which causes the French considerable disquiet. In spite of vehement protests by the Algerian rebel government, Tunisia signed a transit agreement and has even decided that the substantial rental she receives more than compensates for the cooling-off of relations with the Algerian maquis and Cairo. But the French are under no illusions that President Bourguiba might go the way of other Arab leaders and be swept aside by a wave of ultra-nationalism. This would either close the side-door to Saharan oil or at least make the pipeline a trump-card in any policy of blackmail. So the long-term development of Edjeleh is also dependent on a lasting solution of the Algerian problem.

To return for a moment to Conrad Kilian: he did not live to experience the oil-fever in the Sahara. One day at the end of April 1950 he was found hanging from the crossbeam of the window in his hotel bedroom at Grenoble, spattered with blood. After a hurried enquiry a verdict of suicide was pronounced. The unfortunate man had first tried in vain to open an artery with splinters of glass.

Kilian had spent the last years of his life in extreme poverty. A third expedition to the Sahara during the war had ruined his health. He tried to convince the French government that it must at all costs continue to occupy the Fezzan after the war. He bombarded France's leading politicians with memoranda; in his self-styled role of 'Explorateur souverain' he called on them personally, but he was either ignored, spurned or disowned. Kilian, who was anything but a diplomat by temperament, resorted to insult and abuse. A solitary, embittered man, he developed all the symptoms of a persecution mania.

Did Kilian take his own life? His closest friends doubt it. They argue that a man who was so given to making theatrical gestures would hardly have met such a sordid end. And there are other apparent inconsistencies and suspicious features about his death. Was his suicide deliberately staged to conceal a murder? In their view Kilian was a victim of the oil-war that constantly rages behind the scenes. He knew that there was oil in the Fezzan. That is why he urged the French government not to relinquish the territory General Leclerc had conquered. And that, they claim, is why certain (Anglo-Saxon) obscurantists, in whose interest it was that the Fezzan should become part of an independent and therefore weak and anti-French Libya, saw to it that Kilian was removed. This fantastic theory is still quite widely held and openly ventilated in France. The Marquis de Chasseloup Laubat, Kilian's closest friend, propounded it loud and clear on 17 October 1958, before the Académie des Sciences d'Outre-Mer.

The French postal authorities propose to issue a special stamp bearing Kilian's portrait. The Garet el Djenoun, a kind of Brocken in the Hoggar, on which a tablet has been placed commemorating the Saharan pioneers, including Kilian, is to be renamed Mount Kilian on future maps of the Sahara and the first new town in the desert is to be called after him. His friends would like to go further and give Conrad Kilian the official title 'Father of Saharan Oil.' But less prejudiced observers would extend that honour to all the pioneer geologists who blazed the trail on camel-back which their successors are following today by jeep and helicopter.

*The desert is the Garden of Allah, from which
the Lord of the Faithful removed all superfluous human and animal life, so that
there might be one place where he can
walk in peace.*
ARAB SAYING

12. Boom in the Oases

WHEN one arrives at the Transatlantique at Ouargla, tired and
harassed, the first thing one does, having been given the tip by
friends, is to ask the black barman casually if Madame Beauvais,
the Directrice, is around. As an opening gambit it never works.
'You wish a room' he replies, both his expression and the tone of
his voice clearly suggesting that only a lunatic would look for hotel
accommodation.

The hotels in the Sahara, which were built for tourists between
the wars, some with every luxury including a swimming-bath, are
always full to capacity and booked up for months in advance. And
yet the tourist trade is not exactly encouraged. For a trip to the
Sahara one needs permits, visas, passport photographs and all
kinds of papers. 'We'll have to cut down your itinerary because of
transport difficulties,' I was told at the Saharan Ministry in Paris.
But the phrase 'transport difficulties' when applied to the French
Sahara, in which it is possible to thumb one's way from Laghouat
to Tamanrasset, means Algerian rebels. The 'tourists' who are at
present frequenting the Saharan hotels have not come for the good
of their health. At 4 a.m. the jeeps and Land-Rovers begin revving
up; in the evening the men who do business in the desert return,
dusty and grimy. 'Guests are urgently requested not to go from
the bar to the dining-room in their work clothes,' says one of the

notices displayed in the Transatlantique at Ghardaïa. But everyone seemed to ignore it. The dining-room was full of open-necked shirts, shorts and khaki.

Complet—full up: to those familiar with the Sahara there is an obvious alternative, to pay a girl in the 'quartier réservé' to move in with a friend for the night. But this too is a thing of the past. Fatima, the spoilt child of the Sahara's economic miracle, has no unemployed friend who will take her in. Full employment has even spread to the girls in the Sahara.

It is hardly surprising that at El Golea, in place of the Dal Piaz, a palatial hotel has been planned with sixty rooms, each with air-conditioning, bath, W.C. and telephone. The telephone, however, is connected only with the porter's lodge which is invariably empty during the day. 'It's not easy to find a day-porter,' I heard a harassed Saharan hotelier complain. 'They all want to be night porters, for it's at night that the guests usually leave and pay. In the industrialised Sahara the best tips are given in the small hours.'

Living accommodation is also scarce in the oases, particularly at Ouargla, ante-chamber to the largest oilfield in the Sahara. I spoke to a native workman who had spent six months at Hassi Messaoud. During that time he had saved 160,000 francs. Unlike the majority of his fellow-workers he did not spend it on brightly-coloured clothes, sun glasses, revolving pencils, cigarette-lighters, an off-the-peg suit and cheap jewellery; he had invested it in two small houses. Today he is the proud occupant of one and lives on the rent of the other.

The face of the Sahara has changed. At no time was this brought home to me more vividly than at the Feast of Sidi Mohammed. Each time the tambourines fell silent so that burning palm-leaves could be applied to tighten the hide, the clatter of petrol-tins grew louder as the native drummers hammered out the rhythm. I asked the marabout, who was cowering sadly at the foot of his predecessor's tomb some distance away from the singing and dancing, about the change that had come over El Golea and other oases. He pointed sourly at the faded jeans and drainpipe trousers of a group of Moslem youths, who were tucking into a wooden bowl full of couscous. The latest fashion in trousers was obviously like a thorn

in the holy man's flesh, but he had already resigned himself to the
petrol-cans and the ultra modern electric torches which blinked at
us from the mêlée of dancers.

He had nothing to say about the growing bread and meat consumption. The people of El Golea have three times as much bread
to eat today as five years ago. At Ouargla the bleating of sheep and
the screaming of camels have become part of the night-scene. The
meat-consumption, a reliable barometer of the living-standard, is
rising and rising. The old slaughter-house has become too small, a
new one will be built as soon as the necessary permits come
through from the north. Until then, with the tacit approval of the
authorities, a 'black' slaughter-house meets the demand.

In the oases a veritable jungle of notices has sprung up: Parking
forbidden, One way Street, No Cyclists. For the youngsters in
their drainpipe trousers have become fanatical cyclists. These
'Teddy boys' who race through the narrow lanes in packs are not
exactly popular. The shopkeeper in his two-weeks-old Citroën-
2CV-Sahara loses his new-found dignity and curses like any camel
driver. The foreign legionary in his armoured jeep swerves with an
oath. The pétrolier, who is taking his boss from Paris for a drive
through the oasis in the Land-Rover, jams on his brakes but not
without a sidelong glance of proud satisfaction at his visitors, as
much as to say: 'This is all our doing!' The 'routier' or long-
distance driver who skitters across the desert with his trailer, en-
throned in his driver's cabin like the captain of some ocean-liner,
blows his fog-horn. The dromedary chewing in the corner of the
market place, alone and unnoticed, curls his upper lip in scorn. As
for the pedestrian, there is no more room for him in the Sahara.

All this is no exaggeration. The authorities in the growing town
of Ghardaïa, who recently felt impelled to name their streets
(rue Laperrine, rue Charles de Foucauld etc.) are now thinking of
introducing traffic lights; the noise on its arterial road is already
intolerable; when I was there I counted 127 traffic signs. And they
have also spread to the desert. Tarred roads are creeping southwards. The blue-black ribbon that is unrolling under the steam-
rollers, shovels, excavators and tar-mixers becomes half-a-mile
longer every day. Each half-mile of Saharan highway consumes

some 65,000 gallons of water and, depending on the terrain, anything from thirteen to twenty million francs. The budget of the Joint Organisation for Saharan territories (OCRS) provided for an expenditure of twenty-six milliard francs on roads and highways in the years 1958/1960. As a rule it is water, not money, that is hard to find. The stretch of road from In Salah to Tamanrasset, which is due to be completed some time in the next year or two, is already a nightmare to the road builders because of the lack of water in the Hoggar.

Until recently the Sahara had to make do with tracks, not unlike country cart-tracks: a network of tyre-marks to which each driver tries, whenever possible, to add his contribution, for it is usually easier and more comfortable to keep to the side of the track. Only where the road dips into a wadi, where the track crosses shifting sand or a spur of rock, do drivers stick to the beaten track, though never without a certain sense of uneasiness, for the same ground that was firm yesterday may have been undermined by a sandstorm, a cloudburst or simply by wear and tear of heavy vehicles.

For the transport companies these tracks are a constant headache. The potholes take their toll of even the most robust vehicles. Before the Oil Road was built, a twenty-tonner lost a complete set of expensive tyres on one trip from Algiers to Edjeleh and back. Apart from this there is the damage done to freight by the constant shaking and by the vicious climate. Contractors reckon that transport costs on the ordinary desert-tracks are more than twice as much as on made-up roads. As well over 50,000 tons of freight are carried each year on any one stretch, the cost of building roads is obviously justified.

But there are technical as well as economic reasons why road-building in the Sahara has received top priority. To give only one illustration, the amount of freight carried between El Golea and In Salah jumped from 3,500 tons in 1951 to 25,000 tons in 1955. Naturally these figures represent an increase in the number of vehicles but more important has been the steady increase in their carrying capacity. The search for oil immediately raised the volume of road traffic; with the development of the oil-field at Hassi Messaoud, the track linking it with Ouargla was so ravaged by the

monsters of the road that ordinary five- and ten-ton vehicles could
no longer use it.

Today one can travel through the Sahara without having to dig
the truck out of the sand. The desert unwinds itself on either side
as smoothly as a film, fascinatingly unreal. The Oil Road runs
from Biskra past the Rhir oases through Touggourt, Ouargla and
Hassi Messaoud to Fort Lallemand on the edge of the Great
Eastern Erg. Another road runs from Laghouat through the
swampy country of the Dayas to Ghardaïa and from the Mzab
capital through the foothills of the rocky Chebka plateau to El
Golea. Should one suddenly feel the urge 'to go into the oil,' there
is an excellent road from Ghardaïa to Ouargla, and on the way
back north one can branch off to El Oued in the Souf country.
Colomb Bechar in the west of the Algerian Sahara is equally
accessible from Ain Sefra.

This network of roads is by no means complete. The Oil Road
from Fort Lallemand to Edjeleh is being built, and work has
started on the important connecting-road from Berriane, north of
Ghardaïa, through Guerrara to Touggourt. Plans are also under
discussion for an extension of the central trunk-road beyond El
Golea to In Salah and later presumably to Tamanrasset (unless it
is linked up with the Oil Road by way of Amguid and Fort
Flatters). A direct connection between Colomb Bechar and Laghouat is also under consideration. Apart from that, the Roads
Department of the OCRS is awaiting fresh instructions from the
Great God Oil. Every year a special team of surveyors puts a
thousand miles of road on the stocks. As soon as a new oilfield is
discovered, the 'seven dwarfs' of the 'Ponts et Chaussées' are
ready to roll out the carpet for the high priests of the All-powerful.

One of the leading figures in Saharan transport is Wolfram
Heimke, an engineer, who was taken prisoner when Rommel's
Africa Corps retreated. After his release from P.O.W. camp he
worked his way up to a senior position in the 'Union Industrielle
Africaine.' For him the Sahara is a technical challenge. His firm
sells the American Kenworth trucks which were originally designed for Saudi Arabia.

The French motor-manufacturers have naturally resisted the

American invasion of the Sahara. A desperate struggle has developed between French firms on the one hand and between them and their foreign competitors on the other. The result has been bigger and bigger vehicles. The T-100 is more than four yards wide and fourteen yards long; with 600 h.p. it ploughs through the sand on six special tyres (diameter: $2\frac{1}{2}$ yards). The driver's cabin is air-conditioned and has a radio-transmitter. The T-100 has a total weight of between 80 and 120 tons, depending on whether it is an ordinary commercial vehicle or an articulated lorry. Each of the four vehicles at present in service is a prototype specially designed for the desert. One of these monsters with its six-wheel drive can transport a heavy pump or a complete drilling-rig without any need to build expensive roads.

I met Heimke in a Kenworth in the sand-dunes south of Ouargla, where a group of motor engineers were testing the climbing-performance and tractive-power of their road-giants on different kinds of terrain. With a few nomads and camels looking on, one might almost have been at a motor-rally. The men who stood watching these prehistoric monsters straining at the chains that held them stationary while a dynamometer measured the energy they were expending, those men were as keen as a bunch of model-boat enthusiasts.

The engineers and technicians from the 'Ponts et Chaussées', on the other hand, looked anything but enthusiastic as they tested the wear and tear of these giants on a section of the road between Ouargla and Hassi Messaoud. The motor manufacturers try their best to allay the road-builders' fears of producing wider and wider tyres. The specific surface-pressure of a T-100 is no greater than that of a camel's foot. But the drivers too have their fears. 'One of these days,' grumbled one long-distance driver, 'they'll stop us using the roads altogether. . . .'

But that is perhaps the least of his worries. The 'routiers' live in pairs for weeks at a stretch in the glass cabin of their vehicle. From time to time the rebels set an ambush, the European falls riddled with bullets, the truck blazes like a huge torch, and the Mohammedan 'graisseur' who has made his escape returns to base with yet another story to add to the general sense of insecurity. Then there is the Fech-Fech, powdery sand which has putrefied under a treacherous, hard crust. Hamida, who had been too smart for the fellagha on more than one occasion and who drove his GBO across the desert as effortlessly as other people drive along the Route Nationale, was eventually trapped by the fech-fech. He had parked his lorry and as usual, fallen asleep under it. During the night the lorry sank slowly, crushing Hamida and his mate beneath it. Another of the 'routier's' bitter enemies is scurvy. Unlike the 'pétrolier' who receives ample supplies of fresh vegetables, meat and fruit by air, he lives out of tins.

The 'routier' has little time for high-sounding phrases like 'Patriotism' or 'opening up the desert.' The sound that appeals to him most, the sound that helps to soothe the nagging fear, is the rustle of banknotes. His much-vaunted sense of comradeship has accordingly its limits. It is one of the unwritten laws that, if you are in a jam, you must not ask more of a colleague than you would be prepared to do for him. The routier's motto is 'every man for himself.' An ingenious system of bonuses keeps him constantly on the move. Time is money. If, for example, he does the journey from Algiers to Edjeleh and back, a distance of 2,500 miles, in eighteen days, he receives a bonus equivalent to eighty-five per cent of his basic wage. As a rule the journey takes three weeks. Even then he earns a sixty per cent bonus, which is, however, not payable after twenty-four days. With allowances, expenses, profit-sharing, tips, and so on a routier can usually treble his monthly earnings.

The exploitation of the desert has made freight-transport a major industry. A twenty-tonner pays for itself with three trips from Algiers to Hassi Messaoud and back. With luck a contractor can reckon to do this within a month. But the time is past when four wheels and an old motor could chug their way across the sand. The competition is fierce. The giants are agreed only on one thing, to keep competition within bounds and not to allow the little man to take any of the pickings. The Yellow Map, which the routiers speak of with as much reverence as if it was Holy Writ, lays down the freight quotas, decides who is entitled to claim how big a slice of the cake. The right to ply a lorry in the Sahara is worth much more today than the lorry itself.

The desert has been mechanised at the expense of the camel. A modest five-ton lorry, which covers a hundred and ten miles between sunrise and sunset, is equivalent to two hundred and fifty camels, a Berliets Super-truck to five thousand. A further handicap under which the camel labours is that the two hundred and sixty pounds it normally carries must be carefully distributed on its hump, otherwise it staggers. This does not mean, however, that the camel has been pushed right out of business. Every year large salt-caravans with thousands of camels, the Azalaïs, still leave Taoudenni and Amadror with blocks of rock salt and Bilma with common salt for the ports on the southern border of the desert, for the Sudan, the Niger and Chad countries. And the camel is still the vehicle used by the nomads to collect their supplies. It is thanks to the camel, in fact, that the Saharan nomads are not nearly so frugal in their way of life as they are alleged to be. The nomads of Mauretania, who 'do their shopping' in Morocco or still more in the Sudan and Senegal, buy from forty to fifty thousand tons of millet, four to five thousand tons of sugar, eight hundred tons of tea and six to eight thousand tons of cloth every year. Even the industrialised desert has not entirely dispensed with the camel's services. It carries petrol to outlying airstrips and petrol-dumps. After all, tanker-aircraft consume half as much fuel as they can carry and even road tankers have a thirst that makes them uneconomic. Mournfully the camel allows himself to be made a fool of, as he digs his own grave. A wave of unemployment is engulfing the 300,000 camels in the Sahara and herding them into the slaughter-houses. In the oil-booming Sahara Allah's decree that the camel should be man's brother is much less relevant than a saying once current in the French Army in Africa: 'Camel meat is just as good and just as healthy as beef, but cheaper.'

* * *

The old Saharans are sulking. Who are they? There is the Commandant, who for twenty long years dreamt of the spring-floods and the bracing air of Brittany, only to find when he retired from the army that he could not leave the desert. There is the German ex-legionary who spent his indemnity on a small bar

where he always serves up the same tough cutlets and stale jokes.
There is the First Lieutenant from the Camel Corps who refuses
to talk to anyone who has done less than six thousand miles of
meharée through the desert. There is the doctor who learned from
the natives that the flesh of the desert lizard will cure a horned-
viper's bite. There is the mystic who sought God in the desert, the
fool who tried to find the emeralds of the Garamanti, and the sage
who took refuge in the eternal stillness.

In Saharan sandals and baggy trousers they sit over their glasses
of Saharan milk, aniseed, and air their grievances. They complain
bitterly of the heavy trucks that thunder past, of the whisky-
drinking pétroliers, of their boots, shorts and boy-scout hats, of the
driller's tin helmet and the tiny souvenir flask of oil from Hassi
Messaoud among the caps and the blue and white kepis, which
hang like votive offerings on the wall behind the bar.

Above all, they are furious with themselves. They have realised
too late that they were had. The geologist whom they helped because, like them, he slept in the open, because, like them, he drank
the brackish water from the goatskin guerba, because, like them, he
rode through the desert on a white camel—the geologist was not,
after all, one of them. He was an accomplice of the driller with the
high boots, rubber gloves and gleaming helmet.

Sometimes the fury bursts into rhyme; Jean Le Muletier published a six-verse poem in the Saharan house-magazine, 'Bulletin
de Liaison Saharienne.' It was called 'Colère d'un vieux Saharien':
'Go to the devil, old Sahara. Your camels will perish, your son will
be air-conditioned, and in the valley of the dunes salad is sprouting. . . .'

The Saharans are offended. But there is more to it than that.
They know the desert better than those who have wakened it from
its long sleep merely to knock it out again. The boom arouses in
them something more than the hurt of a lover whose beloved has
run off with the first good capitalist to appear. It also stirs in them
a paternal sense of responsibility.

'The natives, encouraged by the oil-prospectors and other
treasure-hunters, are about to saw off the limb they're sitting on.'
The remark was made by a lean-jawed officer who was born

twenty years too late. He sounded both nettled and worried. 'I don't like exhaust fumes in Allah's garden. I'm behind the times, I know, but it's not just sentimentalism that makes me and many others wince when we hear the phrase "Industrialisation of the Sahara." The last few years have plunged the Sahara oases into a crisis they will probably never recover from. The engineers and the technicians think that they have the desert beaten, that they've been too clever for it. That's not true. They've built a few air-conditioned villages which are only kept going thanks to air transport. At the same time, they've undermined and ruined the only source of livelihood the desert people have: dates. The oilmen have won a pyrrhic victory.'

In fact, of course, the crisis of the oases is an old one. It began with the emancipation of the slaves. The black slaves became tenant-farmers or Khammes. The word means in Arabic 'the fifth part.' The Khamme receives from the landowner in principle a fifth of the produce in exchange for his labour. The method of sharing out varies from one oasis to another and depends very largely on the irrigation. At Beni Abbès, for example, where there is spring water, the share-cropper keeps a third of the dates and the grain and half the fruit. At El Golea with its artesian wells the Khammes can claim one bunch of fruit per tree together with half the vegetables and grain. In the Souf the landowners cultivate their own dates, but they are exceptional. Most of the palm-groves do not belong to the peasants. The white proprietors and main beneficiaries live either as nomads a long way off or as rentiers in the Ksar.

In the slave period the landowner performed an important function: he was a banker and he controlled all the means of production, the soil, water and labour. In 1899 a male slave, depending on his age, was worth from 150 to 200 gold francs. The price the entrepreneur had to pay for labour was correspondingly low: it was equivalent to 'amortisation' and the upkeep of the slave and his family. With the abolition of slavery the cost of labour rose sharply. But the returns from date-growing were small and the means of the landowner limited. Many jobs remained undone, the yield dropped, money became even scarcer . . . and so on. Today the landowner is not even in a position to play the part which his legal rights require him to play: the capitalist. He is merely a parasite, a burden on the economy of the oases.

Date-growing is not good business. It is little more than a form of insurance against death by starvation and in years of bad harvest it is not even that. In the French Sahara there are nine million palms, seven of them in Southern Algeria. Compare this with the date-plantations at Basra in Irak which alone have ten million trees. The average yield of a date palm in the French Sahara is 55 lb. In the Souf each date-grower has on an average twenty trees, at Biskra a hundred and twenty, at Ouargla four hundred but half of them bear no fruit. In other parts of the Sahara as many as half a dozen owners have a share in one single tree.

The share-cropper who must be content with a fifth of the crop clearly has too little to live on and too much to die on. Freed from slavery he remained a prisoner of the oasis. To try to escape on foot was certain death, and it is much easier to buy a car in Europe by instalments than it is to hire a camel from the Saharan nomads cash down. Not until the motor-truck invaded the desert was escape possible. Growing numbers of blacks migrated north-wards, to Algeria, Tunisia and France, looking for work. They fled from a poverty-stricken agriculture and by fleeing made it poorer still.

The oases were also subjected to another form of pressure. In 1934 Tindouf was occupied and with it the last of the warring nomads were subdued. Their morale very soon suffered. With the previous ban on the slave-trade the French had taken away their most lucrative line of business; now the caravan-trade, on which they depended, was slowly being squeezed out by motor-transport. More and more nomads fled the open desert and gathered, as if flung there by some centrifugal force, on its northern fringes or clung like drowning men to the oases. But, having become sedent-ary, they did not take to working in the palm-groves which, in fact, partly belonged to them. Capot-Rey reports that several members of the Chaamba tribe became 'gentlemen farmers' at El Golea, but most of the former desert pirates were quite content to find com-pensation for their humiliation in an even greater contempt for the date-farmer. They agreed with the Tuareg: 'The hoe brings shame on the house.'

While the population of the oases increased as a result of the influx of nomads and the successful fight against epidemics and child mortality, the flight of tenant-farmers reduced the supply of home-grown foodstuffs. In 1930 the Algerian Sahara produced 900 lb. of dates per head of population; in 1950 it was barely a quarter of that amount. The fact that the natives lived on this bare subsistence-level for so many years without rebelling is due, on the one hand, to their primitive mode of living, on the other to the solidarity of the tribal structure, their form of welfare state. In a society of egoists many would have starved to death. Yet their group solidarity and their altruism also explain their complete lack of economic dynamism.

I heard a marabout quote an old desert saying: 'Kill a ewe and you kill a bee, kill a bee and you kill a palm, kill a palm and you kill seventy prophets.' In the last few years thousands of prophets have been liquidated. Their murderers have perfectly clear consciences and are moderately prosperous.

If France can be reproached with anything at all, it is that she did too little to adapt the conditions she found in the Sahara to twentieth century requirements. She contented herself with castrating a traditional social order which was felt to be unjust. The administrators succeeded in breaking down the iron law of the desert that war, hunger and pestilence can be relied upon to keep the balance between population and natural resources. But not enough was done to make the lives of those who had been saved from death worth living. The nomads were prevented from waging war and trading in slaves but they were also allowed to degenerate into 'living fossils.' The slave became a wage-earner but was not paid a living wage.

It would be unfair, however, to blame the French altogether. The fact that the steps they took were not forceful enough was due not to too little but to too much love. The Saharans who for decades had the desert to themselves were torn between two conflicting emotions. On the one hand there was the desire to give the natives a decent, European-style standard of living, which would include better hygiene, better irrigation and better agriculture. But there was another school of thought which saw in the rocky, sandy wastes the ideal breeding-ground for self-discipline, endurance and courage. The exponents of this doctrine lived with the nomads, sided with them against the administrators, tried to be poor, proud and dignified like them, cultivated their sense of honour and colour. No one would deny that a troop of the white-clothed, red-girdled Camel Corps make a splendid picture on a ridge of yellow dunes, but they have no future.

The Saharans were confident that the development of the desert would come gradually. Although they themselves, in pacifying the desert, had started a revolution, they went on talking of an evolution. Even without the oilmen they would have run into serious difficulties. The pétroliers are merely carrying out a sentence which was passed long before. They have merely brought the date of execution forward. For them the desert is no longer 'art for art's sake' but a capital investment, which has to pay its way. If they borrow from the vocabulary of their predecessors such phrases as 'the mystique of the Sahara' and 'the call of the desert', then only because they want to interest the French public in a new loan. The Sahara, which in the days of the blue kepi with the gold crescent and star was a testing-ground for all the masculine virtues, is now a testing-ground for guided missiles and atom-bombs. And out of this desert the Meharist is slinking away like 'a walking shadow, a poor player, that struts and frets his hour upon the stage, and then is heard no more.'

What can be done to stay the crisis?

In Tamanrasset they reintroduced slavery—a modern form of it with identity cards, stamps and duties, but no different from the old. Captain Bret, who rules the Hoggar district and who is known ironically amongst the people as 'the little king,' looked very sour when I called a spade a spade. He rolled his cigarette nervously from side to side of his pink mouth as he explained: Anyone who wants to work for the diamond, platinum and uranium-prospectors or for any organisation concerned with developing the desert is obliged to get permission. Those who need it most are not given it. The wretched share-croppers and slaves, who with rumbling stomachs cultivate the small grain-oases of the Hoggar for the benefit of the Tuareg and for whom a wage-packet of 500, 600, and 700 and more francs a day has a very special appeal, are excluded from the boom. Anyone who leaves his job without permission is fetched back by the police. Le Capitaine's justification for this grave interference with the liberty of the individual was that the gardens had to be protected, otherwise their fate would be sealed. And he added with such a consciously casual air that I took this to be his main reason: 'Besides, we have certain obligations towards the Amenokal.' It is, of course, vitally important to the Amenokal or Supreme Chief of the Hoggar-Tuareg that the slaves and share-croppers who feed him and his idle subjects should not desert. France's accommodating gesture will probably make him a little less receptive to Cairo's warnings and the seductive words of the 'Front de Libération' which even penetrate into the mountain fastness of the Hoggar.

It is clear that measures of this kind conceal the disease for a time but can never cure it. And by agreeing to adopt a 'guided' policy of employment, the companies which are changing the face of the Sahara cannot do more than check the flood. Whether they compete for one another's labour or not, at sundown the oil-derricks still throw long shadows across the desert.

So the question still remains: What can be done to alleviate or possibly to avert the crisis?

One solution would be to improve and expand what is already there: more water-points to protect the nomads' sheep-herds from the appalling havoc of drought, dugouts as shelter from the cold in the hibernation areas, instruction in livestock breeding to increase the yields. The nomads suffer heavy losses at present through having to drive their herds to the north to be slaughtered: forced marches, days spent in railway-trucks and even in ships (bound for France) take a heavy toll both of the quantity and the quality of meat delivered. The construction of slaughter-houses with modern equipment within easy reach of the grazing-areas and the introduction of a special air-service to transport the meat would encourage the nomads, who have suffered particularly severely from recent droughts. Measures of this kind would naturally mean swimming against the current without any possibility of quick results.

Spectacular experiments are at present few and far between. The experts have realised that an extensive programme which comprises a great many small adjustments and improvements is a better way of dealing with the emergency than a small programme with a few ambitious showpieces. The SAS officers and the Water Board officials, who are trying in this way to give the natives fresh confidence in the agricultural potentialities of the oases, are pitting themselves against the desert. At present they are achieving comparatively little. But their hour will come as soon as the desert fever has passed.

A second solution that is frequently suggested is the ruthless conversion of the oases into suburbs of the industrial Sahara. The exponents of this policy envisage the erection of multiple garages, palatial hotels, workshops, administrative buildings, food depots, transport companies, and even banks. They point to oases which have already been used as staging-points in the search for oil. But they also refer back to the past, when, in fact, the oases were less important as producers of food than as markets and meeting-places for the desert nomads.

I have met men who accept neither of these two solutions, who refuse to speak of a crisis in the oases at all. For them there is only a human crisis, the crisis of men who live in the desert. The impact of capitalism on the barter-economy of the Sahara was like the breaching of a dam and the unleashing of an irresistible flood. The most one can hope to do is throw the victims something to cling to. Or teach them to swim. The men engaged in this rescue operation are a small minority, and they do not have the enormous resources at their disposal which those behind the economic miracle can call upon. But their enthusiasm and their human effort are out of all proportion to their budget. They are the men who are really battling with the desert.

13. Schools for Nomads

THE teacher's living quarters are next to the school. Should he ever wake up during the night and wonder if the school is still there, he does not even have to get out of bed. All he need do is stretch out his hand and feel for it. The schoolhouse and the teacher's lodgings consist of a few posts driven into the sand and covered by a blue awning. And the furniture is equally primitive: a table, a chair and a camp bed with an air mattress in the teacher's tent, a mat for sitting on and a blackboard in the school tent. The whole thing is called the Koudia nomad school and is situated in the grotesquely-shaped mountains of the Hoggar.

I clambered on to a large rock immediately behind the two tents and gazed across a tongue of sand in the midst of black granite boulders. At the lowest point of the depression a small wadi snaked away between the rocks. Beyond it seven orange-coloured Tuareg tents stood out against the sand and the rocks, sprawling hide tents about four feet high, each one with a forecourt surrounded by a mat fence. In the forecourt of the main tent I could see Claude Blanguernon, the 'schoolmaster of the Sahara', sitting cross-legged with six heavily-veiled Tuareg men round him. He was busy concocting a letter for one of them to send to some Ministry in Paris. The greatest care had to be taken to find the correct French equivalent for each Tamahaq word. I had seen Blanguernon at work before and knew exactly what was happening. He was giving these men a lesson without their realising it. For Claude Blanguernon, founder and director of the nomad schools, is a born teacher. Not that he looks the part. He wears nails, desert sandals which consist almost entirely of soles to protect the feet against the hot sand, baggy trousers and a boubou, a sleeveless shirt which is slit up the sides as far as the armpits.

Immediately below me I could see Pierre Dumez, the official inspector, listening to two of the pupils who were sitting beside him on a mat in front of the tent, while their teacher, Marcel Antoine, stood anxiously by. It was an extremely picturesque scene. From where I stood the two Tuareg boys looked like two bundles of indigo-blue cloth, from which two pairs of brown feet and two tufts of blue-black hair peeped out. Abdallah, a cheeky, intelligent boy of eleven, had his wispy, dishevelled hair plastered down on his forehead with goat's butter. Sliman on the other hand, who at fifteen was almost old enough to wear a man's veil, wore his hair plaited in a great many short ringlets, a Tuareg style that looks all the more unusual as the front part of the scalp is shaved. Dumez in his creased trousers and smart pullover looked as if he had stepped out of a tailor's catalogue.

A great deal has been written about the veiled men of the Sahara, so I shall confine myself to a few essential facts.

The Hoggar-Tuareg, who today number some 5,500 souls, form—as do the Ajjer-Tuareg and other groups of the same people —a tribal confederation in which not all the member-tribes are on an equal footing. The Imouhar are the élite, the aristocrats, while the Imrad are tributary vassals. How this hierarchy developed is not precisely known. It may correspond to two waves of immigrants, the second of which subdued the first. The king of the confederation, the Amenokal, to whom all the land belongs, comes from the Imouhar tribe, although the Imrad chiefs also have a say in his election. On the bottom rung of the social ladder are the Iklan, the slaves, the descendants of negroes from the Sudan. The women cook, sew, wash and carry water; the men look after the animals. The Iklan also work, together with the Haratin, in the small grain-growing oases. The black Iklan, who number about 1800, must not be confused with the Haratin who, at least theoretically, are free. The Iklan and their descendants are the property of the master, who is obliged to clothe and feed them and give them lodging. A slave who is dissatisfied with the way his master is treating him can ask to be transferred. If his master, not surprisingly, takes an unfavourable view of the request, the slave has yet another remedy: he simply cuts an ear off a goat belonging to the master of his choice and by Tuareg law the injured party can claim him body and soul. The fourth caste, that of the Enaden, has no definite position in the Tuareg social scale. As craftsmen they are both respected and ostracised.

The particular tribe from which the Amenokal has been chosen for many decades past is the Kel Rela, and the most important Imrad tribe, tributary of the Kel Rela, is the Dag Rali. Dangouchi, the leader of the camp I visited, was also the Amrar or Supreme Chief of the Dag Rali. At the court of the nomad ruler Dangouchi's word carries a great deal of weight, more than that of all the other chiefs put together. The reason is quite simple: the 'pacification' of the desert. The Imouhar were a caste of warriors. Imouhar means: men of the ruling race. It is also related to the word 'plunder.' The right to plunder was regarded amongst the Tuareg tribes as a privilege of high birth. The Imouhar lived by raiding. They would lie in wait for caravans passing through their territory and either impose a levy or rob the merchants. They attacked oases which refused to pay their taxes and defended the Imrad and the Iklan against enemy attacks. The Imrad supplied them with remounts, bred camels, assembled a few caravans and kept goats and sheep. When occasion demanded it, they would also take up arms and fight by the side of the noble Imouhar.

Like the medieval knights, the Tuareg were unable to hold out against firearms. The French reduced the Imouhar in particular to a state of impotence. They forbade slave-trading, stopped the feuds between hostile tribes and brought security to the caravans. The Imrad, on the other hand, who had organised caravans, profited by the pacification of the desert and became more prosperous.

Dangouchi's tribe is almost four hundred strong; each of its members has a slave from the Iklan. The tribe's main source of wealth is 1,200 goats and 1,000 camels. The yearly tribute which the Dag Rali pay to the Amenokal is about twelve sacks of dates, eight leather bottles full of buttermilk, a dozen sheep for milking and ten goats for slaughtering. Families with caravans of their own engaged in the salt and date trade pay a special premium.

From the very beginning the French approached the Tuareg

problem from two different angles. As the 'protecting' power they dealt with the bandits amongst them by putting them out of business. Some joined the Camel Corps. Apart from that, however, the 'Protector' made no attempt to give the Imouhar a fresh means of livelihood. On the contrary, the French were not insensitive to the romantic legend of the veiled cavaliers of the desert and gave them the sort of protection accorded to an ancient monument. The Hoggar was turned into a kind of nature reserve and zoological garden, whose specimens were a source of wonderment to the occasional anthropologist or privileged visitor. Indeed, no great importance was attached to the emancipation of the slaves, which was a mere formality.

The nomad school was intended as a rescue operation. Claude Blanguernon, who was a school teacher in Constantine, learned of the slow decline of the Tuareg. Having won the government over to his plan, he opened a school at Tamanrasset in 1947. But the only pupils to appear were children of the Haratin, the black oasis-peasants. Not a single Tuareg child showed up, not even the sons of slaves. Blanguernon did not give up. As the pupils would not come to school, the school would have to go to the pupils. One Targi declared in the somewhat braggart language the veiled men are fond of using: 'I would rather strangle my sons with my own hands than send them to your school.' The Amenokal said bluntly: 'My son will never go to school.' Blanguernon, however, explained to him in his native Tamahaq just what advantages a nomad school could offer and the Amenokal gave in. But he was not prepared to take the decision alone; Blanguernon would have to plead his cause with all the Tuareg leaders, then there would be a general show of hands.

Blanguernon's method was both simple and effective. In each camp he called the men together and put three questions to them. Firstly: 'A camel is worth twenty thousand francs. How much are two camels worth?' The Tuareg had no difficulty in answering. Secondly: 'How much are four camels worth?' This time the reply came after a few minutes' thought. Thirdly: 'How much are a hundred camels worth?' As soon as Blanguernon had put this question, he wrote the answer on a slate and laid it face down on the sand. When the men returned after an hour of intensive calculation with the result, Blanguernon lifted the slate and showed them that he had arrived at the same result in a matter of seconds. Impressed by this magic, the Tuareg agreed to support nomad schools.

The position of Tuareg women is unique in the Islamic world. The Targia, unlike her menfolk, does not wear a veil. She will not tolerate another woman in the house; the Tuareg are all, without exception, monogamous. If a Targia thinks she has been badly treated, she can demand a divorce. She marries comparatively late, often not before she is twenty-five. Before marriage she leads a completely free life and seems to enjoy it. At the so-called Ahal or Court of Love, which is held on moonlight nights in some fairly secluded spot, young men and women, widows and widowers make music and recite poetry. These occasions have been compared to the courtly ceremonies of the Minnesänger but the Ahal appears to be much less platonic; not without reason Pater de Foucauld maintained that there was no word in the Tamahaq language for virginity. The Targia is the guardian of tradition; she knows the Tifinagh script and keeps the legends, myths and battle songs alive which fell into disuse with the longswords; she plays the Amzad, a fiddle with a hollowed-out gourd covered with goat's hide as a resonance-chamber and one string made of horse's hair. The Targia is expert in the use of herbal medicines and nature cures. During the long months when her husband is away she is in sole charge of the tent and commands great respect. Her prestige rests on the right of succession, for the Targi succession is not through the father but through the mother. When the Amenokal dies, it is his sister's sons who are next in the line of succession.

To set up a modern school in an archaic society that is so markedly feudal, matriarchal and even prehistoric inevitably creates problems. In starting the nomad school Blanguernon's aim was not to push the Tuareg into the twentieth century from one day to the next but, on the contrary, to lessen the shock which was bound to come in bridging the gulf of centuries. His idea was that the Tuareg should learn to write, read and count just enough to enable them to form a judgment of their own. That is why the

nomad children are not taught in a permanent schoolhouse, why
the teachers live in the camps and move on with the Tuareg as
soon as the water-points and grazing are exhausted. Blanguernon
demands of his teachers that they should adapt themselves to the
habits of the tribes, however much self-denial this may involve.
No attempt is made to extol the virtues of the sedentary life. Pater
de Foucauld maintained that the Tuareg would only become
civilised if they could be made sedentary. The French have long
since abandoned this idea, partly for selfish reasons. Experience
has shown that, when former nomads did settle, more problems
were created than solved.

Blanguernon had an ulterior motive in setting up the nomad
school: to gain access to the hitherto mysterious, closed world of
the Tuareg. Now that this has been achieved, the nomad classes
are a living expression of the 'présence française.' They fulfil a
definite function, for the marabouts who come down from the
North professing to preach Islam invariably carry the Koran in one
saddlebag and the latest manifestos of the Algerian maquis in the
other.

Claude Blanguernon summed up the situation when he said: 'If
we were rich and honest, there would be hundreds of nomad
schools. But as we are neither rich nor honest, there are only three.
We are not honest, because these three nomad classes are, in the
last resort, propaganda—and an expensive form of it too. It will be
two or three years before we can hope to take one or two Tuareg
boys and train them as teachers in future nomad schools.'

Blanguernon argues that it would be better to submit all the
Tuareg boys to a few tests, to pick out the most intelligent, put
them in special schools and eventually let them loose on their
fellow-tribesmen and their children. But I cannot imagine that
Blanguernon seriously believes such a method would work. He has
too much insight for that. There is another reason for the bitterness
with which he speaks of his own creation and for his desire to
train Tuareg teachers in quantity: the sort of school he once
dreamt of, a school that would equip the young Targi when he
reached the crossroads, to decide for himself which direction he
would take, this school is now out of date. It has been outdated by

the economic development of the desert. There is no room in an industrialised Sahara for the Tuareg way of life. Not even as an island.

Today it is no longer surprising or unusual to find a Tuareg working for a mineral prospector in the mountains or helping to build a road. When the Iklan, who finds it more lucrative to work as labourers than to be paid slaves, return to their masters after a few months with the money they have saved and sacks of sugar and tea, the Targi has no scruples about sharing the booty, but he is also clever enough to realise that his Akli slave will probably not come back a second time and certainly not a third. The chances are, therefore, that the Targi, tormented by the memory of so much tea and sugar, will eventually join the Akli in swinging a pick or listening to the fateful whisper of a geiger counter.

The power of the landlord is dwindling day by day. Not long ago a group of marabouts, who went to Dangouchi with the recommendation of the Amenokal, were sent about their business. The Kel Rela, to whom Dangouchi's tribe have to pay tribute, are already known somewhat pointedly amongst the Dag Rali as 'people who cost a great deal.' The Amenokal owns the land, in which, according to the French, there are rich natural deposits. To whom do these belong? To the Amenokal? The Imrad are already turning this question over in their minds. The tribal hierarchy, which stood the test for centuries, has, during the last few decades, begun to crack and crumble—a victim of peace, platinum and the combustion engine.

*　　*　　*

'Mohammed looks after the sheep belonging to a member of his tribe. One day a "chantier" is set up nearby. He would like to take a job there and learn a proper profession that will help him in the future. But he hesitates, for his master, a just and good man, wants him to stay. What will Mohammed do, and why?'

Henri-Jean Cottin, his pale face framed in coal-black muttonchops, put this question to Mohammed Boukhetta, a sixteen-year-old boy who looked thoughtfully at the drawing with which Cottin had illustrated the question: a shepherd standing beside a drilling-rig.

'He must stay with his master,' said the boy firmly. 'It is better. Perhaps he will not find a job. Or perhaps the drilling will stop and he will be dismissed.'

Cottin wrote the reply on a form and produced his second test-question.

'Mohammed is about to lose a good job, which he has held for a long time, because his master is moving to another district. What will Mohammed do, and why?'

'If he has done well by his master,' replied the boy unhesitatingly, 'he should follow him. But naturally only if his travelling-expenses are paid.'

This quiz was held in the Davel Askri or House of the Soldiers at Ouargla, which the military authorities had placed at the disposal of the Study Group for Human Problems in the Desert Areas. Cottin and his colleagues were conducting what they called 'Operation Mekhadma' and had turned this neglected building and its small forecourt into a modern laboratory with all kinds of gimmicks used in psychological research.

Mohammed Boukhetta is only one of about four hundred Mekhadma tribesmen who are being tested. The heart and soul of 'Operation Mekhadma' is Dr. Claude Vigan, the 'doctor of the Sahara,' who advises companies working in the desert on all problems concerning the welfare of their employees in difficult climatic conditions. He, however, sees his professional obligations in a much wider context than do his employers, for he is interested in helping not only them but also the natives. For a European transplanted to the desert the main problem is one of adapting himself physically to the climate. For the native, on the other hand, the problem of becoming acclimatised to completely new working-conditions is primarily a social and psychological one, which in the case of a nomad is all the more acute if he has inherited a profound contempt for hard work.

The Mekhadma gravitated, together with other nomadic tribes —the Chaamba, the Beni Thour and the Said Otba—round the Ouargla oasis. Nomads and sedentary 'Ksourians' or oases-dwellers proved to be complementary. The peasant dug wells and maintained them, fertilised the date-palms, grew vegetables, corn and dates, and, in an emergency, allowed the fighting men of the desert to take refuge behind his fortified walls or even, in periods of war or drought, to draw on his supplies. The nomad, on the other hand, took over transport, delivered meat, wool, butter and cheese, and protected the peasant if he was attacked by other nomads. But the alliance between them was neither voluntary nor based on mutual respect. Sheer necessity and a threat of force compelled the peasants, who had become lethargic in the moist oasis climate and in many cases had been weakened by swamp-fever, to seek protection from some tribe of desert raiders. They hated and feared their masters, who in turn—and in common with other raiding tribes—despised the 'corn-eaters.' Every year the Mekhadma pitched their tents in the Ouargla neighbourhood when the dates were ripe, in order to supervise the harvest, to buy corn, tea and sugar, to build up their supplies and store up the surplus in barns. Ouargla for them was both a trade and a war-depot. Their grazing grounds lay to the west; once they had exhausted the grazing and the water-supply in the Oued Mya, they moved their flocks into the Mzab towards Zelfana and Metlili.

Then peace broke out in the desert and the combustion engine arrived. The social hierarchy, which placed the fighting-man over the 'Ksourian', collapsed; the inter-regional caravan trade, which had been the main source of income, dried up, and the Mekhadma became poor. Between 1885 and 1945 they lost two thirds of their livestock and a large proportion of their date-palms. Madeleine Brigol has also pointed out another important factor. Formerly the Mekhadma were a patriarchal community. This was in keeping with their way of life as nomadic cattle-breeders. They had to hold together; problems of grazing, migrating and breeding required a great deal of experience. But with peace came security, and the seeds of a new individualism were sown. Strangely enough the army, which attracted many nomads, failed even to keep alive much less strengthen the traditional sense of collective loyalty. The nomads who had done their military service proved to be the most arrant individualists. And so the whole tribal system began to break up. The tribe gave way to the clan, then to the family and finally to the individual. But a single tent lacked the experience and the means to breed large flocks and cope with variations in the climate and the market. The result was a growing tendency to settle in the oases. Principal cause—and effect—was the fall-off in livestock. If, for example, the number of camels drops to two or three for each tent, the nomad is no longer in a position to keep his family in supplies, much less to join in any caravans. But once he has become sedentary, he loses interest in livestock breeding.

The first Mekhadma settled in 1908; between 1920 and 1930 the movement to the oases increased; since 1950 it has assumed massive proportions. Today the 4,500 members of the Mekhadma tribe can no longer be regarded as nomads. The tribe comprises four classes. In first place are the Schorfa who trace their descent back to Mohammed or to his grandson Hassan. Then come the Zoua, who are, as it were, born marabouts, born holy men. So Schorfa and Zoua together form a kind of religious aristocracy, entitled automatically to alms and subsistence from their fellow-Moslems. Below them in the hierarchy come the Harrar, the 'free' —free by contrast with the black slaves and descendants of slaves. Eighty-five per cent of all Mekhadma are Harrar. The blacks, who were formerly treated not as human beings but as commodities to be bought or bartered, have been largely absorbed into the Mek-hadma society. Their position is not comparable to that of the Tuareg slaves, a reminder that life in the desert is as varied as its landscape. The freeborn Mekhadmi may raise his eyebrows when he sees one of 'his' emancipated blacks and, when he talks about them, an undertone of contempt may creep into his voice, but he has long since become resigned to doing manual work himself which was formerly done by his slave. In terms of blood-relationship, too, the barriers between the various castes are fast disappearing.

Madeleine Brigol made an ingenious comparison between the house of the 'Ksourian' and that of the nomad. The house of the Ouargli has an inner court, stairs and terraces. The nomad's living-quarters, on the other hand, are always on ground-level and have no terraces. Originally the building was simply a store-room, while the family lived in a tent, the only difference being that the stores were protected against weather and possible robbers.

Later, when the nomads gave up their wandering, they built on two or three rooms and added a courtyard for the animals. The result is nothing more than a tent in stone! The confused state of mind of nomads exiled from the desert is most clearly reflected in the pitching of a camel-hide tent in the courtyard. It gives the impression of being the focal point of the house. Its function varies from one family to the next. It is sometimes used to accommodate the women, sometimes as summer-quarters, sometimes it is occupied by the mother of the master of the house because she cannot get accustomed to having a permanent roof over her head. I found a tent of this kind in the precincts of every house that had recently been occupied by a Mekhadma family—including the Caïd himself.

Once he has settled, the nomad is in no hurry to acquire the habits, good or bad, of the 'Ksourian.' The Mekhadma women still walk about the oasis unveiled, a habit which they acquired in the desert and which their more orthodox sisters view with the greatest envy from behind their veils. Cultivating the land is not one of the Mekhadmi's special talents. A quarter of the water which Ouargla's first Alb-well brings bubbling up from Savornin's sea was allotted to the Mekhadma—a handsome gesture by the French when one considers that the Mekhadma least of all natives believed that a river could be conjured up out of the earth. Today the SAR, the model-plantation, begins immediately behind the Caïd's house: young date-palms stretching as far as the eye can see at regular intervals of ten yards . . . In the close network of irrigation channels the artesian water steams at a temperature of more than 100 degrees. It looks as if an agricultural future has already dawned for the Mekhadma. Yet there are still quite a few sceptics. The Mekhadma were neither willing nor competent to prepare the ground for the SAR. Two hundred settlers had to be imported from the salt-marshes of the Chott, excellent farm-workers who help to look after the Mekhadma palms. Whether the Mekhadma will themselves become proficient farmers or whether in a few years their date-plantation will have degenerated to a wilderness, only time can tell.

*   *   *

His Eminence Monseigneur Georges Mercier, 'Bishop of the Sahara,' is not lacking in civic courage. When the sands of Hassi Messaoud were already pouring out black gold and the desert was in the grip of the oil-fever, he issued this warning: 'The Sahara possesses only one source of wealth that is steadily increasing: its young people.'

Monseigneur Mercier is an unusual Prince of the Church. He attaches no importance to ceremony. Tributes paid by believers to his office embarrass him. The clothes of his order, the White Fathers, the white burnous and the red, fez-like hat are a most effective disguise. The ring on his finger and the cross round his neck are the only badges of rank he wears. Monseigneur Mercier's official residence is at Laghouat on the northern fringe of the desert, but he is seldom to be found there. His Bishopric is the largest in the world (820,000 square miles) and he runs it by living like a nomad. He is eternally on the move, by air, Land-Rover and camel. But his interest is by no means confined to his own believers; the Moslems of the desert look upon the White Father and Bishop of the Sahara as the successor of Pater de Foucauld, the unforgotten white marabout before whom even followers of the Prophet knelt to kiss the hem of his garment. Monseigneur Mercier is conducting an intensive campaign for the canonisation of the venerable hermit. Nothing would please him more than that Rome should present the Sahara with a saint at a time when treasure-hunters are burrowing beneath it and rockets are being launched into its blazing sky. But the natives respect, in fact, revere him for more solid reasons. The young people of the Sahara, whom he plays off against the underground riches of the desert, have him to thank for their technical schools.

'We are teaching them to swim, so that they will not drown in the economic flood that is breaking over them.'

The White Fathers started technical schools in the Sahara in an attempt to improve the hopeless situation of young people in the desert. Out of 180,000 boys and girls of school age at most thirty per cent attend elementary school and only a small percentage of these enter for or pass the school-leaving examination. (For example, not a single Mekhadma at Ouargla has passed it.) And, of those who have in fact obtained the 'Certificat d'Etudes Primaires' (CEP) the majority forget all they have learned at school in the three or four years between leaving it and finding a job. The vast majority of the Saharan population, unless they choose to lead a near-starvation existence in the date-gardens, have only two possibilities open to them at the age of eighteen: to join the Army and look forward to a modest pension at thirty-five, or to find casual work of some kind, which means spending a lifetime of uncertainty and humiliation looking for work. The most they can hope for is to remain day-labourers until the end; many of them become petty thieves or worse. The invasion of oil and ore prospectors, of road and airfield builders, water drillers and all the others who are turning the Sahara into a hive of industry has made little or no difference to the problem as such. The fact that the natives can find work remarkably easily and at wages which by their standards are exceptional has, of course, relieved the situation. In a great many cases, however, the real problem, which is a human not a labour problem, has merely been pushed out of sight.

The original object of the technical schools was to give the young people in the oases elementary training in some trade that would help them find better paid positions in northern Algeria and in France. But work in these 'Centres de Formation Professionelle' had barely got under way when the old dream of industrialising the Sahara began to take practical shape. As a result, the White Fathers' protégés are not exported northwards but are all absorbed locally.

The White Fathers, who could hardly have realised their particular dream unaided, receive encouragement and support not only from the Algerian authorities but also from quite a number of firms which operate in the south. Their motives are neither social nor humanitarian but entirely selfish. I remember a conversation I had with the Head of the Personnel Branch of an oil company. 'We are trying wherever possible to replace the northern Algerians by native-born, local labour,' he said openly. 'First of all for climatic reasons. The autochthonous population is naturally better adapted to the desert climate, particularly to the intolerable summer heat. But there is also the fact,' he added after a moment's hesitation, 'that the people here are fresher, not so spoilt. The contact the northern Algerians have had since childhood with Europeans and European civilisation hasn't been an unmixed blessing. You understand. . . .?' I understood.

So far five technical schools have been opened: at Laghouat, Ouargla, Colomb Bechar, Ain Sefra and El Golea. They train masons, general mechanics, electric fitters, motor mechanics and drivers. The courses last at least six months, at most two years. The various schools are so situated that they attract pupils from more or less the whole of the Algerian Sahara. The entry-age is theoretically between eighteen and thirty-five but the eighteen year-olds or specially gifted seventeen year-olds are in the majority. There is, of course, no discrimination of colour or religion; Moslems and Christians, nomads and oasis-dwellers, pure Arabs, Berbers and descendants of negro slaves are all accepted. Not only are the courses free, the pupils are paid a monthly subsistence with, in some cases, children's allowances.

Over a cool glass of beer in the headmaster's kitchen at El Golea the Bishop of the Sahara explained to me how he saw the development of the Sahara.

'Every year the White Fathers' technical schools turn out about a hundred and fifty young people. I realise, of course, how few that is, very few when you consider the magnitude of the problem. But we must begin somewhere, then we can set our target higher and higher both in terms of quantity and quality. But to do that we must have help. Even the modest scale on which we are working at the moment is really beyond our even more modest means. . . . We are guided by two convictions. The first is that the future of the Sahara must depend on how the human factor is dealt with. Man will always be a country's most precious capital and he must be "developed." That applies as much to the Sahara as anywhere else. Employers of native labour frequently complain that their workers have no team-spirit and are incapable of staying in one place of work. And it is true that most of the natives return to their oases as soon as they have earned enough to keep themselves for a few weeks or months. But this is hardly to be wondered at. Finding work is important but it is not everything; one also has to be taught to work. The development of the desert is for me, for us, something that must begin with these poor devils, who inhabit the desert. We must get right down to their basic needs and their misery, try to bring them salvation as soon as possible and show them a way out. There is no sense in laying the administrative foundations of a modern State—all by ourselves and without the people who need us—if we put no thought into it, whether for good or ill, but simply go on the frivolous assumption that the poor devils will adapt themselves somehow and one fine day will fit into our system. Did I say it makes no sense? More than that, it is short-sighted and a sin against our neighbour. It is our duty to probe deep into their thoughts and way of life and, with their help and the aid of our technical skill, to improve them. As Pater de Foucauld once wrote: "If we do not do our duty, if we exploit instead of civilising, we will lose all and the concord we have given this people will turn against us." Today, of course, the word "civilisé" has acquired a peculiar flavour of its own. But just the same we know exactly what Pater de Foucauld meant by it fifty years ago. If we develop the desert without taking account of its human capital, if we try to displace them, push them aside or throw them a bone to chew, then the day will come when their reactions will certainly be exploited and we will reap a harvest of rebellion.'

'The second possibility, on the other hand, binds us to them from the beginning. By constant teaching we can help them to break free gradually from the slavery of their environment and from their archaic bonds. We can lead them step by step into the structure of society and industry, which we are building for and with them. There can only be one programme for the future, for the very near future; to improve what is already there, namely the traditional way of life of the cattle-breeding nomads and date-farmers, and to prepare what must come: absorption in a modern economic system, in industry.'

Monseigneur Mercier then went on to explain what he understood by improving what is already there. Above all he is in favour of replacing the existing elementary schools, which were imported direct from France and are much too intellectual for the oasis

population, by a basic type of school which would set out to prepare its pupils to work as peasants or manual labourers. He would
also like to see the school leaving-age extended by two years to fill
the present unfortunate gap between leaving school at fourteen
and reaching adolescence. But the Bishop of the Sahara admits
that, however important and necessary this may be, he believes not
so much in what already exists as what is to come: industry.

'I said that the first and the main pillar of our work is the conviction that we must begin with the needs of the desert peoples.
The second is our belief in the industrialisation of the Sahara.
Even though at the moment it is hedged about with "ifs" and
"buts", it is still the only hope for the desert and its inhabitants.
The natural resources are not sufficient and not reliable enough. It
is only the constant underground wealth of the Sahara that can give
its people a higher standard of living and maintain it. The Sahara
has no agricultural future and it is now losing such crafts-
manship as it had. In future we must think first and foremost
in terms of craftsmen and peasants. A worker's wage-packet can
cultivate a peasant's date-garden. This is a basic law of the Saharan
economy which the industrious Mozabites discovered a long time
ago. "The palms of the Mzab," say the Mozabites, "have their
roots in the shops of Algiers." But we must not allow the native
to enter the promised land of an industrialised desert merely as a
casual labourer and a "maid-of-all-work." One day all the pipelines will be laid, the pumping-stations in operation, the roads and
airfields built. Prospecting for oil requires much more intensive
effort than exploiting it. As the demand for skilled labour rises, the
market for unskilled labour will shrink. What happens then? Will
the natives, who in the drilling-camps have seen, tasted and
enjoyed all the material blessings of modern civilisation—things
that a few years ago they only knew from hearsay—will they leave
the opulent meals in the camp-canteen without a murmur and go
back to dates and water? Or will they take their revenge on those
who destroyed the house of their fathers without building a new
and more spacious one? Will they blow up the pipelines, set the
trucks on fire, attack the oil-towns—in short, will they rebel because they realise they have been exploited instead of "civilised"?

I am far from believing that a technical education will solve all problems. What I d   eve is that it is a practicable course which leads to a desirable

The midday su   ed through the closed shutters into the small kitchen. We   he warm shadow and wiped the perspiration from our fore

'The process of integration which I have been trying to outline needs financiers and technicians. There has not exactly been a shortage of them in the Sahara. But for a sound policy towards the youth of the Sahara we need men, men who want to be not bureaucrats but lay apostles. More than half a million young Frenchmen have fought in Algeria. Sometimes I cannot help thinking just how much these young men could have achieved if they had been recruited as civilians to preach in peace and friendship the gospel of magnanimity and spiritual power. It is peace that must be humanised, not war. The heart of the problem will always be the same: responsibility. The responsibility of peoples who are doing well towards those who are not so fortunate. The greater their misery, the greater is our responsibility. Could it weigh anywhere more heavily than in the Sahara, where all records of poverty have been broken?'

Words like 'Eurafrica' and 'French Union'
have an unreal, ghostly sound against the
background of the Algerian tragedy; yet pre-
cisely because this appalling conflict between
a legal fiction and a reality can only end with
the destruction of a myth, the myth of the
'mother country of the peoples', so it will
become the threshold across which France
finally steps out of the magic circle of histori-
cal self-adulation into the open: as a nation
amongst nations. The question is not whether
this will happen but at what cost and how
late?

HERBERT LUTHY, *Frankreichs Uhren gehen anders*

14. Cement of Eurafrica?

ACCORDING to his friend Charles de Foucauld, Laperrine jeopardised his career when he gave France the Sahara against her will.
Laperrine shared this fate with most of the courageous, enterprising Frenchmen who built up an empire behind their country's
back. At the same time, the Sahara, unlike the other colonial
possessions which were a constant thorn in the French government's flesh, never aroused the anti-colonial passions of the Left.
It always enjoyed a certain undisputed popularity, for, if its dunes
were not the scene of some current film, then its mountains formed
the background of a novel or its hammadas and regs were used as
starting-point for a journey into space. Between times it would be
forgotten. There was no Ministry for the Sahara, no Sahara budget
—nothing to trap the spirit of that overwhelming, fascinating
Great Desert in a neatly-labelled bottle. The Sahara consisted of
appendices to various administrative units and its internal borders
reflected the rival claims of officers, who had penetrated into the
desert from north and south and 'taken possession' rather than the
division of grazing-grounds, of pasturage rights and caravan-
tracks amongst the nomads. Those parts of the Sahara which belonged to French West Africa and French Equatorial Africa came

under the Ministry for Overseas Territories. The Algerian 'Territoires du Sud' on the other hand, the remoteness of whose southernmost tip is a tribute to Laperrine's energy, came in the last instance under the Ministry of the Interior but were covered by a special statute which gave them an almost exclusively military administration. Without any fuss, without a portfolio and without any appreciable budget the 'Képi bleu' governed 750,000 forgotten square miles of mountains, rubble, gravel and sand. The desert officers watched with jealous eyes to see that no outsider stepped on to this immense stage, on which dramatic scenes of courage and self-sacrifice and legendary feats of human endurance had been performed. In Paris 'meharisation' and the secret understanding between governors and governed were sneered at, but the unorthodox officers who showed more interest in flint arrow-heads than the silver stripes and gold braid of their uniforms were left to go their own way.

Then came the day when the Sahara was promoted to a rich and productive desert. For the Army it is not a promotion but a downgrading. Their administration, which had proved itself and had been tailored to suit local conditions, was declared ripe for demolition. The desert officers had based their ideas on the native but had failed to progress sufficiently from this promising beginning. Once they came under the spell of the desert, they no longer wanted to change it. Now the pioneers of a new Sahara were staking their claim. They blandly dismissed local idiosyncrasies and indeed found them a hindrance to their all-embracing plans for the desert. They were not impressed by the existence of different political statutes and administrative systems, different currencies and taxes, different financial dues and mining royalties, to say nothing of customs barriers. Imperiously they demanded the unification of the desert.

The year 1957 saw the foundation of the 'Organisation Commune des Régions Sahariennes' (OCRS) and of a Ministry for the Sahara. At the same time the 'Territoires du Sud' were turned into two French départements, which together are three and a half times the size of Metropolitan France: the départements of Saoura (capital: Colomb Bechar) and Oasen (capital: Laghouat). In 1959 the Ministry for the Sahara was dissolved, at least in name, and the OCRS was reorganised to bring it into line with the 'Communauté.'

The main territory covered by the (re-formed) OCRS is France's two Saharan départements, but it also extends its activities, wherever possible, to other territories, particularly those formerly included in the French Union. The OCRS comes under the wing of the Minister responsible for the Sahara, and it is run by the Delegate General who has a technical committee and a committee for social and economic questions to advise him. The Delegate General's post is filled at present by the Minister responsible for the Sahara.

The OCRS has financial autonomy. Its main source of revenue is oil, for the profits accruing to the State—after a deduction has been made for the development of Algeria—go to the autonomous Saharan Organisation. France therefore acts on a sound economic principle: the profits derived from the desert are ploughed back almost entirely into the expanding and flourishing enterprises in the Sahara. In theory half the oil profits go to the OCRS, but, in view of the enormous investments which have to be paid off, the Saharan oil will not be showing a profit before 1964. So if the OCRS were only to acquire its share when the oil companies began to make a profit, it would have to wait a long time for working capital. The Oil Code therefore provides that, as soon as the oil leaves the drilling-hole, the OCRS receives $12\frac{1}{2}$ per cent of its value; the remainder is taken later by the State in the form of a profits tax. In this way the OCRS can reckon with some fifty million pounds revenue until 1963.

The administrative change-over in the Sahara has not been going altogether smoothly. The newly-created prefectures and subprefectures are to a large extent absorbing the administrative officers, but the latter are not accepting their new status with a very good grace. Behind the scenes the army is defending every position grimly against the civilians. The old Saharans complain angrily about the 'greenhorns from Paris' who are 'stealing' the desert from them without knowing what to do with it. 'They're barbarians who have no sense for the beauty of a sunset,' said one

Lieutenant to me, snapping his fingers contemptuously. 'They're turning everything upside down and in the same breath they're even disrupting the traditional system of administration which would have given the native, whose personal, family and tribal life is breaking up, something to lean on.' 'Sorry,' reply the civilians, unmoved. 'This is no time to gaze at sunsets. What the industrial Sahara needs is not sentimentalists but managers. . . .'

The outside observer might well dismiss these petty jealousies and intrigues as normal symptoms of a transition period, if the energy and drive of the new men were impressive. But precisely this is in doubt. Many Frenchmen regard the OCRS as a somewhat cumbersome super-bureaucracy.

According to its Charter the OCRS's main object is to co-ordinate economic schemes for the development of the desert, but it also has the task of stimulating the social development of the Sahara. It is primarily concerned itself with the building of roads and airfields, laying-on of water-supplies, telephone and radio communications.

Eirik Labonne is the man who first worked out a plan for industrial combines in the desert. The 'Zones d'Organisation Industrielle et Stratégique en Afrique' (ZOIA) were widely spoken of at one time but today suspiciously little is heard of them. The ZOIA of Colomb Bechar was to be industrial zone No. 1 with a thermal power-station, a ferro-manganese and an artificial manure factory. A sufficient supply of industrial water, labour power and raw material—all of them essential—was thought to be already there. But to more objective observers ZOIA No. 1 seemed like a cat that kept chasing its own tail. The copper ore at Bou Kais can be exploited, it is said, as soon as the industrial combine has been set up at Colomb Bechar. This will only be realised when it is proved that there is enough ore to exploit . . . ZOIA No. 1's safest bet seemed to be the nearby testing-ground for long-range and guided missiles (Centre Interarmées d'Essais d'Engins Spéciaux), the world's biggest inland shooting-range (in which NATO has recently been showing an active interest)—a fact which did not exactly allay the suspicions of the economists. In the meantime the construction of the power-station has been deferred and ZOIA put off indefinitely. The Labonne Plan has not thereby been proved wrong but merely premature.

The OCRS, to judge by its own self-avowed aims, is another ZOIA on a gigantic scale. Its protagonists see in it a major industrial, economic and social experiment on the lines of the famous Tennessee Valley Authority in the United States. But the OCRS is so severely handicapped from the start that its chances of success are not particularly rosy. The proposal made in 1951 to nationalise the Sahara has not been forgotten. Quite a few people regard the OCRS as a resurrection of the Sahara State after it had already been buried by the experts on the grounds that the human problems of the desert, both in terms of population and social structure, were too complex. The somewhat quixotic development of the OCRS not along purely economic lines but in an administrative and political direction naturally revived these fears, as did also the combining of the Delegate General's post with that of the Minister for the Sahara and the creation in 1958 of the 'Ordre du Mérite Saharien'—as it were, an Order of this disguised Saharan State—which decorates the chests of deserving Saharans with the Southern Cross.

The assurance that the OCRS would not impinge on the political structure of the Sahara was not taken very seriously and from the beginning this mistrust has had unpleasant consequences. Mauretania remained outside the Sahara Pool, although its participation would have been extremely welcome. Not only does it possess a seaboard with a harbour at Port Etienne, it also has iron deposits at Fort Gouraud and copper at Akjoujt. It was only after prolonged bargaining and after the OCRS had given numerous and very binding assurances, that the Niger State agreed to pool its tin deposits in the Aïr Mountains. The growing politicisation of the OCRS during 1958 caused increasing uneasiness in the southern areas of the Sahara. The French Sudan, since de Gaulle's referendum made it autonomous, has not renewed its contracts with the OCRS. Up to the present, therefore, the OCRS has fallen far short of achieving its original aims; only the Niger and Chad Republics have given their assent to the communal effort in the Sahara and even they have made quite a number of reservations. If the OCRS remains permanently restricted in this way, then its basic purpose, to establish a uniform economic area in the common interest, must go by the board.

Another handicap under which the OCRS has been labouring is, of course, the uncooperative attitude of the neighbouring states. The OCRS reckons that it will later be able to bring in Morocco, Tunisia, Libya, Spain (with the Spanish Sahara) and perhaps even Khartoum on a common scheme for the development of the Sahara and its natural resources. This is an attractive but at the moment completely utopian idea. It is, for example, a disturbing fact that the OCRS has not even succeeded in winning over Mauretania and the Sudan, both members of the French Commonwealth. The division of Southern Algeria into two départements and the foundation of the OCRS gave a new lease of life to the plan for a federation of the Maghreb, a Western Islamic Federation. The reorganisation of the French Sahara was regarded in the Maghreb as an attempt to salvage the wealth of the desert in time before France's Algerian policy went bankrupt—a suspicion which became a firm conviction in the autumn of 1959 when de Gaulle promised Algeria and the Algerians self-determination: in this solemn proclamation the same right was not given to the inhabitants of the Sahara. It is this attempt to treat the Sahara as a separate political entity that has given rise to the Maghreb proposal that a barrier should be erected from Morocco to Libya, which would stand between the OCRS and the Mediterranean. France can chalk up on the credit side Habib Bourguiba's decision to allow the oil from Edjeleh to be transported across Tunisian territory, but Bourguiba's decision ran counter to the solemn vow taken by all the North African nationalist parties at the Tangier Conference (Spring 1958) to work for a Maghreb one and indivisible. France cannot fail to realise that, the longer the Algerian conflict lasts, the more radical the nationalist elements in Tunisia and Morocco become, so that both Bourguiba and King Mohammed might become virtually the prisoners of the FLN (Front de Libération Nationale) if they are not in fact swept aside by a surge of nationalism.

A further obstacle in the way of the OCRS is the frontier

disputes and more particularly Morocco's territorial claims. The fact is that south of a point level with Colomb Bechar there is no de jure frontier between Morocco and Algeria. The Convention of Lalla Marnia, which was signed by the French and Moroccan governments in March 1845, merely divided up the oases and tribes south of the Teniet-Sassi Pass and added: 'As regards the land south of the Ksour (oases) of the two governments, a demarcation of the frontiers is superfluous, as the area is waterless, uninhabitable and desert.' Today the French tear their hair at the thought that they could have allowed more than a century to pass without any final demarcation. Now it is too late. The map of Greater Morocco, which Allal el Fassis, its prophet, brought back from Cairo at the end of 1955 and which hangs today in the headquarters of the nationalist leaders, boldly includes Colomb Bechar, the Saoura, the Touat, Tindouf, Spanish Sahara and Mauretania in Moroccan territory. The Niger and the Senegal rivers form the southern border of this Sherifian Empire which includes more than twice as much territory as the existing State of Morocco. The historical arguments on which the claim to Mauretania in particular is based are partly fantastic, partly grotesque. The main Crown witnesses are the Almoravides who in the eleventh century founded an empire which stretched from Senegal to Castile, from the Atlantic to Cyrenaica. The Moroccans blithely ignore the fact that the Almoravides, who stemmed from Senegal, could be cited rather more convincingly in support of Moorish claims to Morocco, Western Algeria and Moorish Spain. Of late, however, the Moroccans themselves have shown a decreasing enthusiasm for the historical evidence, preferring instead to invoke the wish of the people in the disputed territories to 'return to their homeland,' a slogan which, at least in Mauretania, can hardly reflect the growing national feeling.

Nevertheless 'Greater Morocco' has long since ceased to be a mere joke. The Moroccan partisans, of whom King Mohammed is both sovereign and prisoner, adopted the title of 'Army of Liberation for the Moroccan Sahara' and have since caused the French considerable trouble in the whole area claimed by Morocco, including Mauretania. At the same time the political position of

France and the OCRS deteriorated. To begin with, Greater Morocco was a concept more or less confined to Allal el Fassis and a number of militant nationalists; the throne did not commit itself. At the end of 1957, however, a Saharan Department was created in the Moroccan Ministry of the *Interior*, which was headed by a colleague of Si Allal, and in 1958 King Mohammed came out into the open. During a tour of the south in February he took over Si Allal's claims lock, stock and barrel. In March of that year a Mauretanian prince and several local dignitaries paid homage to him as the ruler of the 'occupied' territories. In April, Spain, in accordance with a previous agreement to terminate the 'protectorate', relinquished the most southerly area, the province of Terfaya, though the impression made on the Moroccans was short-lived. The Italian oil magnate, Enrico Mattei, who has been described as 'the most powerful Italian since Augustus,' was given prospecting rights and, as Rabat has pointed out rather ominously, Tindouf is now within range of Moroccan artillery: the Military Council of the Maghreb nationalists in Tangiers endorsed Rabat's claims to Mauretania. Morocco tried to use its claim to sovereignty as a means of sabotaging a World Bank loan for the exploration of the ore deposits at Fort Gouraud. In Rabat a Congress for the Liberation of Mauretania was held. When France granted the first concession for oil prospecting in the Tindouf area, which stretches right up to the Moroccan frontier, Morocco managed to persuade an American and a German company to apply for this and other concessions in what is French territory. And in 1959, when Spain encouraged prospecting in her Saharan possessions, Rabat again protested violently against drilling in 'disputed areas of the Sahara.' Morocco's annexationist propaganda is broadcast on a special Saharan wavelength by Radio Morocco and is also disseminated through the Arabic weekly 'Sahara el Maghreb' and the French monthly 'Perspectives Sahariennes.'

The dispute over the Algerian-Tunisian border in the Sahara also appears to have unpleasant possibilities. In an interview at the beginning of February 1959 President Bourguiba stressed the fact that this border had never been clearly defined. He complained that France had slammed the Saharan door in Tunisia's face and protested against the granting of prospecting rights to the 'Esso Saharienne', the Saharan subsidiary of Standard Oil, and the French companies associated with it. He maintained that the greater part of the concession area was under dispute. Tunisia, he declared, had submitted the dispute to France and to the Algerian National Liberation Front and was determined to obtain satisfaction by placing a complaint before the International Court at the Hague.

*   *   *

J. R. von Salis in his 'World History in Recent Times' writes: 'The 1880's had seen a precipitate, ruthless, energetic, grandiose manifestation of European rule in Africa, the driving force of which was similar to that which in the same century had led to a rapid expansion of the United States right across the vast American Continent to the shores of the Pacific Ocean. From a political viewpoint however, the large number of European competitors in Africa, the fact that in many parts of the Black Continent the Europeans encountered organised native states, and factors of geography and climate all combined to give developments in Africa quite a different character from the expansion in the Middle and Wild West, in Texas and California, Oregon and Alaska. Above all, settlement by whites on a massive scale was not possible, any more than a physical annihilation of the natives, so that the only conceivable solution was a colonial protectorate by the Europeans over the natives as the first step towards an eventual partnership between the whites and the coloured peoples.'

What contribution could the Sahara make to a partnership of this kind? At this point one must recall the ideas put forward by two men who were pioneers in the cause of Eurafrica. One was a German, Herman Sörgel, the other a Frenchman, Eirik Labonne.

In the 1920s Sörgel produced his Mediterranean plan. Impressed by America's power, he saw the future of Europe in a close link with Africa. The Mediterranean was to be the power-house of this union. Sörgel's plan was to lower the level of the Mediterranean by building dams in the Straits of Gibraltar and the

Dardanelles which would cut off the inflow of water from the Atlantic and the Black Sea. As the Mediterranean normally loses more water through evaporation than it receives from its rivers and from rainfall, the level would sink about a yard every year. Sörgel wanted to use the dams and the river-mouths as a means of producing electric power which would remove the salt from the sea-water and pump it into the Sahara. Later Sörgel, who was known to his friends as the 'Dalai Lama' because his head was constantly in the clouds, carried this idea still further by envisaging the restoration of a prehistoric sea in the Congo which would influence the climate in the interior of Africa, prevent Lake Chad from drying up—as it was then assumed it would—and providing a second source of power where it flowed into the Atlantic.

During this same period Eirik Labonne, former Resident General in Morocco and Tunisia, compared the Atlas mountains with the Urals and issued this warning: 'A disintegrated and impoverished Europe is measuring its tiny strength against the vast development of the United States and Soviet Russia. Africa is its only hope: the Continent which, if Europe can decide on a joint plan for its development, will enable the Europeans to break away from their small, peninsular existence and find their unity in a common effort.' Both Sörgel and Labonne agreed with Saint-Exupéry: 'Force them to build a tower and you will make them brothers.'

Today when parts of Africa are drawing closer together and supra-national industrial groups are appearing in Europe, the dream of Eurafrica seems nearer to being realised than ever before. And yet, as even the most casual newspaper reader knows, a genuine Euro-African partnership, despite all that is said and written about it, is still only in its infancy. Some progress has been made in the countries of French Africa, in which the members of the Common market, particularly Western Germany, plan to invest large sums in the next few years. In the Southern Sahara France has initiated a wide policy of de-colonisation. It was General de Gaulle who in the autumn of 1958 exercised the authority inherent in the de Gaulle legend to cut through the tangle of legal and legislative red tape. The territories in the French

Union (with the exception of Guinea) elected to become member-states of the 'Communauté française,' which soon began to develop in the direction of a loosely-constituted Commonwealth. Following the sobering example set by Guinea, Paris is placing as few obstacles as possible in the way of the increasing drive towards emancipation on the part of France's former protectorates, which are no longer content to accept self-government alone but are striving for full independence.

If France carries through this process of de-colonisation, then Eurafrica will have gained a victory for which France's European partners cannot be too grateful. At the same time, it is precisely France who is undermining her own position, and therefore the future of Europe, in Africa.

Since 1956 a new and unexpected form of anti-colonialism has been gaining ground in France. It began with a series of articles in the illustrated weekly *Paris-Match* by Raymond Cartier. Cartierism is based on the thesis that Metropolitan France is being exploited by her former colonies, which are costing considerably more than they bring in. It would be better, so the argument goes, to invest the capital and technical resources at present being spent on them in underdeveloped areas at home. 'Cartierism' would like to see France's former protégés 'condemned' as soon as possible to a freedom which is also free from subsidies. If this conception, for which there are very strong economic arguments, were to be universally accepted, it would be tantamount to a betrayal of the moral obligation to help the undeveloped countries in general and, above all, it would mean the end of the Eurafrican idea at a time when it is beginning to show promise.

But the development of black Africa by France, which is so important to Europe as a whole, is threatened by something even more serious than Cartierism: the war in Algeria. Professor Herbert Luthy, the least suspect of witnesses, has called it an abscess in which the French crisis has come to a head. The Algerian maquis only have to invoke the battle-cry of the French Revolution—Liberty, Equality, Fraternity—to bring home the cruel paradox of the French position in Algeria. If this abscess is to be lanced, then it can only be with the help of, not in spite of, France.

And any non-Frenchman who regards this as a reason for being cautious in his comments on the Algerian war cannot ignore its effect on the rest of Africa. The slogan 'Hands off Africa', which was prominently displayed at the first Pan-African conference at Accra, was directed not only at the Colonial powers but at the new Europe. This anti-European demonstration was staged partly and by no means least on behalf of Algeria, for the Algerian crisis is imposing more and more pressure on those states which, thanks to the smooth transition to post-colonial systems of administration, are today ready to cooperate with France and her European partners. It must be remembered that Eurafrica is not the only proposal that has been put before the Africans. The philosophy of Nasser's revolution dreams of a close link between Africa and Asia, which will be achieved by islamising the black continent. Those best qualified to say how much progress Islam has made in Africa in the last few years are the Christian missionaries: they have been helpless to stem the mass-conversion which brings a hundred thousand African souls to Mecca every year. Algeria, where the Christians are alleged to be conducting a war of annihilation against Allah's children, is a heaven-sent gift to Islam's propagandists.

French publicists proudly describe the Sahara as the cement of Eurafrica, as the great magnet that draws Africa and Europe irresistibly closer. How seriously is one to take this?

In the first place the Sahara provides convincing evidence to support the thesis that Africa must be a joint European enterprise. Quite a proportion of the desert's natural wealth can only be extracted if Europe is prepared to consume it. On the other hand, the potential consumers are putting capital, technicians and technical equipment, wherever possible and wherever necessary, into the search for this wealth and its extraction. Here are two examples.

Such is the magic of the word 'oil' that the natural gas of the Sahara has been somewhat overlooked. In fact, throughout the world as a whole, natural gas has for a long time been the poor relation in the hydrocarbon family. Quite wrongly. In the past two decades it has had a resounding success as a source of power in the United States; today it supplies a third of America's power. In

Canada the natural gas industry is developing by leaps and bounds. Since the war Europe has also become increasingly interested in it. In Italy the natural gas of the Po Valley, the Abruzzi and Sicily is completely revolutionising the country's power consumption; the field at Lacq has become the basis of industrial development in south-west France; since the signing of the State Treaty Austria has been expanding her natural gas industry; in Western Germany and in England hope has been by no means abandoned of finding larger deposits. True, the known supplies of natural gas in Europe are not likely to reduce Western Europe's deficit in home-produced power, for that deficit is expected to increase threefold by 1975. But the natural gas of the Sahara would help to tide Europe over, till atomic energy is available in sufficient quantity.

At present there are three extensive deposits of natural gas in the Sahara, one south of In Salah, the second at Hassi Messaoud, the third at Hassi R'mel. The fields south of In Salah produce almost pure, dry methane. But the CREPS is in no hurry to develop these fields, for they are almost seven hundred miles, as the crow flies, from the Mediterranean coast. Hassi Messaoud will probably produce mostly liquid gas (butane and propane). Hassi R'mel's annual production might be as much as one eighth of the total yearly output of the United States and more than five times the present production of the whole of Europe (the Soviet Union excepted). The Hassi R'mel field at its nearest point is three hundred miles from the coast, but the transportation of natural gas through high-pressure pipes is cheap, so long as there are considerable quantities being transported.

Algeria will not be in a position to consume one milliard cubic metres (about forty-five milliard cubic feet) of natural gas a year— the minimum needed to make the Hassi R'mel supplies competitive—before 1963 at the earliest, and only then if the industrialisation plans drawn up at the beginning of 1959 are implemented. Moreover much greater supplies would be necessary, to say nothing of a long-term development of the Hassi R'mel field, to make them cheaper than imported fuel. Considerations of this kind are, of course, relatively unimportant now that France has decided, for political reasons, to use the natural gas of Hassi R'mel as a basis for the industrialisation of Algeria. A 24-inch gas pipe-line is already under construction which will link up with Oran and Algiers and which, when completed, will have a yearly capacity of three milliard cubic meters—more, much more, than Algeria itself will be able to consume in the foreseeable future. France is looking to Western Europe, which—though to the detriment of other types of fuel—could easily consume 50 milliard cubic metres of Saharan natural gas a year.

Unfortunately between Hassi R'mel and Europe lies the Mediterranean. Two possible ways of surmounting this formidable barrier are being considered, namely to transport the liquefied gas by sea in special tankers or by special long distance submarine pipelines. The one solution does not rule out the other. To begin with, a plant is to be built at Arzew (near Oran) which will liquefy some of the gas from the Sahara by cooling it to minus 160 degrees. This will reduce it to one six-hundredth of its original volume. Methane tankers will bring it to Europe, where it will be stored, if necessary restored to normal temperature and fed into the distribution-system. This solution, which presupposes an adequate supply of methane tankers and satisfactory results from the shipping of liquid gas, is to be replaced as soon as possible by the second: a submarine pipeline. If the straits of Gibraltar are chosen as the transit point, only three to four miles of pipe will be needed under water. But the crossing could also be made further east. Until now no submarine pipeline has ever been laid at such a depth or over such a long distance, but a survey of the sea-bed between Mostaganem (near Oran) and Carthagena in Spain has revealed a submarine valley 150 miles long which is covered by a thick layer of mud. This mud has oxygen-consuming bacteria which would protect the pipeline against rust. But by German calculations, even with the detour via Gibraltar and with a 1750-mile journey through Algeria, Morocco, Spain and Southern France, the price of Saharan natural gas in Strassbourg would still be extremely low—assuming that it can be transported in very large quantities and continuously. The maps inspired by 'Eurafrigas' even show pipelines from France to England, Germany and the Benelux countries. The realisation of these ambitious projects depends entirely on whether Europe will decide in the coming years to pool its resources of energy. But one thing is already established, that the gas from Hassi R'mel could contribute to an unprecedented upswing in Europe's gas industry.

The desert provides yet another argument in support of the thesis that Africa's development is only conceivable as a concerted European venture: the iron ore deposits at Fort Gouraud and Gara Djebilet.

At present the world's iron and steel industry consumes six hundred million tons of ore. Russia and the United States both have adequate supplies of their own; fresh deposits have been found in Venezuela and Canada. Western Europe, however, is not in such a happy position. It runs the risk of suffering from an ore shortage, if something is not done very soon to expand its supplies overseas. For geographical reasons alone Africa is naturally an interesting source, but to exploit Africa's deposits is beyond the capacity of any one European country by itself.

Before mining can begin at Fort Gouraud, this remote desert spot must be connected with the coast. The nearest port, Villa Cisneros, is silting up, so the railway will run to the small Mauretanian fishing-place, Port Etienne. As it nears the coast it will have to cross about sixty miles of shifting sand-dunes, crescent-shaped sand-hills which are creeping southwards. The track is so planned, however, that it is unlikely to subside for at least twenty years. An attempt is also being made to strengthen the windward slope of the dunes by spraying them with oil. As Madrid has refused to allow the railway to pass through Spanish territory, as was planned, it will have to negotiate further sand-dunes and sand-hills, which in this case, however, are not mobile, in the area where the frontier protrudes, and a tunnel will have to be built through a high plateau. This detour will greatly increase the initial outlay and the running-costs. Six million tons of ore will be transported every year over the three hundred and fifty miles of railway-line, which will later have a branch line to Akjoujt. Difficult working-conditions and high freight costs, handicaps peculiar to almost all African ore-deposits, make it far from certain that these ores would be an economic proposition in Europe. The Fort Gouraud project, where following a strong financial injection by the World Bank (more than 40 per cent of the minimum sum required), mining could begin in 1960, is intended as a test-case. The first ore is not expected to be delivered before 1964. Yet the 'Société des Mines de Fer de Mauritanie' (MIFERMA), in which French, British, Italian and German interests are represented, is sanguine of success. The political risk implicit in Morocco's claim to Mauretania is not taken too seriously, as the mines, whoever they might belong to, must improve the living standard of the natives.

The Commission which has been studying the economic potentialities of the Gara Djebilet deposits is an international body with French, Belgian, Luxembourg, German, Italian and Dutch experts. The ore at Tindouf contains phosphorus and is of a kind only used in four of these countries. On the other hand the proportion of Thomas-type ores in the world supply of iron-ore is comparatively small, so that the addition of rich, new deposits could play an important part in Western Europe's long-term planning.

* * *

From a scientific, technical and economic viewpoint the battle of the Sahara has been won, won by France for Europe, and Europe must now help her to pursue the victory. France is anxious that the people who live in the great desert should have a share of the 'manna from heaven.' She is aware, however, that drilling-rigs, ore-mines and industrial combines in the desert are not only sources of higher living standards but must inevitably give rise to social disturbances unless something is done quickly but patiently to educate the natives to work and to develop a sense of responsibility towards the community.

There is no denying that as yet the Sahara is both socially and politically underdeveloped. A delegation of black parliamentarians from French West and Equatorial Africa, who visited the Sahara in 1957, were astonished at the low level of education amongst Moslem officials. The notables, the caïds and sheikhs, seemed to them mere 'Beni oui oui,' indefatigable Yes-men who would look decorative at a New Year reception but carried little or no political weight, collaborators who were publicly decorated with the Légion d'Honneur but privately despised.

France would like to keep the Sahara apart from an Algeria that might opt for independence, yet paradoxically she is trying to throw the wealth of the Sahara into the scales as a stabilising factor in Algeria. A steelworks is planned for Bône; refineries, cement-works and petro-chemical combines are to be built; André Malraux spoke of creating a model province in Algeria. In every case the Sahara is to supply the power or the raw materials. This indus-trialisation is the backbone of the Constantine Plan which also provides for agricultural reform, an anti-unemployment drive and an increase in the number of schools, to be financed in part from the oil of the Sahara. From this plan France expects a social regeneration of Algeria, a climate of confidence in which politics can finally be discussed. It is certainly true to say that a people must be made immune against colonisation before colonialism is properly overcome—but it is late in the day to apply it in a politically-conscious Algeria.

In the Sahara France has fled forward. Disillusioned by the quarrelling and back-biting amongst France's political parties and by the setback to French 'grandeur' in the world at large, France's young men turned to the desert in their desire to achieve some-thing great and unique. It now looks as if their achievements will only come to fruition, will only acquire real significance for Europe and Africa—a significance that cannot be measured by balance-sheets and order-books—if France can also bring herself to make a 'forward flight' in Algeria.

God made Nature, man the desert.
JOHAN HUIZINGER

15. The Taming of the Shrew

THE only endemic disease of the Sahara, Gautier once remarked, is madness. . . .

Two projects which go back to the 'heroic' period in the desert are still talked of in the dawn of its 'industrial' era: the Trans-Saharan Railway and the Saharan inland sea. They are prize examples of the lack of realism in the majority of large-scale plans—lack of sound economic and scientific foundation.

The idea of a Trans-Saharan railway, which had its roots in an age-old, mystical desire to link North Africa and the negro countries through the Sahara, began to take shape in the 1870's. The father of the first concrete plan, Adolphe Duponchel, was an enthusiast for technical progress. He planned a pipeline to carry wine from Beziers to Paris. He proposed that highly-compressed jets of water should be used to complete the Panama Canal, and he suggested the same process to wash down certain lime ridges in the Pyrenees in order to cover the marshes in south-west France with fertile mud. The Saharan Railway, however, was his pet obsession. Thanks to him, the National Assembly in 1880 had three possible routes mapped out. Then came the massacre of the Flatters expedition, which had been sent out to investigate the route farthest east, and for the next decade the Saharan Railway sank into obscurity. When Lord Salisbury recognised France's claims to the desert in 1890, the railway took on a fresh lease of life but only to subside once more into the background when it was discovered that Lord Salisbury had given something away which neither he nor France really owned. Not until Laperrine's camel corps had brought peace to the desert did the 'Transsaharien' again come into the news. This time, after a further look at the plans, something was really done. A narrow-gauge railway line was laid to Colomb Bechar, where the constructors apparently began to wonder rather anxiously what on earth their railway was supposed to carry. The track stopped there.

Much of the history of the 'Transsaharien' reads like the report of a gigantic hoax. Mysticism, idealism, tomfoolery, patriotism, megalomania and prestige all contributed to the desire to see steam-trains rushing through the desert. There was even a strong element of missionary zeal, for in the same year that Flatters was killed three White Fathers were murdered by Tuareg near Chadames on their way to Central Africa—a tragedy which turned Cardinal Lavigerie, the founder of the Society of White Fathers, into an active supporter of the Trans-Saharan Railway.

The chief quality which distinguished Duponchel from a common crook was his naive ability to take his own daring statements seriously. When the financiers enquired about the possible economic merits of such a railway, he referred them to the 'hundred million consumers' at the southern end of the track who were waiting for French industrial products and to the paradisaic treasures of the tropics, which could be transferred to Paris in a matter of six days. So he was very annoyed by the agreement reached with Lord Salisbury in which France gave up those very areas where his railway was to terminate. Moreover he was very fond of making comparisons with the United States. Had the railway which since 1869, despite deserts and tomahawks, linked the Atlantic and the Pacific, not led to the foundation of villages and towns along the line? Duponchel chose to overlook the fact that the American Transcontinental railway had been laid through areas rich in minerals in a climate which white settlers could tolerate. He also omitted to mention (if he ever knew) that, before the work began, the Americans had despatched a commission to the still relatively unknown lands between the Mississippi and California and that the report on the investigations filled fourteen volumes. Duponchel, on the other hand, who had never been farther than Laghouat, boasted that he could build a railway, without any preliminary survey, from any point in Algeria straight into the heart of black Africa.

Not all those who supported the railway were as sure of their ground as Duponchel, whose slogan was: 'Traffic begets traffic.' Plans to stimulate freight and tourist traffic were concocted; it was a high holiday for charlatans. A certain Mr. Fock proposed that a marabout should be stationed at a suitable point on the line and, for a substantial monthly remuneration, should stage a number of miracles to encourage pilgrim traffic from the Sudan. It is hardly to be wondered at that a wealthy fool named Jacques Lebaudy, who proclaimed himself Emperor of the Sahara, was another enthusiastic champion of the Trans-Saharan Railway, till in 1915 he became an inmate of the lunatic asylum on Long Island.

The irony of it is that the idea of a Trans-Saharan Railway is still very much alive. From time to time between the wars the file was taken out of the cabinet, dusted off, then stowed away again. In the meantime, however, 180 miles of normal gauge track had been laid north of Colomb Bechar, and one of the last decisions of the Third Republic was to continue it as far as Kenadsa, where coal-mining was to begin. In 1941 the Vichy Government suddenly decreed that the Trans-Saharan Railway should be built. As a sort of bridge over the Sahara, it would demonstrate that France, though humbled, was still great, and the enemy would be put to shame. In any case, with the British Navy menacing the sea-route, it seemed the right moment to restore a land-link with French Equatorial Africa. The Germans appeared at first to favour the plan, then suddenly their interest switched to the idea of a trans-Saharan pipeline for groundnut oil. This rival project would, to say the least, have retarded the railway, but the Allied landing in November 1942 put paid to both. In 1945 the 'Mediterranée-Niger' Company was given official status but since then the railway line has only advanced about sixty miles beyond Colomb Bechar to Abadla, and the main function of the Railway company, ironically enough, is to maintain 2500 miles of desert track.

The drafts and blueprints—plans which are naturally as different from Duponchel's improvisations as chalk from cheese—have been lying ready since 1947. The railway is to pass through the Saoura Valley and the Tanezrouft desert to In Tassit, where a branchline through Gao and Niamey (1550 miles) would connect up with the Nigerian railways and via Timbuctoo-Segon (1800 miles) with the Senegalese network. The track south of Colomb Bechar would have a total length of more than 2000 miles. From a technical point of view a desert railway of this kind would not present any great difficulties today, but its economic justification is still as much in doubt as ever. In 1930 a special Commission estimated that goods traffic between Colomb Bechar and Gao would rise very quickly to at least 250,000 tons a year. By 1950, however, the figures were still a miserable 997 tons in one direction and 994 in the other—just enough to keep one goods train going.

It is fair to say that since then the development work in the desert has brought an appreciable increase in traffic, but for the time being there is no question of pushing the 'Transsaharien' beyond the proposed extension to Adrar. It is possible that in the foreseeable future the existing 'Mer-Niger' network will be expanded to transport ore from Djebel Guettara (95 miles from Abadla) and lead from the Moroccan mines at Taouz (170 miles from Colomb Bechar). These, however, would hardly rank as forerunners of the future Trans-Saharan Railway but merely as projects to meet local demands.

*   *   *

A close parallel to the Trans-Saharan railway, as regards both its date of birth and its longevity, is the plan for a Saharan inland sea. About the middle of the last century the discovery was made that the surface of the chotts in the north-eastern part of the Algerian Sahara and in the South-Tunisian Sahara lies partly below sea-level. This gave François Roudaire, who was then a Captain on the General staff, the idea of forming a 'Mer Intérieure Saharienne.' He suggested that the rocky escarpment at Gabes should be pierced to allow the Mediterranean to flow into the interior of the Sahara. He started from the assumption that the entire chain of chotts—nearly 250 miles long—must be depressions, and he therefore reckoned with a canal little more than ten miles in length. Ferdinand de Lesseps, who in the decade between the completion of the Suez Canal (1869) and the inception of the Panama Canal (1879) appears to have taken an interest in any ambitious plan that was put forward, waxed even more enthusiastic over Roudaire's project than over the Trans-Saharan railway. His support naturally gave the plan maximum publicity. The Saharan inland sea became common gossip in Paris. Jules Verne used it as the theme of his 'L'Invasion de la Mer'.

In 1874 the National Assembly unanimously approved a somewhat niggardly loan for a detailed survey of the chott area. Roudaire carried it out in 1873 and 1876 in the worst possible conditions and discovered that only the Melrhir and el Rharsa Chotts are depressions, whereas the Djerid Chott, which lies nearer the coast, is above sea-level. But Roudaire was undismayed. He revised his plan to carry the canal round the north of the Djerid Chott into the depressions. There was still a sufficiently large area below sea-level to produce a sea of more than 3,000 square miles. The fact that the canal would have to be ten times longer took the edge off public enthusiasm but did not quench it altogether. After all, the Suez Canal, which was very little shorter, had been built under very similar climatic conditions.

Roudaire, being an Army officer, naturally foresaw that a navigable waterway as far as Biskra would make the sending of French reinforcements to southern Algeria (and since 1881 to Tunisia) considerably easier. But his main argument was the green Sahara. He hoped that the inland sea would raise the level of subsoil water in the coastal areas, thus bringing large tracts of hitherto barren land under cultivation. Evaporation would increase air moisture, produce rainfall and thereby form a natural barrier against the desert climate. From a scientific viewpoint Roudaire's plans and views were open to countless objections. Experts in the Academy of Sciences warned against engaging in such an unpredictable adventure, particularly as even the precise level of the chott had not been established. Without questioning Roudaire's integrity, they pointed out that on the salt surface of the marshes mirages and other optical illusions were said to be quite common and that even the most practised observer might be a yard or two out. A yard or two could make all the difference to the size of the inland sea and the eventual fate of the neighbouring oases. In 1878 Parliament had approved fresh credits for further geological research, in which Lesseps himself took part. In 1881/82 an official Commission was set up to examine the financial implications of the plan. Six times as much earth and rock as in the case of the Suez Canal would have to be moved. The Commission estimated that it would cost 1.3 milliard francs, a figure that horrified the Finance Minister. Roudaire and Lesseps themselves mustered rather more than a ninth of this sum. If the plan was finally and quietly dropped after Roudaire's death in 1883, it was due partly to the violent opposition of a certain geologist.

The success Roudaire's idea had enjoyed had depended largely on the assumption that his Saharan sea actually existed in prehistoric times: Lake Triton whose fertile, well-populated shores were acclaimed by ancient authors. Amongst the scientists who rejected the theory of a quaternary sea in the Sahara none was more vehement than A. Pomel. When he first spoke out in 1872 no one took him seriously. Eight years later, after he had made a close study of the geological conditions in the Gulf of Gabes, he again opposed the theory. To the much-harassed French Finance Minister the geologist's intervention was highly welcome. By proving that the Gabes escarpment could not possibly be a new formation, Pomel compelled the champions of the Saharan Sea to abandon their most forceful argument: that they had merely copied their plan from nature.

Unfortunately, while Pomel's premisses were quite correct, his conclusions were false. The controversial quarternary sea has recently come back into circulation. In 1952/53 drillings by oil-prospectors produced evidence that pointed to a link between the chott and the Mediterranean in the ice age. It was not, however, the Gabes escarpment that had subsequently emerged but the Mediterranean that had dropped by a good thirty yards. As a result, Lake Triton degenerated to a lagoon and a salt-marsh.

Not surprisingly, this discovery immediately reawakened interest in the Saharan Sea. In June 1957 the French 'Journal Officiel' announced the formation of the 'Association de Recherche Technique pour l'Etude de la Mer Intérieure Saharienne' (ARTEMIS). Count Yves Michel de Perredon reactivated the Roudaire Plan, which his great-grandfather Michel Pasha, lighthouse-builder for the Ottoman Empire, had supported together with Lesseps. In 1958 Artemis managed to pass a document about the Saharan Sea to General de Gaulle. In spite of this attempt to arouse interest in high quarters, the French authorities preserved a significant silence. Artemis finally drew the obvious conclusion in 1959 and, at least temporarily, went into liquidation. Its place has been taken by a research syndicate, with the French mining concern HERSENT as its spokesman, which is pursuing the project with an option from the Tunisian Government and in collaboration with the Tunisian Ministry of Public Works.

To judge by the document which Artemis drew up, the most up-to-date version so far of Roudaire's plan, the project has lost none of its appeal in seventy-five years.

Roudaire had planned a canal fifteen yards deep and thirty yards wide. Artemis proposes something on a very much bigger scale, which will be at least 400 to 700 yards deep and between one and a half and two and a quarter miles wide, to say nothing of a barrage at Tozeur to produce electricity. Roudaire wanted to route his canal to the north of the Djerid Chott; Artemis plans to take its gigantic channel right through the salt marsh. Roudaire estimated it would take five years to complete the constructional work and nine years for flooding; Artemis had promised to carry out its entire operation in a few months and is confident that its inland sea will cost a mere fraction of Roudaire's.

Has Artemis found Columbus's egg? Not at all. It is quite simply pinning its hopes on the hydrogen bomb. One H-bomb of 20 megatons, which explodes at a depth of 2,500 feet, makes a crater of about 2 miles in diameter. A maximum of fifty such explosions, which would be set off either simultaneously or at intervals of a few seconds, would, it is calculated, be enough to excavate the channel from Gabes to the edge of the El Rharsa Chott.

According to Artemis, the oil-companies should be a hundred per cent in favour of this project, for several hundred miles of pipelines and expensive pumping-stations could be saved if the oil from Hassi Messaoud and Edjeleh were transported by tanker from the shores of the Saharan Sea. The pétroliers, however, dismiss the Artemis project as pure fantasy. No provision has been made in the estimates for port installations and for making the depression navigable; at its deepest point the Melrhir Chott is only a hundred feet below sea-level. But what irritates the oil-people most about the scheme is that there is no indication when it might be implemented. They are in a hurry; time for them is money. Artemis does not even know where it could purchase the necessary H-bombs.

*   *   *

Louis Kervran, who in 1953 had brought Roudaire's plan out into the open again but only to return it to its shelf, has in the meantime found a means of killing both birds—the Trans-Saharan railway and the green desert—with one stone. He published his plan in November 1958. It is to divert water from the Niger near Timbuctoo northwards into the area round Taoudenni. From there half the water would flow in a wide curve through the Mauretanian desert and debouch into the Atlantic at Nouak Chott. The other half would flow from Taoudenni towards In Salah, from there by pipeline and canal to Fort Flatters where it would enter the fossil bed of the Oued Igharghar and find its way to the Melrhir Chott. Kervan maintains that only minor excavations would be needed to create this network of waterways. The necessary power would be provided by the gas at Berga.

Kervan's plan was not hatched in the lumber-room of the past, but, after various committees have applied themselves to it and waxed enthusiastic, it will doubtless suffer the same fate as its predecessors.

*   *   *

Can the Sahara be tamed?

The answer to this question is mainly one of energy, of cheap energy. For lack of energy is, so to speak, another word for 'desert.' No one expects now to find any sensational coal-deposits in the Sahara. Sometime in the remote future the natural gas deposits south of In Salah may lead to the establishment of some industrial combine, but one of the essential features of the desert, distance, is not easily overcome. Hence the frantic search in all desert countries for sources of energy which are not handicapped from the beginning by high transport costs.

The strong permanent winds of the Sahara are, of course, not wasted. The Saharans have long since become accustomed to wind-driven power-stations: the windmill drives a dynamo, the dynamo feeds a buffer-battery which produces just enough of a red glow in the fort's naked bulb to enable the solitary officer to read his month-old newspapers. Wind-motors on a much bigger scale are being tried out. At Adrar I visited a German-made plant which had been working experimentally since 1953: a windmill with three vanes, each about twenty-five feet long, on a 65-foot tower and directly connected with a pump. At a wind-velocity of twenty-two to twenty-five feet a second enough water was produced to irrigate two hundred acres of green plantation in the middle of the desert. On the 'Great Wind' hill near Algiers I saw the last word in wind-motors, a small wind power-station which had been built in England after a design by the French engineer Andreau and which had a most ingenious method of transmitting the power. The two vanes of the windmill, as well as the tower, are hollow. As the vanes whirl round, they expel air through openings in the tips. This sets up a suction which draws air in at the bottom of the tower. The resultant stream of air drives a turbine with an alternating-current generator with a capacity of 100 kilowatts. The Andreau system should have a great future in the desert.

One young technician to whom I spoke prophesied that sooner or later the Sahara would be equipped with gigantic wind-power plants. By 'gigantic' he meant windmill wheels with a diameter of three hundred yards and more erected on enormous derricks like the Eiffel Tower. But the experts point out that the frequency and force of the Saharan winds are still relatively unknown.

Wind-driven power-plants are becoming more and more ingenious. They turn automatically into the wind; they can start, adjust their speed and stop in the event of a storm automatically. The vanes are made of such synthetic materials as, for example, polyester resin reinforced with glass-fibre. In spite of all these elaborate devices the production cost of electric or mechanical power generated by the wind is, even for the desert, an economic one. The only drawback is the unreliability of the wind, for in summer a wind-driven pump that is used for irrigation has to be out of action for only one day to endanger the whole crop. On the other hand, it is a costly business to install a combustion engine to cover periods of lull. Hence the reluctance of the experts to entrust the desert's future to the wind.

What of the sun?

It is hardly surprising that the inhabitants of the desert, who have been so poorly endowed by nature, should gape in open-mouthed astonishment when they hear how much energy emanates free, gratis and for nothing from the sun. On a sixty-mile square of the Sahara the sun discharges each year some forty billion kilowatt-hours, roughly forty times the present world output of electricity and five times the heating capacity of the proved petroleum deposits in the Sahara. On the principle of the solar battery, which has an efficiency ratio of more than ten per cent, this area of two and a half million acres of desert could be transformed into a gigantic electricity plant producing a yearly current of four billion kilowatt-hours. The construction of this power-station would present no basic technical problems. On the other hand, actually to cover the area in question with silicon plates which are sensitive to light and produce electricity would be fabulously expensive. To trap and utilise sunshine is expensive, and the more so if it is not only expected to work but is to have its hours of work prescribed.

'The awkward question of cost,' stressed Fridal Juston-Coumat, a young physicist whom I met at Bouzareah, 'varies from place to place. One square yard of ground in the Central Sahara is subjected on an average to three times as much solar energy as the same area in, say, Zurich. In Zurich, too, coal and oil are much cheaper than in the Sahara. In other words, any device to harness solar energy must have far greater economic potentialities in the Sahara, where you can reckon with 4,000 hours of sunshine a year, than it would have in Zurich.'

Bouzareah is the solarium of Algiers and Fridal Juston-Coumat is the Director of the largest solar furnace in the world. The 122 aluminium mirrors in its parabolic reflector (diameter: 27 feet) concentrate the sun's rays in a two-and-a half-inch sphere at three thousand degrees Celsius. The ARESA or 'Association pour la Recherche sur l'Utilisation de l'Energie Solaire en Algérie', which operates this highly expensive instrument, has so far used only the ultra-violet part of the solar spectrum for its experiments, but even in this limited field the solar furnace generates one kilowatt, which for photo-chemical experiments is an astonishingly powerful source of ultra-violet energy.

Juston-Coumat's experiments at Bouzareah are also indirectly linked with the development of the desert. Ultra-violet energy of this kind might be used in the Saharan industries of the future to crack hydrocarbons and, for instance, to break down the 'wet' gas of Hassi R'mel to light benzines, acetelyne and numerous other products. In ore-processing centres solar-furnaces would be capable of pure smelting. In agricultural areas they could convert the nitrogen and oxygen in the air into nitrate fertilisers.

A more immediate use for solar energy, however, lies not so much in industry as in the home. ARESA is with good reason interested in creating the ideal Saharan house, which is cooled by the sun in summer and heated by it in winter. Drinking, cooking and bath-water, hot or cold as required, is drawn from the solar distillation plant on the roof, which, moreover, is covered by a dome, the natural type of roof for the Sahara because the full heat of the sun can strike only one point at any given time.

Apart from ARESA, a study group of the BIA called the 'Société d'Etudes et d'Applications Industrielles de l'Energie Solaire' (ENERSOL) has also been doing intensive research, particularly on the possible development of an American miniature solar power-station. The sun's rays heat a storage battery, and thermal units convert the heat into electric current. ENERSOL proved that, with a capacity of anything from ten watts up to ten kilowatts, a power-station of this kind in the desert could compete with a motor-generator of the same capacity driven by oil or benzine. Louis Armand, former President of Euratom and the DIA and a man who is both shrewd and farsighted, has estimated that the experimental stage both in the laboratory and in small plants should be completed in twenty-five years, after which he maintains, the technical uses of solar energy on a large scale will really begin.

No discussion of the sun and the wind as sources of energy would be complete without a reference to the atom. As one gramme of uranium has the same calorific value as a ton of coal, transport costs are not a serious problem. Small atomic power plants will therefore play an important part in the desert. But atomic energy is not likely to prove the cheap source of power which would be required for long-term development of the desert. In the coming decade it looks as if the atomic bomb will be of more importance to the Sahara than the atomic reactor.

The Sahara is the Promised Land for the peaceful use of atomic explosions. For a long time it was not known when the first French atomic bomb would send its mushroom cloud into the sky at Reggan, but plans to use atomic explosions for industrial purposes were already well advanced. About 1965 a harbour is to be atomically created on the Atlantic coast of Morocco, from which the Tindouf ore will be shipped. Atomic explosions might be used to reactivate the oilfields at Edjeleh and Hassi Messaoud, if they should ever show signs of running dry. And no less exciting are the prospects for the Sahara's water supply.

The French publicist, Camille Rougeron, who as early as 1956 achieved international fame with his book on the peaceful uses of atomic energy, saw in the successful underground explosions of atomic and hydrogen bombs in America in 1957 a new and undreamt-of opportunity for Saharan water.

For some time past hydrologists have been showing particular interest in the oueds, which regularly carry water down from the Atlas into the desert. Hence the dam at Foum el Gherza and the projected barrage at Djorf Torba. In order to achieve an even flow throughout the year the experts are prepared to expend large sums of money, and to resign themselves not merely to heavy losses through evaporation but also to a dangerous increase in salt-content. The possibility has even been considered more than once of building barrages in the interior of the desert. Certain dry wadis in the Saharan mountains, particularly the Tibesti, the Aïr and the Hoggar, could be dammed up, before they enter the plain, to form a useful reservoir for flood-water. Bold plans of this kind have so far foundered on costs and the high rate of evaporation in the Sahara.

In fact, ways and means have recently been discovered of counteracting evaporation. The surface of the reservoir is quite simply covered by a hair-fine protective film. Of the various chemicals which have been experimented with, Hexadekanol, a substance like paraffin, appears to have come out best. It seals the surface of the water off from the air with a layer no thicker than a molecule and is impervious to rain, dust, waves and even boat-traffic. It is also cheap. One pound, costing only a few shillings, will cut evaporation by half on a water-surface of ten acres.

In certain circumstances, however, both Hexadekanol and the barrage could become superfluous. A nuclear explosion at the bottom of a deep drill-hole would create the necessary reservoir underground. The depth of the drilling could be so calculated that there would be no throw-up. The crater of loosened rock over the subterranean explosion would only be visible on the surface in the form of a huge pimple. Rougeron has proposed that the dam-project at Djorf Torba should be replaced by exploding a two-megaton bomb. It would be set off at a depth of 3,000 feet under the east bank of the rocky defile in which the dam is to be built. He believes this would create an enormous sponge of rock which would act as a reservoir. Djorf Torba is, of course, only one of several sites where this method could be applied. Atomic explosions could also produce rock-sponges in the interior of the Sahara. Non-porous formations, over which precious rainfall or floods evaporate instead of being absorbed, could be 'cracked' by atomic explosion, while the areas in which important hydraulic machines are fed by surface-water could be made more permeable. Although only limited experiments have so far been made, they do suggest that radioactive pollution of the water would not be a serious threat, particularly if 'clean' bombs were used. The radioactive particles are burned under the mass of vaporised and molten rock and effectively sealed off.

But that is not the end of the story. Bombs could also increase the yield of deep-water wells. Rougeron has Savornin's Sea particularly in mind. With smaller charges (in the range of a few Kilotons) the output of existing artesian wells, so long as it is not restricted by the piping, could be substantially increased. A case in point is the artesian well at Sidi Khaled, where the water is drawn from a record depth but where the outflow is less than half that of the Alb well at Ouargla and less than a third of Zelfana 11.

Whether bombs are available with the necessary explosive force and which could be inserted in the bore-hole is another matter. This objection would not, however, apply to new wells which were sunk with the aid of nuclear explosives. These might conceivably produce two hundred or more gallons a second. And a well of this kind would also be an important source of mechanical power. At Zelfana the pressure of the water is sufficient to drive a turbine with a generator. Admittedly the cost of installing and maintaining such a plant is disproportionately high but with a volume of 200 gallons a second the cost of electric power would be greatly reduced.

Rougerton goes still further. He points out that the deeper the well the hotter the water. A well fifteen thousand feet deep would, in theory, produce a geyser about two thousand feet high with a temperature of 300 degrees Fahrenheit. Allowing for air-cooling and for a plant with a ten per cent efficiency-ratio, the power generated would still be sufficient to drive a turbine of 200,000 kilowatts and at the same time to irrigate 25,000 acres of land.

The fact that Rougeron frequently indulges in fantasies does not detract from the basic soundness of his idea. Nuclear explosions are not likely to be used on Alb wells, for on the whole their rate of production is regarded as satisfactory. Where they could be very effective is in water-bearing formations which have been tapped by old-fashioned methods and are therefore producing too little to warrant deep boring. An example of this is the Tassili sandstone, which undoubtedly contained large reserves of water but is only yielding about two and a quarter gallons a minute. One atomic explosion would probably increase this a hundred- or even a thousand-fold.

But when all that has been said, however miraculous an expedient the nuclear bomb may prove to be, more water will never be conjured out of the desert than goes into it or is already in it. So one can understand the somewhat resigned conclusion which the meteorologist Jean Dubief and the hydro-geologist André Cornet draw in a joint survey: 'The present state of affairs can be improved upon but one cannot hope to change the Sahara fundamentally. Stick some confetti on the bare wall of a room and you have a picture of the cultivated areas of the Sahara. Now stick fifteen or twenty more pieces of confetti on the wall: then you have an idea what effect unrestricted exploitation of the Sahara's water resources might have. There is still a great deal of desert left.'

Yet I have met men in the Sahara who, although they would wholeheartedly support this judgment, still hope that one day more confetti might appear on the wall.

The use of sea-water to irrigate the desert is an age-old dream, which has so far come to nothing because of the high cost of distilling and transporting the fresh water. New methods of distilling salt and brackish water, which have been tried during the past few years in the U.S.A., in South Africa, Australia, Israel and several European countries and have also stood up to certain industrial tests, give reason to hope that the day will come when the sea will provide fresh water at remarkably low cost. In strictly chemical terms salt water is a simple system of inorganic salts which have melted in the water. As this system is very stable, it requires a comparatively large expenditure of energy to separate its components. Distillation has become an accepted process but large-scale distillation by evaporation is relatively new. In the oil-town of Kuwait on the Persian Gulf various distillation-plants produce more than five million gallons of fresh water a day from the sea and a further plant is being built which will produce another three million gallons. Kuwait, however, is a special case. The power required—natural gas, a 'waste product' of petroleum—is free, and previously tankers had to carry fresh water from Basra in Irak at considerable cost. Solar energy would, of course, also cost nothing and would not be confined to oil-fields. The construction of a solar distillation-plant is perfectly practicable. Salt water evaporates in a hothouse under the sun's heat, the steam condenses on the glass and runs down into a storage-tank. It seems, however, that the capital cost of industrial solar distillation plants is too high.

Recently other processes have been tried out which are both promising and revolutionary. One of these employs selective membranes. The plant consists of a chain of cells, each of which is separated from its neighbour by a membrane. These membranes conduct positive and negative ions respectively. When an electric current passes through, the salt is extracted from one cell and passed on to the next. This process is particularly effective with brackish water. There are also chemical processes whereby, for example, the capacity of certain liquids to 'suck up' large quantities of water at a given temperature and to discard it at another temperature can be exploited.

To irrigate the desert with sea-water requires, of course, more than a process of this kind. When the fresh water has been produced, it must be transported to wherever it is needed. True, the fringes of the desert would probably be the first target but piping fresh water even over short distances would still be too expensive. And this is likely to be so for some time to come. In the more remote future, however, the fusion-reactor, which on the solar principle produces energy by fusing light atomic nuclei, promises to become a source of very cheap power. Professor M. L. E. Oliphant, who is both a nuclear physicist and a realist, wrote to me from Australia: 'I like to imagine thermo-nuclear power-stations on the coasts, which are employed to distil water and to pump the fresh water inland for agricultural, industrial and domestic uses. At the same time the power-plant derives its own deuterium-fuel from the salt water. Large-scale distillation produces substantial quantities of salt which a chemical factory with the energy available turns into fertilisers and other valuable products. Long-distance cables carry electricity into the interior, those consuming the water enjoy air-conditioning and all the amenities of civilisation. Mines and ore-processing industries are established where today it is uneconomic to operate mines.' Professor Oliphant fully realises that he is making out a blank cheque to the future, but he is firmly convinced that, where the future of deserts is concerned, thermo-nuclear power is not just a white 'Oliphant'. . . .

The problem of producing artificial rain is still one that exercises scientists in the Old World. In the United States, on the other hand, the possibilities not merely of artificially increasing rainfall but of doing so effectively is now beyond dispute. After three years of research the Advisory Committee on Weather Control set up by the Government published its findings in January 1957. They were very encouraging.

Under the auspices of the BIA the 'Société de Développement des Techniques de la Pluie Provoquée' (SODETEP) is trying to solve the problem of artificial rain in the Sahara. It is the only official French study group which Morocco and Tunisia have joined. It has also been fortunate in being able to draw on the technical experience of an American Company, the 'Water Resources Development Corporation' (WRDC), which in 1957 covered fifteen per cent of the total area of cultivated land in the United States.

The Sahara was naturally not the ideal place to conduct the first experiments in North Africa. The best ally of the rain-maker is bad weather, which is rare in the Sahara. Moreover, for the time being at least, an increase in rainfall would only benefit a few nomads, sheep and retired camels. That is why the SODETEP chose for their 'targets' the Tiaret area (1,300 square miles) and the Setif district (2,500 square miles) on the high plateau of Algeria. In both cases the 'colons' have every interest in increased rainfall, particularly in Spring, for their winter cereals (wheat and barley). Every centimetre of extra rain that falls in spring and in one shower means an additional yield of about half a hundred-weight per acre.

Charles Dieterle, the Swiss who is in charge of the experiment, explained to me at his headquarters that Spring is the best time for 'hot clouds,' in other words for the sort of weather the rain-makers need. Dieterle and his meteorological staff officers follow the general weather situation, and especially in their own areas, day and night. When a 'hot cloud' approaches an operational area, Dieterle sets the appropriate unit in motion. Each unit consists of a stove and a stoker. In 1959 there were twenty-five of these in the Setif sector and nineteen in the Tiaret sector. The stove is heated with coke impregnated with silver iodide. When the stove reaches a heat of 1,500 degrees, the silver iodide evaporates, leaves the stove and crystallises in the cool outer air. These iodide crystals are practically weightless. The stove, which the rain-makers call a generator, releases 10^{15} crystals a minute, which means a one with fifteen noughts. They are carried up by winds or rising currents into the moisture-laden clouds where, the rain-maker hopes, they will stimulate condensation and produce raindrops. Even if only a small fraction of the crystals reach their destination and a fraction of that fraction form raindrops, the result is still quite a respectable quantity of rain. This particular method is the cheapest of all known rain-making devices.

The Tiaret-Serif experiment started at the end of 1957 and so far the FLN have not succeeded in sabotaging it. Definite results are not to be expected for several years, for it must take years to achieve an artificial rainfall that is sufficiently above the known mean to rule out any element of chance. But the WRDC and SODETEP are optimistic. In the summer of 1957—with the collaboration of the 'Association pour la Pluie Provoquée en Algérie'—they set up twelve additional precipitation-tanks in the Hoggar Massif and established five new weather-stations. Instruments for sun-ray measurement and a weather-radar with a wavelength of 3.5 cm. have since been installed. For the Hoggar, where cloud formations are fairly frequent without any corresponding rainfall, has been earmarked by SODETEP as the first target-area in the Sahara.

Until recently, however, any possibility of developing agriculture in the Sahara seemed to be ruled out not merely by shortage of water but also by the scarcity of cultivable land. It was mathematically most improbable that in the great expanse of the desert, where there happened to be water there would also happen to be irrigable land. But today the scientists view this problem in a much more hopeful light.

To begin with, the sensational discovery has been made that only a few inches under most of the Saharan 'regs', the endless wastes which are so flat that even the smallest pebble throws a long shadow, there is fossil soil. This legacy of the last Saharan rainy period has been preserved under a sterile crust of dust and rubble. In the long run it will undoubtedly prove to be no less valuable than the oil and gas beneath the desert. It is a fascinating thought that under the Land of Fear, the very epitome of barren desert, there is fertile soil waiting to be cultivated, and that the Tanezrouft, where the Targi who has lost his caravan resigns himself to die, would become a paradise if water were made available.

A second reason for new hope is that various methods of so-called water culture with which scientists have been experimenting in all the desert countries have so far proved themselves; plants grow in tanks where they are synthetically fed or in rubble or sand to which the necessary plant-food has been added. Recent research shows that the traditional method of cultivation in the oases, for example in the Rhir area, is nothing more than a culture of this kind: the sand holds the roots, and the water, in which the main mineral salts and even trace elements are dissolved, is Nature's food. The synthetic cultures with which Professor Chouard of the Sorbonne is experimenting in the desert research station at Beni Abbes are producing results which even the most fertile soil could not better.

Professor Chouard's more immediate aim is to stimulate oasis cultivation. A particular thorn in his flesh is the economic absurdity of flying fresh vegetables and fruit from France and North Africa into the drilling-camps. He would like to see the most up-to-date methods employed, as part of an overall plan, to open up the known sources of water and to seek new subterranean supplies, to extend the areas already under cultivation and improve the traditional methods of agriculture. There is, on the other hand, no gainsaying the fact that this would not make large tracts of land fertile. In the foreseeable future agriculture in the Sahara will continue to be confined to the oases. But that does not mean its yield could not be greatly increased.

Professor Chouard maintains, however, that this programme of expansion must go hand in hand with intensive research, the chief aim of which would be to discover ways and means of using the available water more economically. Professor Chouard believes that the present primitive methods of cultivation could be improved upon in a short time sufficiently to cut down water-consumption to a third.

One obvious way of saving water is to reduce loss through evaporation. The prevailing method of irrigation has the effect of saturating the top layer of soil, but it also means that an inch or two below the surface of the soil becomes dried up through evaporation. Professor Chouard's solution is underground irrigation, which he has tried out successfully at Beni Abbes. The water is piped under the ground; the lower side of the pipe is pierced with holes through which the water goes straight to the roots of the plants.

No less important, of course, is to select as far as possible plant species which are suited to the desert and which do not expend water either in evaporation or in sweating. One such plant is chlorella, a minute genus of green alga. The dieticians are not aiming to produce a sea-weed steak; they will be quite satisfied if chlorella makes suitable fodder for cattle or can be mixed with flour in the kitchen. Chlorella's nutritive value has been established. If the cells of the alga break up reasonably quickly, the result consists of forty per cent white of egg, twenty per cent fat and fatty substances, thirty per cent sugar, starch and cellulose and ten per cent mineral salts. Two and a quarter pounds of this dried substance contain 5300 calories. The egg-white, which particularly interests the scientists, is as pure as the albumen of eggs or milk, the finest animal proteins.

Chlorella possesses a further quality which makes it suitable for mass cultivation in the desert. The water it does not need passes not into the atmosphere but into the nutritive juices around it. It requires only a very small quantity of water for structural growth. It would, in fact, be an ideal candidate for industrial tank-cultures in the desert, if only . . . if only the water from the open tank did not evaporate. But if chlorella is cultivated in containers with glass covers, the interior heats up and the alga cells, which are sensitive to heat, cease to separate. Perhaps evaporation could be reduced, by spraying the surface of the water with a protective film, without disturbing chlorella's behaviour and propagation. This, to my knowledge, has not yet been attempted. Professor Chouard, on the other hand, has drawn the geneticists' attention to a plan to breed a heat-proof species of algae which can tolerate temperatures of more than 140 degrees Fahrenheit. It would, of course, be still better if heat-proof salt-water algae could be bred which permit the direct employment of brackish or even sea-water. This may seem utopian, but twenty years ago the mass-cultivation of chlorella at prices that can almost compete with agricultural produce was regarded as utterly utopian. Yet today this is a reality which is assuming more and more importance in an overpopulated country like Japan.

* * *

For the time being any prospect of turning the desert, outside the oases, into a garden is a dream. Yet dreams and fantasies are two different things. Only the rich can afford to shrug off dreams without even trying to realise them. The poor are not in that position. Israel has proved it with her bold plan to make the Negev desert fertile. We live by the law of surplus because we do not think globally. This limited view of life is reinforced by a world economy, which in fact is not a world economy at all but an economy of privilege. To realise this one only has to imagine that the produce of the earth was distributed evenly amongst all its inhabitants, that the industrialised countries had to share demo-cratically with the underdeveloped countries. There would be a serious shortage of a number of commodities, not least food-stuffs. Development of the deserts which form a quarter of the world's continents should be made a matter of urgency—like the Man-hattan Project or the race for the conquest of space.

The fiction of a world surplus can also be exposed in another way. The fact that water limits the population and the scope for development of an area is something that had been learnt mainly from the world's deserts. But it came as an unpleasant surprise to those peoples which are particularly enamoured of the idea of limitless possibilities to learn that the fresh-water reserves are limited even in areas with high rainfall. The United States was shocked when they discovered that in about the year 1975 they will face an appreciable reduction in their drinking and industrial water. Immediately scientists flung themselves on the 'dream' of distilling sea-water and, with large credits at their disposal, worked out in record time processes for producing fresh water.

That is why, in my view, we have also not heard the last of the scientists' dreams in the Sahara. Perhaps it is destined to become more than the cement of Eurafrica—perhaps it will one day give the universal 'homo super mechanicus' a chance to show what he can do when he really turns his hand to peaceful achievements. At all events the way was prepared for the internationalisation of desert research when UNESCO at Delhi in 1956 declared it a 'major project.'

The old Saharan who produces his Bible from a medley of flint arrowheads, a dried horned-viper and a scorpion in alcohol and solemnly reads the passage from Isaiah: 'I will open rivers in high places, and fountains in the midst of the valleys: I will make the wilderness a pool of water, and the dry land springs of water. I will plant in the wilderness the cedar, the shittah tree, and the myrtle, and the oil tree; I will set in the desert the fir tree, and the pine and the box tree together'—is he right after all? Right even in this new world of helicopters spying out fresh pastures, of air-freighters carrying nomads and their flocks from one grazing-ground to another, of distillation plants and plastic pipelines, of solar power stations, wind-driven motors and nuclear power-plants, of industrial centres with their boilers and furnaces, of agricultural areas with mass cultivation of algae in synthetic containers and water containers and water cultures in asbestos-cement basins?

Let us hope he is right. Then the contemporaries of the rich could meet the sons of the fertile desert with a clear conscience.

Glossary

The following is a glossary of words which occur frequently in the book.

Amenokal:	Elected chief of a Tuareg tribal federation
Amrar:	Chief of a Tuareg tribe
Arrem:	Village or hamlet; in the Hoggar a small, usually tree-less oasis where corn is grown
Azalai:	Salt caravan
Bordj:	Fort or fortified settlement
Chaamba:	Nomads of the northern Sahara (sing. Chaambi)
Chebka:	Lit. net; describes a plateau broken up by ravines, the Mzab plateau
Chech:	Head-cloth
Chott:	*See* Shott
Daya:	Self-contained depression, usually green, in which rain-water collects
Djinn:	Spirit or demon (pl. Djenoun)
Edeyen:	Expanse of sand-dunes
Enaden:	Caste of artisans, particularly blacksmiths (sing. Enad)
Erg:	Expanse of sand-dunes
Fech-fech:	Powdery, 'rotten' sand, usually under a treacherous top crust
Fellagha:	Lit. looters; term used for Algerian rebels
Fellah:	In the Souf experts in building wind-breakers (pl. Fellaha)
Foggara:	Subterranean irrigation channel
Gandourah:	Long, flowing cloak, frequently with hood
Gara:	An isolated mountain peak. (pl. Gour)
Gassi:	Lane, free of sand, between two ranges of sand-dunes
Ghibli:	Lit. poisonous wind; used for south wind
Ghout:	Cultivated basin in the Souf (pl. Ghitane)

Guelta:	Rainwater pool
Guerba:	Leather water-bottle
Hammada:	A covering of loose rubble on bare rock
Haratin:	Dark-skinned oasis peasant, possibly descended from the original inhabitants of the Sahara (sing. Hartani)
Hassi:	Well
Horr:	A man of rank, i.e. a freeman (as opposed to a slave); pl. Harrar
Iklan:	Slaves of the Tuareg (sing. Akli, fem. sing. Taklit)
Imouhar:	High-class Tuareg (sing. Amahar)
Imrad:	Vassals of the high-class Tuareg tribes (sing. Amrid)
Jebbar:	Palm shoot
Jebel:	Mountain
Kasbah:	Lit. fortress, citadel; used today to mean a native town or quarter
Kel es Souf:	Spirits, demons
Khammes:	Lit. a fifth; lease-holder, oasis peasant
Ksar:	Lit. fortified place; today any oasis settlement (pl. Ksour)
Ksourien:	Inhabitant of a Ksar
Maghreb:	Western Islam; North Africa
Marabout:	Mohammedan Saint; his grave
Mechoui:	Sheep; mutton
Mehari:	Riding camel (pl. Mehara)
Meharist:	Camel rider, chiefly in the military sense
Mekhadma:	Tribe of semi-nomads, living mainly round Ouargla (sing. Mekhadmi)
Mozabites:	Berber inhabitants of the Mzab; an Ibadite sect
Naïls:	Saharan sandals
Oued:	Dry river-bed, wadi
Redjem:	A cairn of stones used as a land-marker
Reg:	A waste expanse of pebbles, rubble or scree
Rezzou:	Camel-riders who take part in a razzia or raid
Rhtassin:	Builder and cleaner of wells
Rumi:	Lit. Romans; today used of Europeans, foreigners, unbelievers (pl. Ruama)
Sahara:	Correctly pronounced (Sāhara) means dun-coloured; wrongly pronounced (Sahàra) means box or chest
Sahel:	Area in the south which is half desert, half steppe

Sebka:	Depression with no outlet and with very salty soil; often identical with Shott
Serir:	Waste expanse of rubble or scree
Serroual:	Wide, baggy trousers
Shorfa:	Used in Morocco as plural of Sherif, i.e. descendants of Mohammed or his grandson Hassan.
Shott:	Salt marsh or lake
Shurafa:	Pl. of Sherif
Souafa:	Inhabitant of the Souf country (sing. Soufi)
Souk:	Market-place, shopkeepers' and traders' quarter
Taleb:	Moslem scholar
Tamahaq:	Dialect of the Hoggar-Tuareg
Tassili:	Foothill, mainly foothills of the Hoggar
Tibbus:	Inhabitants of the Tibesti mountains
Tifinagh:	Script of the Tuareg language
Toub:	Sun-baked clay tiles
Tuareg:	Berber people, mostly nomads, found between Tripolitania and the Niger bend (sing. Targi; fem sing. Targia)
Zaouia:	Monastic building inhabited by a Moslem fraternity; the fraternity itself
Zoua:	Descendants of the Ouled Sidi Sheikh, a tribe of marabout families (northern fringe of the Sahara)

Bibliography

General

Capot-Rey, R.: Le Sahara français, Paris 1953—*Furon, R.:* Le Sahara, Paris 1957—*Gabus, J.:* Völker der Wüste, Olten 1957—*Gautier, E. F.:* La conquête du Sahara, Paris 1910—*do.:* Le Sahara, Paris 1928—*Lhote, H.:* Les Touaregs du Hoggar, Paris 1955—*Schiffers, H.:* Die Sahara und die Syrtenländer, Stuttgart 1950—*Strasser, D.:* Réalités et promesses sahariennes, Paris, 1956.

Ferner *La Documentation Française:* L'économie pastorale saharienne (No. 1730), Le Sahara français en 1958 (No. 2379 und 2414), L'enseignement au Sahara (No. 2467)—*Travaux de l'Institut de Recherches Sahariennes*, Alger: abbreviated to TIRS in later references, and *Bulletin de Liaison Saharienne*, Alger (BLS).

Chapters 1–4

Balout, L.: Pluviaux interglaciaires et préhistoire saharienne, in: TIRS, t. 8—*Breuil, Abbé, H.:* Les roches peintes du Tassili-n-Ajjer, Paris 1954—*Frobenius, L.:* Ekade Ektab, Leipzig 1937—*Gautier, E. F.:* La conquête du Sahara, in: TIRS, t. 14—*Graziosi, P.:* L'arte rupestre della Libia, Napoli 1942—*Howe, S. E.:* Les héros du Sahara, Paris 1931—*Hugot, H. J./Quézel, P.:* A propos de quelques graines fossiles du gisement préhistorique de Méniet, in: Bul. Soc. Hist. nat. Af. Nord, t. 48—*Lartéguy, J.:* Sahara, An 1, Paris 1958—*Lhote, H.:* Peintures préhistoriques du Sahara, Paris 1957: catalogue of exhibition—*do:* A la découverte des fresques du Tassili, Paris 1958—*Monod, Th.:* Méharées, Paris 1937—*A. Pons / P. Quézel:* Premiers résultats de l'analyse palynologique de quelques paléosols sahariens, in: C. R. Ac. Sc., t. 243— *do.:* Première étude palynologique de quelques paléosols sahariens, in: TIRS, t. 16—*do.:* Premières remarques sur l'étude palynologique d'un guano fossile du Hoggar, in: C. R. Ac. Sc., t. 244—*do.:* A propos de l'étude palynologique de quelques sédiments sahariens récents, in: BLS, No. 29—*Quézel, P.:* see under Hugot and Pons—*Rhotert, H.:* Libysche Felsbilder, Darmstadt 1952—*Staffe, A.:* Die Haustiere auf den nordafrikanischen Felsbildern, in: Forschungen und Fortschritte,

Jahrg. 15—*do.:* Die Herkunft des Kamels in Afrika, in: Zeitschr. f. Tierzüchtungsbiologie, Bd. 46—*Tschudi, Y.:* Les peintures rupestres du Tassili-n-Ajjer, Neuchâtel 1956.

Chapters 5–7

Aris, R./Dervieux, F.: La nappe phréatique du Souf, in: Terres et Eaux, No. 29—*Barrucand, V.:* see Eberhardt—*Bataillon, C.:* Le Souf, Alger 1955—*Berchem, M. van:* Sedrata. Documents Algériens, Série Monographies, No. 11—*Calcat, A.:* Controverses sur la fumure et l'emploi des engrais au Sahara, BLS, No. 18—*do.:* Expérimentation agricole saharienne, Bul. Rens. Agricoles, No. 43–44—*do.:* Economie agricole saharienne, Bul. Rens. Agricoles, No. 43–44—*Cornet, A.:* Essai sur l'hydrogéologie du Grand Erg Occidental et des régions limitrophes (Les foggaras), in: TIRS, t. 8—*do.:* Les ressources aquifères du Sahara, in: Industries et Travaux d'Outre-Mer, June 1957—*do.:* see under Dubief—*Dervieux, F.:* see under Aris—*Drouhin, G.:* Sahara face au problème de l'eau, in: Notre Sahara, No. 3—*Drouhin, G. u. a.:* Quelques aperçus sur l'état actuel des études poursuivies au Chott Chergui, in: Terres et Eaux, No. 27—*Dubief, J./Cornet, A.:* Le problème de l'eau conditionne l'essor saharien, in: Science et vie, June 1958 —*Eberhardt, I.:* Au pays des sables, Paris 1944—*do.:* Mes journaliers, Paris 1923—*Eberhardt, I./Barrucand, V.:* Dans l'ombre chaude de l'Islam, Paris 1906—*Es Sahraoui:* Les Légendes du palmier, in: BLS, No. 18—*Fontaine, H.:* Images du Mzab, BLS, No. 29—*Lablée, J.:* Le déplacement des palmeraies en pays ouargli, BLS, No. 29—*Lô, Capitaine:* Les foggaras du Tidikelt, TIRS, t. 10/11—*Savornin,J.:* Le plus grand appareil hydraulique du Sahara, in: TIRS, t. 4—*Suter, K.:* Die Oase El Oued, in: Vierteljahrsschr. Naturforsch. Gesell. Zürich, Jg. 100—*do.:* Die Siedlungen des Mzab, in: Vierteljahrsschr. Naturforsch. Gesell. Zürich, Jg. 103—*do.:* Die Oase Guerrara, in: Erdkunde, Archiv für wissenschaftl. Geographie, Bd. XI.

Chapters 8–10

Armand, L.: Industrialisation, in: Sahara 57, Musée d'Ethnographie, Neuchâtel—*Bellair, P.:* Les volcans du Sahara, in: BLS, No. 31— *Blanguernon, C.:* Le Hoggar, Paris 1950—*BRMA:* Dix années de recherches minières au Sahara, in: Notre Sahara, No. 3—*Capot-Rey, R.:* Greniers domestiques et greniers fortifiés au Sahara, TIRS, t. 14— *Carrouges, M.:* Charles de Foucauld, Paris 1954—*Côte, M.:* Morphologie de l'Ahaggar, in: Revue de Géographie de Lyon, vol. 32, No. 4— *Dubief, J.:* A propos de l'établissement d'un réseau climatologique local en Ahaggar, in: BLS, No. 29—*Matheron, G.:* Le gisement de fer de Gara Djebilet, Bul. Scient. et Econom. du BRMA, Alger 1955—

Sanlaville, P.: Les centres de cultures de l'Ahaggar, in: Revue de Géographie de Lyon, vol. 32, No. 4.

Chapter 11

Adolph, E. F.: Physiology of Man in the Desert, New York 1957— *Bourcart, J.:* Conrad Kilian, in: Bul. Soc. Géol. de France, t. 1, Paris 1952—*Chasseloup Laubat, F. de:* Hommage à Conrad Kilian, Ac. Sc. d'Outre Mer (17. X. 1958)—*Kennedy, A. L.:* Salisbury, London 1953 —*Krejci-Graf, K.:* Erdöl, Berlin 1955—*Lambert, G.:* see under Metz —*Marsden jr., S. S.:* Drilling for Petroleum, Scientific American, vol. 199, Nr. 5—*Metz, B./Lambert, G.:* Les effets du climat des zones arides sur l'homme au travail, Medical Faculty of Univ. Strassburg, 1957— *Murcier, A.:* Le pétrole saharien, in: Le Monde, 16/17XI/1958— *Verlaque, Ch.:* Les recherches pétrolières dans le Sahara français, in: TIRS, t. 14—*do.:* Evolution de la recherche pétrolière dans le Sahara français, in: TIRS, t. 16—*Vigan, C.:* Médecine du travail au Sahara, in: Archives des Maladies Professionelles, t. 8, No. 2, 1956.

Chapters 12–13

Blanguernon, C.: Le Hoggar et ses écoles nomades, Documents Algériens, Séries Monographies, No. 15—*Brigol, M.:* L'habitat des nomades sedentarisés à Ouargla, in: TIRS, t. 16—*Godard, Commandant:* L'oasis moderne, Essai d'urbanisme saharien, Alger 1954— *Mercier, S. E. Mgr. G.:* La jeunesse du sud, in: L'Algérie et sa jeunesse, Alger 1957.

Chapter 14

arb: Der Schöpfer der Atlantropa-Idee, in: Die Neue Zeitung, 1953, Nr. 2—*Cartier, R.:* En France Noire avec R. C., in: Paris-Match, No. 383 ff—*Kaup, K.:* Erzlager auf dem schwarzen Kontinent, in: Europa, Bad Reichenhall, Nov. 1957—*Lemaire, M.:* L'Eurafrigas, Paris 1958— *Lüthy, H.:* Frankreichs Uhren gehen anders, Zürich 1958—*Mathieu, G.:* L'ensemble économique franco-africain ne peut demeurer dans le 'statu quo', in: Le Monde, Séléction hebdomadaire, 25. IX., 2. X., 9. X. 1958—*Salis, J. R. von:* Weltgeschichte der neuesten Zeit, Bd. 1, Zürich 1951—*Sörgel, H.:* Panropa-Projekt, Leipzig 1929.

Chapter 15

Balchin, W. G. V.: The Purification of Saline Water, in: The New Scientist, Nr. 103—*Bétier, J.:* L'énergie solaire, in: Science et Vie, June 1958—*Chouard, P.:* Peut-on rechercher la mise en valeur agricole du Sahara, in: Rivières et Forêts, No. 9/10—*Depret, P.:* Le 'Méditerranée-Niger', in: Sahara de Demain, Oct. 1958—*Desanges, J.:* A propos du triomphe de Cornelius Balbus, in: TIRS, t. 14—*Fuchs, P.:* Weisser Fleck im Schwarzen Erdteil, Stuttgart 1958—*Hornemann, F. K.:* Tagebuch seiner Reise von Cairo nach Murzuck, Weimar 1802—*Kervran, L.:* Fleuves transsahariens?, in: Notre Sahara, No. 6—*Maurel, G.:* Le Méditerranée-Niger, in: Rivières et Forêts, No. 9/10—*Ozenda, P.:* La végétation ligneuse du Sahara, ibid.—*Rougeron, C.:* L'explosion thermonucléaire, ibid.—*do.:* Les applications de l'explosion thermonucléaire, Paris 1956—*White, G. F.* (editor). The Future of Arid Lands, Washington 1956.

Index

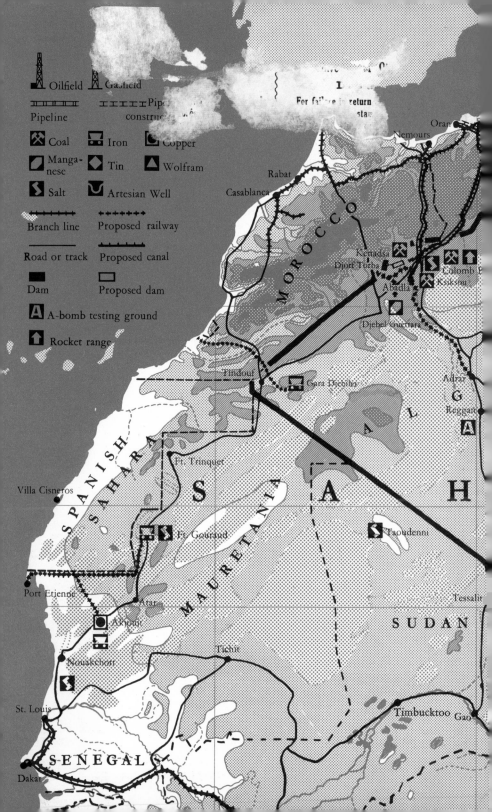

Legend

- **Oilfield**
- **Gasfield**
- **Pipeline**
- **Pipeline construction**
- **Coal**
- **Iron**
- **Copper**
- **Manganese**
- **Tin**
- **Wolfram**
- **Salt**
- **Artesian Well**
- **Branch line**
- **Proposed railway**
- **Road or track**
- **Proposed canal**
- **Dam**
- **Proposed dam**
- **A-bomb testing ground**
- **Rocket range**

Oran
Nemours
Rabat
Casablanca
Kenadsa
Djorf Torba
Colomb B
Abadla
Ksiksou
Djebel Guettara
Tindouf
Gara Djebilet
Adrar
G
Réggan
A
Ft. Trinquet
Villa Cisneros
S
A
H
Taoudenni
Ft. Gouraud
Port Etienne
Atar
Tessalit
Akjoujt
SUDAN
Nouakchott
Tichit
St. Louis
Timbucktoo
Gao
SENEGAL
Dakar

MOROCCO
SPANISH SAHARA
MAURETANIA